FIXED AND VARIABLE CAPACITORS

FIXED AND VARIABLE CAPACITORS

G. W. A. DUMMER, M.B.E., M.I.E.E.

Head of Components Research, Development and Testing at the Radar Research Establishment, Ministry of Supply

HAROLD M. NORDENBERG

Head of the Electronic Parts Unit, Bureau of Ships, Navy Department

McGRAW-HILL BOOK COMPANY, INC.

New York   Toronto   London

1960

FIXED AND VARIABLE CAPACITORS

THE MAPLE PRESS COMPANY, YORK, PA.

PREFACE

It has been said that electronic parts (components) are the bricks with which all electronic equipments are built, and certainly the reliability of a modern complex electronic equipment is determined by the reliability of the weakest part. A better knowledge of the characteristics of parts, therefore, should help designers and users of all types of electronic equipments. This book has been written from the viewpoint of the user to enable him to choose and apply the best part for his particular requirement by understanding its fundamental characteristics.

This is the first time that a book of this nature, devoted specifically to fixed and variable capacitors, has been published in the United States. Although a few European parts are mentioned, American parts are specifically dealt with.

In view of the thousands of electronic parts available, a book of this nature cannot cover every individual type of part. Therefore, military-type parts, supplemented by commercial types to make the text complete, have been chosen as representative of high-quality parts. Also, since they have been standardized, they are fewer in number. Commercial parts generally are not constructed to withstand as stringent environmental conditions but consist of basically similar types.

Electronic-part development takes place comparatively slowly, and often several years elapse between the original research work and full production of a part. Minor modifications and changes may occur, and part manufacturers are usually pleased to provide any such information on their products.

Since no bibliography appears to exist that deals specifically with electronic parts, the authors have collected a number of references to fixed and variable capacitors and have included them as part of the nucleus of such a bibliography.

We hope that this book will fill a gap in the technical literature now available and will aid industry in the development and production of better electronic equipments.

G. W. A. Dummer
Harold M. Nordenberg

CONTENTS

CONTENTS

CONTENTS

CONTENTS ix

CONTENTS   ix

CONTENTS
CONTENTS

CONTENTS

PART 1

GENERAL INFORMATION ON ELECTRONIC PARTS (COMPONENTS)

CHAPTER 1

A BRIEF HISTORY OF THE DEVELOPMENT OF
ELECTRONIC PARTS

In the time scale of civilization, the entire history of electricity and its recent counterpart, electronics, is indeed small. Although static electricity was discovered in 600 B.C. in Greece, it was not until 1745, when the storage properties of the Leyden jar were discovered in Germany, that the first rudimentary capacitor came into being. However, the first radio parts as such (incorporating resistance, inductance, and capacitance) could be considered the constituent parts of the Hertz loop, developed in 1887.

In the 1850s, Faraday's discovery that silver sulfide possessed a high negative temperature coefficient of resistance anticipated the modern thermistor. During the late 1880s, an aluminum electrolytic capacitor was developed in Germany.

Though the first composition resistor was in use by 1885, the first inductor for radio purposes was the Hertz loop itself. In 1904, the two-electrode electron tube was introduced. It was followed by the three-electrode electron tube in 1907. These tubes were used in transmitters and receivers designed for radiotelegraphy. At that time the designer of equipments also constructed all the necessary electronic parts.

The First World War (1914–1918) gave impetus to the development of radio communications. This communications equipment required the first large quantity production of the electron tube. As a result, electronic parts began to assume roughly their present form.

After the First World War, attention was turned to peacetime application of radio for use in communications and entertainment. Electronics history was made in November, 1920, when Westinghouse radio station KDKA in Pittsburgh, Pa., broadcast that year's presidential election returns and instituted the first regularly scheduled radio broadcasts. In 1922, six companies, including Western Electric, Marconi, British Thompson-Houston, Radio Communications, and General Electric, under the British Post Office, formed the British Broadcasting

3

Corporation, which started programmed broadcasts in November of that year.   In September, 1926, the National Broadcasting Company, under the Radio Corporation of America, began nationwide network broadcasting.

The electronic-part industry had its beginning during the 1920s when electronic manufacturers began to specialize in individual parts used especially by the home constructor in making his own receiver.

Resistors were used in large quantities as grid leaks, anode loads, and in similar applications.   These resistors consisted of carbon compositions of many kinds, compressed into tubular configurations and fitted with end caps or radial leads.   Paper-dielectric capacitors were mostly tubular types enclosed in wax-dipped cardboard tubes with wax or a similar material sealing the ends.   Also in common use were stacked mica capacitors, fitted in some cases with screw terminals either in open construction or, later, enclosed in molded cases.   Electrolytic capacitors were primarily the wet types in tubular metal cases.

After 1925, home construction of receivers diminished, and during that period electronic-part manufacture improved to such an extent that by 1940 some 52 million radio receivers were in use in the United States.   However, electronic-part standards were geared only to the needs for producing the domestic radio.   Panclimatic protection was unnecessary, and the self-compensating action of the electron tube made wide tolerances and poor stability generally allowable.   Thus apart from certain telephone, precision-instrument, and military applications, no very high standard was required of the electronic-part manufacturer.

In the late 1920s, the concept of type approval, approval of an item prior to award of contract, was developed by the Department of the Navy.   Use of type approvals to improve the quality of Navy procurements gradually extended to electronic parts and became the basis for future standards and specifications.

It was not, however, until the advent of the Second World War with its unprecedented demands for complicated but reliable weapons that it became essential to produce large quantities of electronic parts quickly.   Also the introduction of large quantities of radar and sonar equipment meant that still more electronic parts, including many new types, were required.   The pressing need for increased production, interchangeability, and higher quality, as well as the shortage of materials, led to interservice standardization of electronic parts.

In the summer of 1942, the director of the Radio and Radar Production Division of the War Production Board, established during the Second World War to facilitate production of war material, initiated a standards program. This program was to be carried out by the American Standards Association through its war standards procedure. As a result, two War Standards Committees were organized: one on radio and one on electrical indicating instruments. Task groups were formed under these committees for the purpose of preparing individual standards. Members for these task groups were drawn from the Armed Services and from manufacturers of electronic parts and equipment.

These task groups prepared approximately 21 war standards, covering such electronic parts as resistors, capacitors, insulators, crystals, switches, and dynamotors. These standards specified acceptable performance requirements, electrical ratings, physical dimensions, test methods, and a system of identification. Later these war standards formed the nucleus of a much more expanded program under the Army-Navy Joint Specification Board (ANJSB), which the two departments set up in 1944 to coordinate specifications. These standards became known as the Joint Army-Navy (JAN) Specifications. The ANJSB has undergone several changes both in structure and name due to governmental reorganizations. Its equivalent now exists as the Armed Forces Supply Support Center.

In May of 1946, the Army Navy Electronic and Electrical Standards Agency (ANEESA) was established by the Departments of the Army and Navy for the purpose of coordinating and handling administrative details, such as qualification approval for joint specifications.

In a governmental reorganization in 1947, which established the Air Force as an independent department, the JAN Specifications were superseded by the military (MIL) series of specifications, to include the Air Force. The name of the ANEESA was changed to the Armed Services Electro-Standards Agency (ASESA), now performing the same duties for all three departments.

Experience in the nation's war theaters, particularly in the Pacific, brought out the inadequacies of electronic parts being used in weapons systems of increasing complexity. A coordinated research and development program was required to keep pace with the ever-more-stringent requirements imposed by this complex equipment. In June of 1946, the Secretaries of War and Navy chartered the joint research and development programs of these two departments. Under the 1947 governmental reorganization, these programs were superseded by the Research and Development Board (RDB), which was responsible to the Secretary of Defense for advice on all military research and development matters.

Under this board, the Committee on Electronics, with its panel on electronic parts (components) and attendant subpanels on specific electronic parts, was established for the purpose of stimulating, planning, and coordinating research and development of electronic parts.

In a reorganization of the Department of Defense in 1953, the RDB was replaced by an Assistant Secretary of Defense for Research and Development. Under the Assistant Secretary of Defense for Research and Development (later changed to Research and Engineering), the Committee on Electronics was retained, but the Panel on Electronic Parts (Components), along with its subpanels, was replaced by the Advisory Group for Electronic Parts (AGEP) with its eight working groups on capacitors: coils, inductors and transformers, electromechanical devices, resistors, frequency-control devices, assemblies and assembly techniques, electronic materials, and transmission lines. Members for these groups are drawn from the military departments and industry.

The AGEP is responsible for coordinating, planning, integrating, monitoring, and recommending budget levels of all research and development contracts on electronic parts. To facilitate the work of this group, a permanent secretariat is maintained under contract to the three departments by the University of Pennsylvania at Philadelphia.

Because of these coordinated research and development efforts, government and industrial researchers have been able to bring about many improvements in electronic-part design within the last 15 years. Some of these developments are the miniature metal-encased hermetically sealed tubular paper capacitor; the high-reliability metal-encased hermetically sealed tubular paper capacitor; the high-dielectric-constant ceramic mixes and resulting disk and tubular capacitors; the tantalum electrolytic capacitor (with both liquid and solid electrolyte); the glass and vitreous-enamel capacitor with electrical properties equivalent to mica; the metalized paper and paper-Mylar combination capacitor; the vitreous-enamel power wire-wound resistor; the hermetically sealed precision wire-wound resistor; the high-stability-metal and cracked-carbon-film hermetically sealed resistors.

Further developments are transformers capable of operating for 2,000 hr at ambients of 200°C; fluoro-chemical gas and liquid-filled transformers for high-powered pulse and high-voltage applications, capable of operating 10,000 hr at 125°C ambients; resin and silastic encapsulated transformers using various materials and techniques, and many other parts, such as sealed relays, ruggedized meters, and switches. In addition, the techniques for large-quantity production were developed as required.

Each one of these developments has resulted in improved electronic parts for the ever-more-demanding applications in military electronic equipment, with the result that the electronic part of today bears little resemblance to its earlier counterpart. It is smaller, lighter, and capable of operating over a wider temperature range under adverse environmental conditions. Even so, modern requirements ask for still higher standards, particularly higher operating-temperature capability, greater stability with varying ambients, greater reliability, and more miniaturization. There is little doubt, therefore, that research and development work will continue in an effort to improve the performance of electronic parts as we know them today.

TEMPERATURE AND HUMIDITY CATEGORIES OF ELECTRONIC PARTS

Prior to and during the Second World War there was no general specification covering environmental conditions for electronic parts. Some of the early military specifications, and later the war standards, began to include these requirements for individual parts. The spread of the war into different climates and the arduous operational conditions led to the development of various environmental tests for electronic parts.

These tests were later introduced into the JAN and MIL electronic-part specifications. A further step in this evolution was the issuance of Military Standard 202, an omnibus standard of all types of tests, environmental and electrical, which are then referenced as required in the individual-part specification.

CLASSES OF ELECTRONIC PARTS

Specifications and requirements for electronic parts vary according to the conditions of use. Table 1-1 summarizes the main classes of electronic parts.

As a guidance document for current and future research and development as well as standardization, the Armed Forces Supply Support Center has recently issued Military Standard 446, titled "Environmental Requirements for Electronic Component Parts."

Table 1-2 summarizes the environmental characteristics and groups listed in this standard.

Environmental Groups

The following groups contain the various environmental requirements of the three military departments:

Group I. It covers electronic parts that are exposed to conditions no more severe than natural climatic conditions and that are characterized by such parts as those used in portable manpack communications equipment; radio-frequency (r-f) and other cables, meters, audio cords, waveguides, and fittings.

TABLE 1-1. CLASSES OF ELECTRONIC PARTS

Class of part	Use	Requirements
Commercial...	Radio, television	Cost should be competitive. Good availability; long life. Need not be miniature or panclimatic
Professional...	Industrial, electronics, communications, computers	Cost may be higher. High accuracy and permanence of electrical characteristics essential. Reliability and long life required (40,000 hr minimum). Need not be miniature
Military.......	a. Ground, shipboard communications, radar, sonar, test equipment, and computers	Reliability essential. Must be panclimatic and capable of operating over a wide range with a minimum life capability of 10,000 hr
	b. Airborne communications, radar, computers	Reliability essential. Must operate under severe conditions, be panclimatic, lightweight, miniature or subminiature, with minimum life capability of 2,000 hr
	c. Guided weapons	Reliability essential. Operational conditions severe. Must be panclimatic, miniature or subminiature, and compatible with potting resins if necessary. Must cover wide temperature range. Short operational or test life (500 hr) but long storage periods (up to 5 years) necessary
Military.......	Transistor	Reliability essential. Must be panclimatic and capable of operating over wide temperature range with minimum life capability of 10,000 hr. Reliability essential. Must be comparative in size with transistor
Commercial...	Transistor	Cost should be competitive. Must have good availability and be comparative in size with transistor

TABLE 1-2. ENVIRONMENTAL REQUIREMENTS CHART

Environmental characteristic	Group I	Group II	Group III	Group IV	Group V	Group VI	Group VII	Group VIII
Temperature:								
Operating	−55° + 55°C	−65° + 85°C	−65° + 125°C	−65° + 125°C	−65° + 200°C	−65° + 200°C	−65° + 350°C	−65° + 500°C
Storage	−65° + 71°C	−65° + 85°C	−65° + 85°C	−65° + 85°C	−65° + 85°C	−65° + 85°C	−65° + 85°C	−65° + 85°C
Thermal shock	*	−65° + 85°C	−65° + 125°C	−65° + 125°C	−65° + 200°C	−65° + 200°C	−65° + 350°C	−65° + 500°C
Pressure:								
Operating	20.58″ Hg	1.32″ Hg	20.58″ Hg	0.326″ Hg	0.326″ Hg	0.043″ Hg	0.043″ Hg	0.043″ Hg
Altitude, feet	10,000	70,000	10,000	100,000	100,000	150,000	150,000	150,000
Nonoperating	3.4″ Hg		3.4″ Hg					
Altitude, feet	50,000		50,000					
Moisture	*	100 per cent relative humidity with condensation for all groups						
Vibration:								
Cycles per second	10–55	10–2,000	10–55	10–2,000	10–2,000	10–2,000	10–2,000	10–3,000
Acceleration, gravitational units	*	10	*	10	15	15	20	40
Shock:								
Acceleration, gravitational units	50	50	50	50	50	50	50	50
Time in milliseconds	6	11 ± 1	11 ± 1	11 ± 1	11 ± 1	11 ± 1	11 ± 1	11 ± 1
Air-induced vibration:								
Cycles per second	*	*	*	150–9,600	150–9,600	150–9,600	150–9,600	150–9,600
Decibels above 2×10^{-4} dynes/sq cm	*	*	*	165	165	165	165	165
Explosive atmosphere	‡	‡	‡	‡	‡	‡	‡	‡
Nuclear radiation (reactor):								
Neutron flux level (fast): Neutron/cm²-seconds				*	*	10^{10}	*	10^{10}
Time, hours				*	*	1,000	*	1,000
Gamma photon flux level: Photon/cm²-seconds				*	*	10^{11}	*	10^{11}
Time, hours				*	*	1,000	*	1,000
Thermal neutrons	†	†	†	†	†	†	†	†
Nuclear radiation (pulse):								
Neutron flux level (fast): Neutron/cm²-seconds				10^{17}	*	10^{17}	*	*
Time in microseconds				10^{17}	*	10^{17}	*	*
Gamma flux level: Roentgens/seconds				10^{8}	*	10^{8}	*	*
Time in microseconds				80	*	80	*	*
Sand and dust	Applicable only to moving parts§							
Salt atmosphere, hours	96	96	96	96	96	96	96	96
Flammability	Should not sustain combustion§							
Fungus resistance	Nonnutrient in all groups§							
Life, hours:								
Operating	30,000	30,000	30,000	2,000	20,000	2,000	2,000	10,000
Storage	Five years for all groups§							

* Not applicable.
† Thermal neutrons are not listed as a requirement, but since all neutron fluxes have some thermal component, this component should be measured and reported with all tests.
‡ The part to be tested in accordance with Procedure I of MIL-E-5272 for all groups.
§ For additional details refer to Department of Defense, "Environmental Requirements for Electronic Component Parts" (Military Standard 446).

9

Group II. It covers electrical components of the precision type used in oscillator tuning or frequency controlling circuits where electrical stability is of prime importance.

Group III. It covers electronic parts intended for general use in shipboard and ground electronic equipment.

Group IV. It covers electronic parts for use in electronic equipment of high-performance aircraft and surface-to-air and air-to-air missiles.

Group V. It covers electronic parts for use in electronic equipment of high-performance aircraft and specialized shipboard applications.

Group VI. It covers electronic parts for use in electronic equipment of nuclear-powered aircraft and ballistic missiles.

Group VII. It covers electronic parts for use in specialized applications in electronic equipment of high-performance aircraft and missiles.

Group VIII. It covers electronic parts for use in electronic equipment of nuclear-powered weapons.

CHAPTER 2

GENERAL INFORMATION ON CAPACITORS

CAPACITANCE

Capacitance is present between any two adjacent conductors. A capacitor consists basically of two metal plates separated by a dielectric material, such as air, gas, paper, ceramic, or an oxide film. When a voltage is applied between the two metal plates the capacitor will become charged, and the amount of charge will depend primarily on the voltage. The capacitance of the capacitor is the ratio of the charge acquired to the voltage applied, or

$$C = \frac{Q}{V}$$

where Q = charge, coulombs (or amp-sec)
V = voltage, volts
C = capacitance, farads

The farad is the unit of capacitance, and a capacitor has a capacitance of 1 farad if its potential rises by 1 volt when it receives a charge of 1 coulomb. This unit is inconveniently large for practical usage, and the submultiples microfarad (μf—one millionth of a farad) and micromicrofarad ($\mu\mu$f) or picofarad (pf—one million millionth of a farad) are normally used.[1]

The energy of the charge is stored up as electrostatic energy in the dielectric and is equal to $CV^2/2$. If this energy is absorbed at a uniform rate over a time t, the power required is

$$P_{av} = \frac{\frac{1}{2}CV^2}{t}$$

where P_{av} = average power, watts
C = capacitance, farads
V = voltage, volts
t = time, sec

[1] Throughout this book the more convenient term picofarad has been used.

11

Under a-c conditions the rate at which energy is supplied to and returned by the capacitor is

$$P_{av} = 2\pi C V^2 f$$

where f = frequency, cps
V = rms voltage

When a direct voltage is applied to a capacitor, the electric field within the dielectric is displaced, and the bound electric charges are polarized or displaced from their normal position of equilibrium. Work is therefore done in charging the capacitor. The work done in joules (or watt-seconds), which is available as stored potential energy, is

$$J = \tfrac{1}{2}QV, \text{ or } \tfrac{1}{2}CV^2, \text{ or } \frac{Q^2}{2C}$$

where J = joules or watt-sec
C = capacitance, farads
V = voltage, volts
Q = coulombs or amp-sec

The fundamental formula for the capacitance of two flat plates separated by a dielectric material is

$$C = \frac{\kappa A \times 10^{12}}{4\pi d \times 9 \times 10^{11}}$$

which becomes
$$C = \frac{0.0885\kappa A}{d}$$

where C = capacitance, pf
κ = dielectric constant[1]
A = area of one plate, sq cm
d = distance between plates, cm

When more than one plate is used $(N - 1)$ is added to the top line of the above two formulas, where N is the number of plates. Owing to edge and fringe effects, this formula is not strictly true; the capacitance should be slightly higher, and the following corrections should therefore be added to the plate dimensions:

For straight edges, . . add $0.44d$ to the sides
For circular edges, . . add $0.11d$ to the sides

The equivalent circuit of a capacitor may be represented as in Fig. 2-1,

---

[1] The symbol κ (Greek kappa) is used in capacitor work, together with the contraction high-K for high dielectric constant.

where C = capacitance of capacitor

R_s = resistance due to leads, plates, and contacts

R_p = resistance due to the dielectric and case material

L = inductance of leads and plates of the capacitor

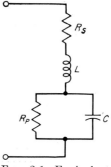

FIG. 2-1. Equivalent circuit of a capacitor.

The behavior of the capacitor at various frequencies is described later in this chapter (page 24). It is important to remember that capacitance is never constant, except under certain fixed conditions. It changes with temperature, frequency, and age, and the capacitance value marked on the capacitor strictly applies only at room temperature and at low frequencies.

CHARACTERISTICS OF DIELECTRIC MATERIALS

Dielectric materials used for capacitors can be grouped in the following five main classes:

1. Mica, glass, low-loss ceramic, etc.: used for capacitors from a few to a few hundred picofarads

2. High-dielectric-constant ceramic: used for capacitors from a few hundred to a few tens of thousands of picofarads

3. Paper and metalized paper: used for capacitors from a few thousand picofarads up to some microfarads

4. Electrolytic (oxide film): used for capacitors from a few to many microfarads

5. Dielectrics, such as polystyrene, polyethylene terephthalate (Mylar[1]), polytetrafluoroethylene (Teflon[1]): range of use from a few hundred picofarads to a few microfarads

Many factors which affect the properties of a material when it is used in a capacitor, among them being the dielectric constant, power factor, leakage current, dielectric absorption, dielectric strength, and operating temperature, are discussed briefly below.

Dielectric Constant[2]

The dielectric constant, permittivity, or specific inductive capacity of any material used as a dielectric is equal to the ratio of the capaci-

[1] Registered trademark for E. I. du Pont de Nemours & Company.

[2] Dielectric constant will be used throughout this book, since the term is commonly used in this country. However, it is not precisely correct. It is not a constant because it varies with temperature and frequency.

tance of a capacitor using the material as a dielectric, to the capacitance of the same capacitor using vacuum as a dielectric. The dielectric constant of dry air is approximately equal to one. A capacitor with solid or liquid dielectric of higher dielectric constant than air or vacuum can therefore store κ times as much energy for equal voltage applied across the capacitor plates. A few typical figures for capacitor dielectrics at 25°C are:

Dielectric constant K

Vacuum	1.0
Dry air	1.00059
Polystyrene	2.5
Polytetrafluoroethylene (Teflon*)	2.0
Polyethylene terephthalate (Mylar*)	3.0
Impregnated paper	4.0–6.0
Mica	6.8
Tantalum oxide	25.0†
Aluminum oxide	7.0
Ceramic (magnesium titanate, etc.)	Up to 20
Ceramic (titania)	80–100
Ceramic (high-K‡)	1,000 and upward

* Registered trademark of E. I. du Pont de Nemours & Company.

† Approximate value, with general acceptance.

‡ The high dielectric constant in high-K ceramic capacitors comes from the fact that the electric charges in the molecular structure of the material are very loosely bound and can move almost freely under the polarizing voltage, resulting in high total capacity.

Dielectrics can be classified in two main groups—polar and nonpolar materials. Polar materials have a permanent unbalance in the electric charges within the molecular structure. The dipoles within the structure consist of molecules whose ends are oppositely charged. These dipoles therefore tend to align themselves in the presence of an alternating electric field (if the frequency is not too high). The resultant oscillation causes a large loss at certain frequencies and at certain temperatures.

In nonpolar materials the electric charges within the molecular structure are balanced and the dipoles do not rotate under applied fields, although they may distort. No sharp loss peaks with frequency and temperature therefore exist. Polyvinylchloride (PVC) is an example of a polar material, having a dielectric constant of 10 at low frequencies, falling to 3.0 or 4.0 at a few megacycles per second, while polystyrene is an example of a nonpolar material, having a dielectric constant of approximately 2.5 for direct current and for alternating currents up to many thousands of megacycles per second.

An exceptional material having special properties is high-dielectric-constant ceramic, which is a nonpolar material in that it maintains its dielectric constant for frequencies up to many thousands of megacycles per second, but has very high induced polarization effects. Under voltage stress, the molecular structure distorts to such an extent that it becomes extremely sensitive to temperature, mechanical pressure, and applied voltage. Under these circumstances, the dielectric constant becomes very high.

Losses in Dielectric Materials

Losses occur due to current leakage, dielectric absorption, etc., depending on the frequency of operation. For a good nonpolar dielectric the curve relating loss with frequency takes the approximate shape given in Fig. 2-2. For a polar material the loss-frequency curve may be shown approximately as in Fig. 2-3.

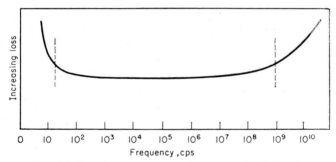

FIG. 2-2. Loss frequency curve for a nonpolar dielectric.

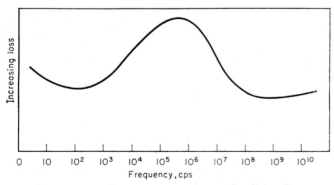

FIG. 2-3. Loss frequency curve for a polar dielectric.

The variation of dielectric constant with frequency is negligible so long as the loss is low. Increased losses occur when the process of alignment cannot be completed, owing to molecular collisions, and in these regions there is a fall in dielectric constant. Viscous drag in the molecular structure limits the frequency at which full alignment can be carried out. If the applied frequency is comparable with the limiting frequency, losses will become high.

Equivalent circuits showing series and parallel loss resistance can be given but are greatly dependent on the system of measurement at any particular frequency. The important criterion is the ratio

$$\frac{\text{Power wasted per cycle}}{\text{Power stored per cycle}}$$

This is the power factor of the material, and for good dielectrics, it is independent of frequency. Power factor, phase angle, and phase difference are defined as shown in Fig. 2-4.

When alternating current flows in a capacitor, the current leads the voltage by a little less than the theoretical 90° (angle ϕ in Fig. 2-4). This is the phase angle. The complement of this angle (δ) is termed the loss angle. The cosine of the phase angle or sine of the loss angle is the power factor. The dielectric loss is therefore $EI \cos \phi$ or $EI \sin \delta$. The loss angle normally is so small (for power factor values of less than 10 per cent) that tan δ, the dissipation factor, can be considered equal to sin δ. While it is more convenient to use tan δ rather than sin δ or cos ϕ, since it is easier to meas-

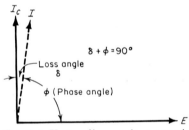

FIG. 2-4. Vector diagram for a capacitor.

ure, both notations are used to describe dielectric losses in a capacitor. In a perfect capacitor with no dielectric loss, $\delta = 0$. The dissipation factor is

$$\tan \delta = 2\pi f R C \times 10^{-6}$$

where f = frequency, cps
   R = equivalent series resistance, ohms
   C = capacitance, μf

The power factor can be represented as the ratio of the power loss in the dielectric to the product of the applied voltage and current. That is,

$$\frac{\text{Total power loss in watts}}{\text{Volts (rms) applied} \times \text{amperes (rms) flowing}}$$

The power factor can therefore be calculated from

$$\cos \phi = W \times \frac{10^6}{2\pi f C E^2}$$

where W = watts (total)
$\quad C$ = capacitance, μf
$\quad E$ = voltage, volts
$\quad f$ = frequency, cps

The Q of a capacitor is the reciprocal of the dissipation factor. It may be defined as the ratio of the pure reactance to the effective resistance.

Dielectric Absorption

If a capacitor were completely free from dielectric absorption, the initial charging or polarization current when connected to a d-c supply would be

$$i = \left(\frac{E}{R}\right) e^{-t/CR}$$

where i = current flowing after a time t
$\quad E$ = applied voltage
$\quad R$ = capacitor series resistance

and the polarization current would die off asymptotically to zero. If R is small, this takes place in a very short time, and the capacitor is completely charged. In all solid-dielectric capacitors it is found that, after a fully charged capacitor is momentarily discharged and left open-circuited for some time, a new charge accumulates within the capacitor, because some of the original charge has been "absorbed" by the dielectric. This produces the effect known as dielectric absorption. A time lag is thus introduced in the rate of charging and of discharging the capacitor.

Dielectric absorption is due to the finite time taken to displace the bound charges in the dielectric from their normal positions because of the viscous forces which resist their motion. Polarization time varies with different dielectrics—the polarization may be almost instantaneous or it may take many hours. Even within the same dielectric a few electrons or ions become free to move only after a period which may be seconds or even days. The effect is exceedingly complex and, for example, in the case of an impregnated-paper capacitor, the polarization times of paper and of impregnant are different.

The effect of dielectric absorption is to reduce the capacitance as the frequency of operation is increased and also to cause unwanted time delays in certain pulse circuits or in circuits requiring rapid charge and discharge characteristics.

Leakage Currents and Time Constants of Capacitors

Losses due to leakage currents when a capacitor is being used on direct current prevent indefinite storage capacity being realized, and the charge acquired will leak away once the source is removed. The time in which the charge leaks away to $1/e$, or 36.8 per cent, of its initial value is given by RC, where R is the leakage resistance and C is the capacitance. If R is measured in megohms and C in microfarads, the time constant is in seconds. This can also be expressed as a product of either megohm-microfarads or ohm-farads. Some typical time constants for various dielectrics used in capacitors are:

Polystyrene.. Several days
Impregnated paper................................ Several hours
Tantalum-pellet electrolytic capacitors.............. 1 or 2 hours
High-dielectric-constant capacitors (ceramic).......... Several minutes
Plain-foil electrolytic capacitors .... Several seconds

It should be borne in mind that below capacitance values of about 0.1 μf, the time constant is generally determined by the structure, leakage paths, etc., of the capacitor assembly itself rather than the dielectric material. Leakage current increases with increase of temperature (roughly exponentially). In good dielectrics at room temperature it is too small to measure, but at higher temperatures the current may become appreciable, even in good dielectrics.

INSULATION RESISTANCE

The insulation resistance of a dielectric material may be measured in terms of surface resistivity in ohms or megohms, or as volume resistivity in ohm-centimeters. Surface and volume resistivities are measured using apparatus similar to that shown in Fig. 2-5.

The specimen is mounted in mercury and a potential difference of 500 volts d-c is connected across the inner and outer metal rings with mercury electrodes to the top surface. Typical surface insulation resistance figures for some good dielectrics measured in this way (to ASTM:D257) are given in Table 2-1.

For capacitors, a figure of "ohm-farads" is often quoted (see paper-

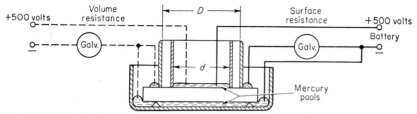

FIG. 2-5. Typical arrangement of apparatus for surface and volume resistivity test.

dielectric capacitors), as the insulation resistance product, and varies with capacitance, particularly in the higher capacitance values.

Volume resistivity is measured similarly between the top and bottom surfaces, as shown on the left side of Fig. 2-5. Typical figures for volume resistivities are shown in Table 2-1. It is important to remem-

TABLE 2-1. TYPICAL INSULATION RESISTANCE FIGURES
FOR SEVERAL GOOD DIELECTRICS

Dielectric	Surface resistivity, ohms	Volume resistivity, ohm-cm
Polystyrene..............................	10^{16}	10^{17}–10^{19}
Polytetrafluoroethylene (Teflon*).....	3.5×10^{13}	10^{16}
Polyethylene terephthalate (Mylar*)...	10^{13}	10^{13}

* Registered trademark of E. I. du Pont de Nemours & Company.

ber that the insulation resistance of good dielectrics in a capacitor (glass, mica, etc.) may be reduced by any encasing material having a lower insulation resistance, such as the phenol resins, particularly under conditions of high humidity or temperature.

THE INSULATION RESISTANCE OF FIXED CAPACITORS

Methods of measuring insulation resistance of dielectric materials have been described in the previous section, but the insulation resistance of the assembled capacitor is important in circuit use. The insulation resistance of any capacitor will be lowered in the presence of high humidity (unless it is sealed) and will be reduced when operated in high ambient temperatures (whether sealed or not).

For perfectly sealed capacitors used under conditions of high humidity there should be no deterioration, but for imperfectly sealed capaci-

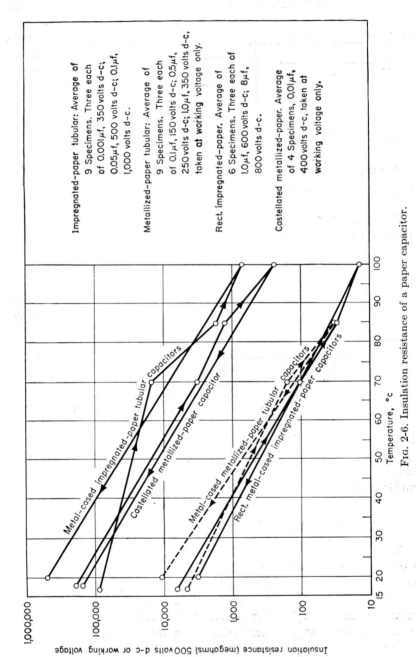

Impregnated-paper tubular: Average of 9 Specimens. Three each of 0.001μf, 350 volts d-c; 0.05μf, 500 volts d-c; 0.1μf, 1,000 volts d-c.

Metallized-paper tubular: Average of 9 Specimens. Three each of 0.1μf, 150 volts d-c; 0.5μf, 250 volts d-c; 1.0μf, 350 volts d-c, taken at working voltage only.

Rect. impregnated-paper. Average of 6 Specimens. Three each of 1.0μf, 600 volts d-c; 8μf, 800 volts d-c.

Castellated metallized-paper. Average of 4 Specimens. 0.01μf, 400 volts d-c, taken at working voltage only.

Metal-cased impregnated-paper tubular capacitors

Castellated metallized-paper capacitor

Metal-cased metallized-paper tubular capacitors

Rect. metal-cased impregnated-paper capacitors

Temperature, °c

Insulation resistance (megohms) 500 volts d-c or working voltage

FIG. 2-6. Insulation resistance of a paper capacitor.

20

tors the drop in insulation resistance will be roughly inversely proportional to the effectiveness of the sealing. Unsealed capacitors will show a large and rapid drop in insulation resistance under these conditions.

Under high-temperature conditions the fall in insulation resistance for most capacitors is given approximately by the formula

$$R_T = \frac{R_t}{e^{-K(T-t)}}$$

where R_T = insulation resistance at high temperature T

R_t = insulation resistance at low temperature t

e = base of Napierian logs (2.718)

K = a constant, as described below

For both impregnated-paper and metalized-paper capacitors, K is taken as 0.1. For mineral jelly impregnation the insulation resistance drops approximately to half its value for every 7°C rise in temperature corresponding to this value of K, and for oil impregnation it drops by approximately half for every 10°C rise in temperature. This becomes more important for the larger values of capacitance.

For both ceramic- and mica-dielectric capacitors, K is taken as 0.05. For ceramic- and mica-dielectric capacitors as normally used the fall is not so steep, and no correction is usually needed.

The sets of curves given in Figs. 2-6, 2-7, and 2-8 show the results of measurements taken on typical impregnated-paper, metalized-paper, mica, and ceramic capacitors. In each case the insulation resistance was measured at room temperature, at 70°C, at 85°C, at 100°C, and again at room temperature. As waxed mica capacitors would not withstand temperatures of 70°C and above without the wax melting, this was removed for these measurements.

All insulation-resistance measurements are in megohms at 500 volts d-c, with the exception of the metalized-paper types. These capacitors were tested at their working voltage with a 10 kilohms resistor in series.

It will be seen from the curves that it is possible for the insulation resistance of a rectangular metal-cased impregnated-paper capacitor to fall to a few tens of megohms at a temperature of 100°C, while the tubular types (having a higher initial insulation resistance) may fall to a few hundred megohms at the same temperature. The fall in insulation resistance of mica capacitors depends greatly on the material in which the capacitor is encased.

Since the measured value of insulation resistance is the result of

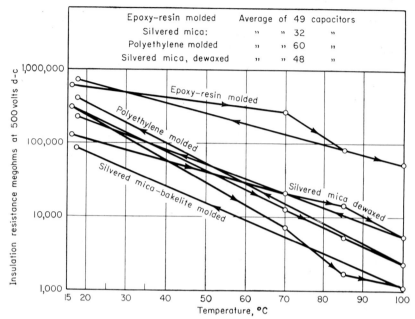

FIG. 2-7. Insulation resistance of a silvered-mica capacitor.

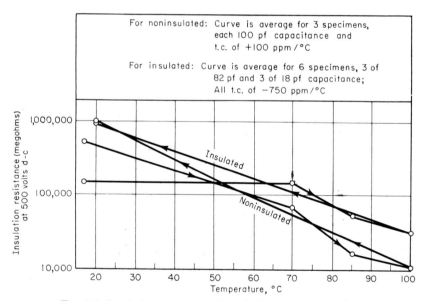

FIG. 2-8. Insulation resistance of a tubular ceramic capacitor.

three separate currents, studies have shown that to determine accurately the insulation resistance of a capacitor, the following steps are necessary:

1. The measurement voltage should be the same as the working voltage.

2. The temperature and humidity must be controlled within very close limits.

3. The electrification time must be specified and must be sufficient for the capacitor to stabilize.

DIELECTRIC STRENGTH

The ultimate dielectric strength of a material is determined by the voltage at which it breaks down. The stress in kilovolts per inch (or volts per mil), at which this occurs depends on the thickness of the material, the temperature, the frequency and the waveform of the testing voltage, the method of application, etc. Therefore comparisons between different materials should ideally be made on specimens equal in thickness and under identical conditions of measurement. The ultimate dielectric strength is measured by applying increasing voltage through electrodes fitted with guard rings to a specimen with recessed surfaces (to ensure that the region of maximum stress shall be as uniform as possible). Preparation of the specimens is important and their previous histories should be known.

A practical limit to the dielectric strength of a material may be conveniently taken as the *discharge inception voltage,* above which progressive breakdown occurs. This is usually much lower than the ultimate dielectric strength for short applications of voltage. Above the discharge inception voltage, a form of corona is created by the discharges, and progressive deterioration takes place. It is an advantage that tests for inception discharge voltage are usually nondestructive tests, as corona produces "noise" which can be detected and measured.

The dielectric strength of a material is always reduced when it is operated at high temperatures or if moisture is present. Few materials are completely homogeneous, and breakdown may take the form of current leak along certain small paths through the material; these become heated and cause rapid deterioration, or flashover, along the surface and permanent carbonization of the surface of organic materials. Inorganic materials, such as glass, ceramic, and mica, are usually resistant to this form of breakdown. The time for which the voltage is applied is important; most dielectrics will withstand a much higher voltage for brief periods. With increasing frequency the dielectric strength is reduced, particularly at radio frequencies, depending on the power factor, etc., of the material.

THE EFFECT OF FREQUENCY ON DIELECTRIC MATERIALS AND CAPACITOR ASSEMBLIES

At very low frequencies and also at very high frequencies there is an increase of loss which sets a limit to the practical use of a capacitor with any given dielectric. At very low frequencies various forms of

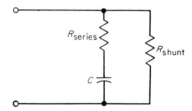

FIG. 2-9. Series and shunt losses in a capacitor.

leakage in the dielectric material have time to become apparent, such as d-c leakage currents and long time-constant effects, which have no effect at high frequencies. At very high frequencies some of the processes contributing to dielectric polarization do not have time to become effective and therefore cause loss. These losses might be simply and approximately represented as in Fig. 2-9.

At very low frequencies the circuit is entirely resistive, all the current passing through the shunt resistance (d-c leakage resistance, etc.). At very high frequencies the current passes through the capacitance C, but all the volts are dropped across the series resistance, and again the circuit is lossy. This series resistance may be due to the resistance of the capacitor leads, the silvering (in the case of silvered mica or ceramic capacitors), contact resistances, etc., in the capacitor assembly itself. These limit the upper frequency independently of the dielectric material used. Similarly, leakage across the case containing the dielectric may limit the lower frequency so that not all the useful range of the dielectric itself may be realized.

The chart in Fig. 2-10 shows the approximate usable frequency ranges for capacitors with various dielectric materials. The construction of the capacitor assembly will affect the frequency coverage to some extent, so that the chart should be regarded as a guide only.

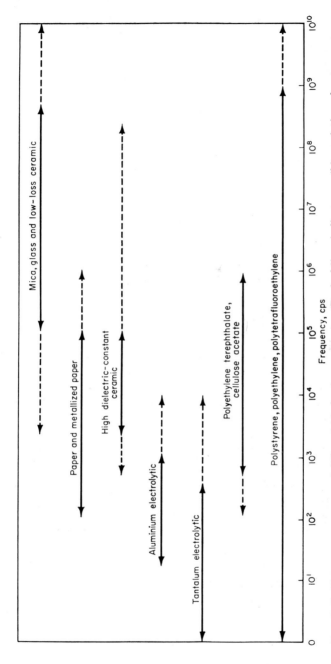

Fig. 2-10. Frequency coverage of different kinds of capacitors. (Dashed lines indicate possible variations due to construction techniques, capacitance value, etc.)

The Impedance of a Capacitor

The current in a capacitor when an alternating voltage is applied is given by

$$I = 2\pi f C V \qquad \text{amp}$$

where C = capacitance, farads
$\quad\;\; V$ = voltage, volts
$\quad\;\; f$ = frequency, cps
and the reactance is given by

$$X_c = -\frac{1}{2\pi f C} \qquad \text{ohms}$$

An ideal capacitor would have entirely negative reactance, but the losses, described previously, due to dielectric, case, and leads, preclude this. In addition, inductance is also present in varying amounts, and therefore as the frequency is increased the inductive or positive reactance increases, and above a critical frequency the capacitor will behave as an inductor. At the resonant frequency the impedance of the capacitor is controlled by its effective resistance, which in turn is made up of the losses described. Every capacitor will resonate at some given frequency (depending on its construction) and, having inductance and resistance, will exhibit a complex impedance, capacitative in one range of frequencies, resistive in another, and inductive in still another. The variation of impedance with frequency of a typical paper-dielectric capacitor is shown in Fig. 6-6.

TABLE OF PROPERTIES OF DIELECTRIC MATERIALS USED FOR CAPACITORS

Table 2-2 gives an indication of capacitor characteristics for most of the materials used as capacitor dielectrics. Most of the recently developed dielectric materials are included.

The most complete tables of properties of dielectric materials are those published by the Laboratory for Insulation Research by A. R. Von Hippel and his associates. These tables are contained in the book "Dielectric Materials and Applications."

TABLE 2-2. PROPERTIES OF SOME CAPACITOR DIELECTRIC MATERIALS

Material	Power factor (at 25°C)		Dielectric constant (K) at 25°C, 60 cps	Capacitance at 85°C relative to 25°C, 60 cps, %	Insulation resistance (ohm-farads) 500 volts d-c		Dielectric absorption 1 min after 2-sec discharge, %	Operating temp range, °C	Remarks
	60 cps	1 kc/sec			25°C	85°C			
Paper (Kraft Cap tissue) with:									
Mineral oil	0.002	0.0035	2.23	102	15,000	100	2.0	−55 to 105	Maximum frequency of operation approx. 1 Mc/sec
Castor oil	0.005	0.007	4.7	96	1,500	50	2.5	−25 to 65	
Silicon oil	0.003	0.0035	2.6	101	20,000	150	1.0	−60 to 125	
Polyisobutylene	0.002	0.003	2.2	101	20,000	150	1.0	−55 to 125	
Chlorinated naphthalene	0.004	0.005	5.2	93	4,000	50	2.5	−20 to 55	
Chlorinated diphenyl	0.0025	0.003	4.9	96	10,000	100	2.5	−55 to 85	
Polyethylene terephthalate	0.0025	0.004	2.8	101	100,000	10,000	0.25	−70 to 150	Losses are high, between 1 and 10 Mc/sec
Above with silicone fluid	0.0025	0.0045	3.0	102	20,000	2,000	2.0	−60 to 150	
Polytetrafluoroethylene (cast film)	0.001	0.0005	2.05	99	1,000,000	100,000	0.02	−90 to 200	Maximum freq. of operation, approx. 10,000 Mc/sec
Above with silicone fluid	0.001	0.0005	2.1	98	20,000	20,000	2.5	−60 to 200	
Cellulose acetate	0.009	0.015	3.8	105	15,000	200	1.5	−70 to 125	
Above with silicone fluid	0.01	0.016	3.8	104	8,000	100	2.5	−60 to 125	
Polystyrene	0.001	0.0005	2.6	99	1,000,000	100,000	0.02	−70 to 85	Maximum freq. of operation, approx. 10,000 Mc/sec
Polyethylene	0.001	0.0005	2.25	96	100,000	1,000	0.02	−70 to 85	
Mica (ruby)	0.0025	0.0006	5.5	100	100,000	1,000	0.7	−60 to 160	Maximum freq. of operation, approx. 10,000 Mc/sec

TABLE 2-2. PROPERTIES OF SOME CAPACITOR DIELECTRIC MATERIALS (*Continued*)

Material	Loss (at room temperature)		Power factor (loss angle tan δ)	Dielectric constant (over operating frequency range)	Dielectric strength, volts per mil (breakdown)	Temperature limits, °C		Remarks
	Limiting frequency of operation							
	Approx. min	Approx. max				Approx. min	Approx. max	
(1)	(2)	(3)	(4)	(5)	(6)	(7)	(8)	(9)
Glass.............. (soft lead-soda)	200 cps	10,000 Mc/sec	0.001	6.5-6.8	<500	No limit	+200	
Glass.............. (hard, borosilicate)	100 cps	10,000 Mc/sec	0.001	4.0	<500	No limit	+200	
Quartz.............. (fused)	100 cps	>10,000 Mc/sec	0.0002	3.8	1,000	No limit	+300	
Ceramic.............. (low-dielectric-constant types) Magnesium silicate	100 cps*	10,000 Mc/sec	0.001	5.4-7.0	200-300	No limit	+150	
Ceramic-dielectric-constant.......... (Medium-dielectric-constant types) Titania Rutile (TiO_2)	500 cps*	5,000 Mc/sec	0.001	70-90	100-150	No limit	+125	
Ceramic.............. (High-dielectric-constant types) Titanate	1,000 cps*	1,000 Mc/sec	0.01	Approx. 1,000– over 7,000	100	−100	+120	Characteristics dependent on temperature. Sharp max in dielectric constant at 120°C. Dielectric constant depends on volts. Below 120°C hysteresis occurs and loss dependent on volts. Other high-*K* materials exist with different peaks

* Can be direct current, but slow capacitance change is possible.

CHAPTER 3

CHARACTERISTICS AND SELECTION OF CAPACITORS

CHARACTERISTICS OF FIXED CAPACITORS

The major characteristics of a capacitor are determined by its dielectric material. Therefore, capacitors are usually categorized by their dielectric material: paper, mica, ceramic, etc. Since it is useful for the electronic-equipment designer to know these characteristics, Table 3-9 outlines some of the important characteristics of fixed capacitors, and Table 3-11 provides comparable information for variable capacitors.

The military specifications which are listed in Chaps. 5 and 14, for fixed and variable capacitors, respectively, are performance documents providing individual specifications written for each specific dielectric material. Although throughout the book an occasional reference is made either to these specifications or to the type designation for a particular type of capacitor, the military specification system as such has not been dealt with in detail. Whenever additional information is required with respect to military specifications, volume I of "Techniques for Application of Electronic Component Parts in Military Equipment" should be consulted (see Bibliography).

Impregnated-paper Capacitors

Impregnated-paper capacitors are general-purpose capacitors, constructed by rolling two or more sheets of paper, which is the dielectric or insulator, between two metal foils, and then filling with an impregnant.

The following characteristics are pertinent to this type of capacitor (compared with a mica capacitor):

1. Cost: relatively inexpensive
2. Power factor: relatively high (up to 0.01 at 25°C, measured at 1 kc; 0.005 to 0.04 at −55°C, depending upon the impregnant)
3. Capacitance to volume ratio: high
4. D-c working voltage: average
5. Capacity tolerance (initial): wide ($\pm 5\%$ possible, usually $\pm 10\%$ or larger)

29

The maximum permissible d-c working voltage of an impregnated-paper capacitor is dependent upon the ambient temperature.   The life of such a capacitor is approximately inversely proportional to the fifth power of the operating voltage up to 85°C.   All capacitors in accordance with military specification MIL-C-25 are rated at 40°C. Voltage derating curves are given in this specification for each specific style of capacitor.   The per cent of voltage derating required varies with the capacitor characteristic (which indicates a different kind of impregnation) and the energy content of the capacitor when fully charged.   In general, for normal service, rated voltage is specified for up to 45°C, for characteristics D, E, and F; up to 75°C, for characteristics A and B; and up to 85°C, for characteristic K for the 0- to 0.5-watt-second group.   For higher-watt-second groups other derating curves are specified.

Reliability studies have shown that capacitors in a typical application have a failure rate in proportion to the percentage of applied voltage to rated voltage.   In one such study the failure rate in per cent per 5,000 hr of operation varied from 0.26 for 25 per cent of rated voltage to 1.6 per cent for 100 per cent of rated voltage.

Impregnated-paper capacitors for use with a-c voltage should be chosen or designed for such applications, since case size (area), impregnant, etc., all affect the a-c voltage rating.   The allowable a-c component for a d-c paper capacitor varies with impregnant and construction.   Therefore, there is a great variation among available capacitors.   Specification MIL-C-25 limits the steady-state d-c plus the peak a-c voltage to the rated voltage, provided the a-c voltage does not exceed 20 per cent of the rating at 60 cycles, 15 per cent at 120 cycles, or 1 per cent at 10,000 cycles.

The insulation resistance of impregnated-paper capacitors, at room temperature (25°C), is equivalent to the product of 1,500 to 20,000 ohm-farads (depending upon the paper and the impregnant) but falls rapidly as the ambient temperature is increased.   In the small hermetically sealed tubular capacitors (characteristic K) the insulation resistance may fall from a product equivalent to 20,000 ohm-farads plus, at 25°C, to 20 ohm-farads at 125°C.   This fall in insulation resistance tends to be inversely proportional to the capacitance from 1 microfarad upward.   The capacitance variation with temperature is a function primarily of the impregnant, and the greatest variations can be expected at low temperatures.   The nominal variations in capacitance at −55°C from the value at 25°C, which can be expected for the various impregnants, are shown in Table 3-1.

TABLE 3-1. PER CENT OF CAPACITANCE VARIATION AT −55°C FROM
THE 25°C VALUE FOR DIFFERENT IMPREGNANTS

Specification MIL-C-25 characteristic	Impregnant	Percentage of variation
D	Castor oil	5 to −15
A and F	Chlorinated synthetic	−20 to −30
B and E	Mineral oil	+2 to −10
K	Polyisobutenes, silicone fluids	−2 to −5
None	Mineral wax	−2 to −6
None	Chlorinated naphthalene synthetic	−5 to −10

The power factor at 25°C varies from 0.003 to 0.01 at 1 kc/sec and tends to increase with frequency. For applications where the capacitors will be subjected to peak voltages of 5 volts or less, or to high-frequency vibration and shock, extended foil construction (see Chap. 6) should be used as some pressure contacts require appreciable voltage to maintain their low resistance. Molded-paper capacitors, such as those covered by specification MIL-C-91, are of poorer quality than the metal-encased hermetically sealed types specified in specification MIL-C-25. The insulation resistance of the molded types is much lower under the influence of moisture and decreases with the aging of the capacitor. Where low capacitance to ground is a requirement, the ceramic-cased hermetically sealed (ceramic or glass end seals) types are suitable. Although capacitors with this type of construction have shown, after a 1,000-hr life test, superior capacitance stability, higher insulation resistance values, and smaller dissipation factor changes over the equivalent metal-encased types, care should be used in their application as this type of construction exhibits seal failures when subject to thermal shock.

Storage studies for a period of two years on representative paper capacitors, in accordance with specification MIL-C-25 and its predecessor, JAN-C-25, have shown that when capacitors are subjected to ambients of 50° ± 2°C, 90–95 per cent rh (relative humidity), a progressive deterioration for the values for insulation resistance, dissipation factor, dielectric strength, and flashover voltage takes place. For equal or lower temperatures in combination with lower relative humidity, deterioration takes place although at a slower rate. Considering all the controlled ambients used, the axial-lead type CP21 and CP04 showed the least variation. Types CP63, CP55, and CP41 followed in that order.

Impregnated-paper capacitors are used for applications such as:

1. Blocking   4. Coupling
2. Buffer   5. Filtering
3. Bypass

For applications which require either a higher order of reliability than that furnished by specification MIL-C-25 or a shock and high-frequency vibration capability, capacitors should be selected in accordance with specification MIL-C-14157. Axial-lead tubular capacitors subjected to high-frequency vibration and shock should always be clamped.

Metalized-paper Capacitors

Metalized-paper capacitors are constructed in such a way that the voids which exist between paper and foil in an ordinary paper capacitor are obviated. These capacitors were developed in Germany and introduced into this country in the late 1940s. In this type of capacitor, one side of the paper is metalized before rolling. Metalized-paper capacitors are smaller than ordinary impregnated-paper capacitors having a voltage rating up to 600 volts. This is particularly true of voltage ratings lower than 100 volts d-c and capacitance values higher than 0.01 μf, where the reduction in volume may be as much as 75 per cent. In addition, under voltage stress, if the dielectric fails and a short occurs, self-healing action can take place. When the paper is punctured, the very thin metal quickly evaporates in the area of the puncture and prevents a permanent short. The maximum voltage at which the self-healing will occur is termed the test voltage. The maximum voltage which may be applied instantaneously without destroying the capacitor is termed the spark voltage. Maximum voltage should never be applied for more than a few seconds as continuous sparking will rapidly destroy the capacitor.

The insulation resistance of metalized-paper capacitors at 25°C is equivalent to the product of 250 to 2,000 ohm-farads and is generally six to ten times less than for the ordinary foil and paper types, although some recent developments (such as Type 116P made by Sprague Electric Company) are comparable to the foil types. Metalized-paper capacitors should not be used for coupling, but may be used for decoupling or smoothing where the primary requirement is low impedance

Metalized-paper capacitors should be used with care on alternating current. The d-c voltage rating cannot be simply translated into an a-c rating. A conversion factor for one particular capacitor rating may be incorrect for other capacitor sizes, d-c ratings, and types of construction.   A-c rating cannot be based upon foil types because of the poor heat conductivity of the metalized winding.   The a-c 60- or 400-cycle peak voltage should never exceed the d-c voltage rating, and while at lower capacitance values this may be the limiting factor, above 10 μf the problem of heat generated in the capacitor is usually the limiting factor.   This rating can be improved by improving heat conduction from the capacitor element to the case.

Metalized-paper capacitors should not be used where frequent surges over the normal working voltages are likely to occur; otherwise, deterioration in capacitance, power factor, and insulation resistance will result.   If two capacitors are used in parallel, a resistor of 1,000 ohms is usually connected in series with each of them to prevent any transient surges which may occur if one capacitor fails, thus keeping the other from being affected.   The power factor of this type of capacitor at 25°C varies from 0.005 to 0.015 when measured at 1 kc.   Military specification MIL-C-18312 has two characteristics: characteristic N for −55 to 125°C operation, and characteristic M for −55 to 100°C operation.

Mica-dielectric Capacitors

Mica capacitors are constructed either by stacking very thin sheets of mica alternately between layers of foil or by bonding a silver deposit directly on the surface of the mica dielectric.   This "stack" is then clamped (to minimize capacitance variation resulting from thermal expansions by excluding maximum amount of air), terminations are made, and the mold or dip coating for mechanical and environmental protection is applied.   The following characteristics are pertinent to this type of capacitor:

1. Cost: more expensive than paper capacitors
2. Power factor: at 25°C, 0.001 at 1 kc, decreasing to about 0.0002 at 1 Mc
3. Q: high [usually in excess of 2,500 (MIL-C-5 requires minimum of 1,200) from 100 to 1,000 μf at 1 Mc.   Q decreases for higher and lower capacitance values]
4. Capacitance to volume ratio: low, when compared to paper
5. D-c working voltage: high voltages possible
6. Capacity tolerances (initial): close (as close as ±0.25 per cent, although ±2 per cent is the minimum listed in MIL-C-5)

The important characteristics of mica capacitors are low power factor (over a wide-frequency range), high-voltage operation, and low capacitance drift with temperature or age.   The stability of the "silvered-mica" type is greater than that of the foil type with a capacitance change for a high-quality unit on the order of ± 3 per cent after 10 years of operation at room ambients.   Precision mica capacitors used as substandards can be adjusted to a capacitance value with a tolerance of better than 0.01 per cent for values over 1 μf.   They are hermetically sealed to prevent environment from affecting stability. Capacitors of this type have remained constant in capacitance within ± 0.2 pf of a value of 10,000 pf for a test period of 10,000 hr at room temperature.   The temperature coefficient is low and is dependent upon the following:

1. Method of clamping the "stack," including the enclosure
2. Source and treatment of mica
3. Capacitor construction (foil vs. silvered mica)

Military specification MIL-C-5 covers the temperature coefficients and allowable capacitance drift, as shown in Table 3-2.

TABLE 3-2. TEMPERATURE COEFFICIENTS BY CHARACTERISTIC IN ACCORDANCE WITH MILITARY SPECIFICATION MIL-C-5

Characteristic for specification	Temperature coefficient	Capacitance drift
B	Not specified	Not specified
C	± 200 ppm/°C	$\pm 0.5\%$
D	± 100 ppm/°C	$\pm 0.3\%$
E	-20 to $+100$ ppm/°C	$\pm 0.1\% + 0.1$ pf
F	0 to $+70$ ppm/°C	$\pm 0.05\% + 0.1$ pf

Since the silvered-mica capacitor has a better temperature coefficient than the stacked-plate type, characteristics C, D, E, and F (axial wire lead or "postage-stamp" types only) are usually of the silvered type.   Both types show slight noncyclic capacitance shifts during temperature cycling although this is more pronounced with the stacked-plate capacitor.   In most of the types available, the temperature capacitance curve is not entirely linear.   There is also a wide spread of mean-temperature coefficients between different specimens of the same batch.   Good temperature coefficients (characteristics E or better with capacitance drift ± 0.05 per cent) can be obtained on the dipped-type capacitors now available for transistor circuitry, etc.

The insulation resistance of mica capacitors, as with other capacitors, decreases with temperature.   As an example, the insulation resistance for a typical CM 35 capacitor (10,000 pf) would decrease from an average 50,000+ megohms at 25°C to an average of 15,000+ megohms at 85°C, and to an average of 200+ megohms at 175°C. Mica capacitors are now available for operation at rated voltage at 125 and 150°C.

The current-carrying capacity of the silvered-mica capacitors is less than that of the foil; therefore, they are less suitable for heavy current work and this imposes a limitation on radio frequency and pulse-loading applications. Storage studies on a limited number of types of CM20, CM65, and CM55 indicate that these types of mica capacitors are not seriously affected when stored at 25°C, ±2°C, 40 to 50 per cent rh; or 50°C, ±2°C, 40 to 50 per cent rh for periods up to 18 months. However, the same capacitors, after six months' storage at 50°C, ±2°C, 90 to 95 per cent rh, exhibited almost total degradation. All samples showed excessive current flow upon the application of the dielectric strength test and insulation resistance values which would be considered short circuits for all practical purposes.

Mica capacitors are used for such applications as:

1. Blocking
2. Bypass (high frequency)
3. Buffer
4. Coupling
5. Filtering (high frequency)
6. Fixed tuning (high voltage, high current)

Button Mica Capacitors

A specialized type of mica capacitor, the button mica capacitor, has characteristics quite similar to those of the molded types described above. Military specification MIL-C-10950 covers two characteristics, B and D, with identical values for the same characteristic according to specification MIL-C-5. On a performance basis, two general types are covered: the nonhermetically sealed type for 85°C operation with relatively low insulation resistance in the presence of moisture and the hermetically sealed button capacitor for 125°C operation with high insulation resistance under all conditions. These capacitors are suitable for use up to 500 Mc/sec for such applications as bypass, coupling, and tuning.

Ceramic-dielectric Capacitors

Ceramic-dielectric capacitors ("ceramic capacitors") are made in three main classes: low-dielectric-constant low-loss; medium-dielectric-constant temperature-compensating; and high-dielectric-constant.

The low-dielectric-constant low-loss types are generally made of steatite or similar material. Steatite has a dielectric constant of approximately 8.0, and other materials may give dielectric constants between 6.0 and 15.0. Their performance at high frequency, from about 50 kc/sec upward, is excellent. The power factor is reasonably low (0.001), approaching that of mica. The temperature coefficient is between $+80$ and $+120$ ppm/°C, and the capacitors are normally very cyclic in behavior. The temperature coefficients vary less between different batches than for capacitors of any other dielectric except glass and vacuum. They operate at comparatively high voltages, about 500 volts (depending upon size), over a temperature range of -55 to about 150°C.

The second class, medium-dielectric-constant ceramic capacitors (K varies from 6 to 110), are primarily temperature-compensating capacitors. The temperature coefficients of these capacitors vary from approximately $+100$ to -800 ppm/°C and are proportional (as well as the dielectric constant) to the amount of titanium dioxide mixed with the other titanates. The power factor is low and may vary from below 0.04 to 0.4 per cent at 1 Mc/sec. Military specification MIL-C-20 specifies by characteristic nominal temperature coefficients (TCs) of $+100$, 0, -30, -80, -150, -220, -330, -470, and -750 ppm/°C. Because of the spread of actual values from the straight-line nominal value, the temperature coefficient must also have a tolerance (TTC). The capacitance temperature curve tends to be nonlinear; therefore, the nominal temperature coefficient specified in specification MIL-C-20 represents the slope of a line determined by ΔC when the temperature is varied from 25 to 85°C. Since the temperature coefficient curve is not a straight line through 25°C, the TCs and TTCs are specified in specification MIL-C-20 as a series of figures, with the TTCs shown as an envelope over the temperature range -55 to 85°C. The TTCs available in specification MIL-C-20 are G, H, J, and K, which approximate ± 30, ± 60, ± 120, and ± 250 ppm/°C for the temperatures between 25 and 85°C. These TTCs have been specified as plus and minus to enable calculation of maximum and minimum deviation from the temperature coefficient. It should be noted that these are approximate only and are applicable only between 25 and 85°C. The exact values should be obtained from the figures in specification MIL-C-20.

Care should be exercised in applying these capacitors to assure that the location is such that the time-temperature curve is the same for the capacitor as for the parts for which the compensation is required.

Capacitors in accordance with this specification have been subjected to high-frequency vibration and shock tests in addition to the other environmental tests. This type of capacitor has characteristics in accordance with Table 3-3.

TABLE 3-3. CHARACTERISTICS OF CERAMIC CAPACITORS (TEMPERATURE-
COMPENSATING TYPES IN ACCORDANCE WITH MILITARY
SPECIFICATIONS MIL-C-20)

Characteristic	Specification MIL-C-20 requirement	Nominal value
Capacitance drift...........	0.2% or 0.5 pf, whichever is greater	0.01–0.15%
Q at 1 Mc/sec.............	Varies from 500 minimum for capacitance value of 5 pf to 1,000 minimum for all capacitance values of 30 pf or more	720–2,500 plus
25°C insulation resistance....	7,500 megohms minimum	750,000–1,000,000 megohms

Storage studies on capacitor types CC20, CC36, and CC35 have shown that after storage for six months at 50°C ± 2°C, 90–95 per cent rh, the result is a high percentage of dielectric-strength failures and a lowering of Q by as much as 1,300 to 190. The insulation resistance of this type of capacitor, as with other capacitors, decreases with temperature. For example, a 24-pf capacitor rated at 500 volts d-c (Type CC21CH240J of specification MIL-C-20B) had an insulation resistance under the specified conditions shown in Table 3-4.

TABLE 3-4. VARIATION OF INSULATION RESISTANCE WITH TEMPERATURE
FOR A 24-PF 500-VOLT D-C CERAMIC CAPACITOR

Temperature	Insulation resistance, megohms		
	500 volts	625 volts	750 volts
25°C................	50,000	50,000	50,000
1 hr at 175°C.........	9,000	8,000	4,000
5 hr at 175°C.........	9,000	7,000	1,000

Temperature-compensating ceramic capacitors are used for such applications as:
1. Coupling
2. Fixed tuning (high frequency)
3. Temperature compensation
4. Bypass

The third class, the high-dielectric-constant ceramic capacitor, provides a very high capacitance in a compact unit. The capacitance and the power factor, however, vary widely with temperature, the changes being neither linear nor very cyclic for either property.   Capacitors using the $K = 1,200$ material, for instance, have a high capacitance peak (Curie point) at about 110°C.   The power factor is at a minimum between 20 and 40°C.   All high-dielectric-constant materials have these characteristics occurring at various temperatures.   In general, the higher the dielectric constant, the more temperature-sensitive is the capacitor.   In addition to changes with temperature, the capacitance is also reduced under d-c voltage stress, especially at the peak points; at 25°C, a reduction in capacity of 10 to 20 per cent will occur, but at the Curie points a reduction up to 50 per cent can be expected. The d-c working voltage is lower than for the lower-dielectric-constant types.   The capacitors are subject to hysteresis and accordingly are suitable only for a-c voltage applications with very small voltages.

Capacitance of the high-dielectric-constant-type capacitor tends to decrease with aging and may decrease as much as 25 per cent for the first 1,000 hr.   This aging effect is usually an asymptotic function with time.   The properties of the high-dielectric-constant capacitor vary so much with temperature, voltage stress, frequency, and age that no general electrical characteristics can be given.   Military specification MIL-C-11015 covers the high-dielectric-constant-type of capacitors. These capacitors are used for such applications as:

1. Bypass (radio frequency)
2. Coupling (interstage, provided the capacitance is large enough under all conditions)
3. Filtering

Glass-dielectric Capacitors

Glass capacitors were originally developed as a substitute for mica, which is a critical material in time of emergency because the majority of the high-grade material is imported.   These capacitors are formed by stacking alternate layers of glass ribbon and aluminum foil and fusing together to form a solid block.   The glass dielectric is formed by extruding it as a very thin ribbon (0.0005 to 0.001 in. thick).   The glass can be made very uniform, and since the K of glass is higher than that of mica, a capacitor of the same capacitance rating will be smaller in size.   The insulation resistance at 25°C is usually in excess of 150,000 megohms, while specification MIL-C-11272 requires a minimum of 10,000 megohms.   Glass dielectric capacitors have a positive temperature characteristic of about 140 ppm/°C; they have very good retrace characteristics, and their capacitance and Q are quite constant. The Q at 1 Mc and 25°C is in excess of 2,000 for values from 10 to 1,000 pf.   Table 3-5 lists the Q requirements of military specification MIL-C-11272.

TABLE 3-5. VALUES OF Q REQUIRED BY MILITARY SPECIFICATION
MIL-C-11272

Minimum Q	Capacitance value, pf
1,500	5–20
1,400	20–500
1,200	1,000
700	10,000

Since the case of the capacitor is made of the same material as the dielectric, the Q maintains its value at low capacitances, while low-inductance direct connections to the plates maintain the Q at high capacitances. The axial-lead or postage-stamp types are covered by military specification MIL-C-11272. Capacitors under this specification are rated at both 85 and 125°C (with appropriate derating). A complete line of glass capacitors has been developed to replace all styles of mica capacitors covered by military specification MIL-C-5. Glass dielectric capacitors are used for such applications as:

1. Blocking
2. Tuning
3. Coupling
4. Bypass

Vitreous-enamel-dielectric Capacitors

Vitreous-enamel-dielectric capacitors ("vitreous-enamel capacitors") are formed either by spraying or silk-screening alternate layers of vitreous enamel and silver conductors to form a built-up structure. This structure or frit is fired at a temperature high enough to "vitrify" the glaze into a monolithic block. Vitreous-enamel capacitors have the following characteristics:

1. Excellent r-f characteristics (dissipation factor decreases from 1 kc/sec to 1 Mc/sec, then increases with frequency to 100 Mc/sec)

2. Total change of capacitance of approximately 5 per cent over the temperature range of −55 to 200°C

3. Temperature coefficient of 115 ±25 ppm/°C

4. Capable of operating at 200°C with proper voltage derating

5. Excellent retrace (less than 0.08 per cent capacitance drift)

6. Very high 25°C insulation resistance (in excess of 100,000 megohms)

7. Q at 25°C and 1 Mc/sec, varying from approximately 1,800 to approximately 3,000

8. Dissipation factor at 25°C, approximately 0.001; at 200°C, will be approximately 0.01

9. 100°C insulation resistance in excess of 10 ohm-farads

As with the glass capacitor, the encasing material is the same as the dielectric material, and therefore all of the corona at high voltages is within the dielectric. Vitreous-enamel capacitors are used in the same type of circuit applications as glass-dielectric capacitors.

Plastic-film-dielectric Capacitors

Plastic-dielectric capacitors (in which the dielectric consists of a thin film of suitable plastic material) are now available with polystyrene, polyethylene terephthalate (Mylar[1]), and polytetrafluoroethylene (Teflon[1]), used as the dielectric, either singly or in combinations. Polystyrene-film capacitors have been available for a number of years. These capacitors have the following characteristics:

1. Insulation resistance: very high. At room temperature (25°C) generally exceeds a product of 10^6 ohm-farads. Insulation resistance decreases very little with increase in temperature (up to +65°C).

2. Maximum operating temperature range: −55 to 65°C (some low-capacitance types good up to 85°C).

3. Power factor at 25°C: approximately 0.0005 (comparable with mica) and independent of frequency.

4. Dielectric absorption: low. Enables its use in long time-constant circuits.

5. Temperature coefficient: negative and varies up to −200 ppm/°C, depending upon the construction of the capacitor.

6. Capacitance drift (retrace): less than 0.2 per cent.

7. Q: in excess of 4,000.

Polystyrene capacitors are used for such applications as:

a. Precision timing circuits

b. Integrating circuits

c. High-Q tuned circuits

d. Laboratory standards

Polyethylene terephthalate (Mylar) is a very promising material and may in time replace paper to a considerable extent. It is, however, temperature- and frequency-sensitive. Its operating temperature is higher than that of paper—up to 150°C. In single foils, Mylar may be impregnated with polystyrene, mineral oil, etc., to fill pinholes, or two or more films may be used as in the case of paper capacitors. The film has good mechanical strength and can be readily vacuum-metalized. Since these films are sensitive to moisture, the capacitors need to be hermetically sealed. Capacitors with Mylar as the dielectric have the following characteristics:

[1] Registered trademark of E. I. du Pont de Nemours & Company.

1. Insulation resistance at 25°C: usually approximately double that of paper capacitors (in excess of a product of 50,000 ohm-farads); at 150°C, usually in excess of a product of 10 ohm-farads

2. Operating temperature: capable of operating as high as 150°C, usually with considerable voltage derating

3. Dissipation factor: not to exceed 0.01 through 85°C; 0.015 through 150°C

4. Dielectric absorption: fair, superior to mica when not impregnated with silicone fluid

5. Capacitance change: less than ±4 per cent over the temperature range −55 to 85°C; ±20 per cent over the temperature range −55 to 150°C

Polyethylene-terephthalate capacitors are used in the same general type of application in which paper capacitors normally would be used but for which paper capacitors are not suitable because of requirements for higher insulation resistance, higher temperature operation, etc.

Polytetrafluoroethylene (Teflon) film dielectric capacitors are capable of operating at still higher temperatures—as high as 200°C—but it is difficult to produce $\frac{1}{4}$- and $\frac{1}{2}$-mil film with the characteristics required. Capacitors constructed with Teflon as the dielectric have the following characteristics:

1. Insulation resistance: high. In excess of a product of 1×10^6 ohm-farads at 25°C. Insulation resistance at 200°C—usually in excess of a product of 200 ohm-farads

2. Operating temperature: capable of operating from −55 to 200°C

3. Dielectric absorption: good, as it is equivalent to polystyrene

4. Temperature coefficient of capacitance: negative; approximately −200 ppm/°C

5. Power factor: low, less than 0.0005 at 25°C

6. Tolerance on capacitance—as low as ±1.0 per cent

7. Q: in excess of 5,000

8. Capacitance change over the temperature range −55 to 200°C: less than ±4 per cent

Because Teflon-film-dielectric capacitors are high in cost, they are used only where there is need for high-operating-temperature capability, low power factor, high Q, very high insulation resistance, and small change of capacitance with temperature. Plastic-film-dielectric capacitors are covered by specification MIL-C-11978.

Electrolytic Capacitors

The outstanding characteristic of this type of capacitor is the very high capacitance-to-volume ratio obtainable. This is especially true if the working voltage is low. Electrolytic capacitors can be constructed by several different methods. Essentially they consist of two electrodes immersed in an electrolyte, with a chemical film that acts as a dielectric on one or both electrodes.

1. Polarized aluminum electrolytics—the oldest type of electrolytic capacitor. This type is made by winding either plain or etched foils on which an oxide has been formed on the surface of one (anode or positive) film in much the same manner that a paper dielectric capacitor is constructed. The etching of the foil (or sprayed gauze foils, which is another method of construction) increases the surface area, and a considerable increase in capacitance can thus be obtained. For constructional details see Chap. 9.

Electrolytic capacitors need to be re-formed periodically if they are stored for a considerable length of time. After six months' storage at room temperature, if the leakage current is high, the dielectric film should be re-formed by the application of sufficient voltage across a series combination of the capacitor, a protective resistor, and d-c milliammeter, as shown in Fig. 3-1, such that rated voltage appears across the capacitor terminals for 30 min. This resistor should have a wattage rating of at least 2 watts and a resistance value, depending upon the rating of the capacitor to be re-formed, as shown in Fig. 3-1. After 30 min, if the capacitance does not fall within specified limits or the d-c leakage current is in excess of that calculated by the following formula, the capacitor should be discarded.

$$I = KC + 0.3$$

where I = leakage current, ma

C = capacitance, μf

K = constant dependent upon voltage rating (Fig. 3-1)

The electrical properties of aluminum electrolytic capacitors change widely under different conditions of use, and some indication of this is given below:

a. Capacitance. There is a slight increase (about 10 per cent) when the temperature is raised from 25 to 85°C, a decrease as the temperature is reduced to −20°C, and a very rapid decrease at lower temperatures. The capacitance also decreases slightly as the applied frequency is increased from 60 cps, giving approximately 10 per cent reduction at 10 kc/sec.

b. Power factor. At 120 cps and 25°C, the power factor varies from 0.02 to 0.35. There is usually a slight decrease at 85°C and a large increase at −40°C. A large increase also takes place as the frequency is increased. To define losses in lieu of power factor or dissipation factor, it is common practice to specify equivalent series resistance. Whereas the power or dissipation factor is a function of both reactive and resistive parts of the capacitor, the equivalent series resistance is a measure only of the resistive elements, e.g., the metallic losses and the resistivity of the electrolyte. Usually, the value of the equivalent series resistance is determined largely by the conductivity of the electrolyte and to a lesser extent by the metallic resistances of electrodes, tabs, and terminals.

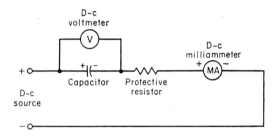

Resistance value of the protective resistor		
Capacity, μf	Voltage D-c, volts	Protective resistor, ohms
8–100	15–50	1000
8–100	Above 50	5000
100 and above	15–50	1000

Values of K	
Rated voltage	K
15–100	0.01
101–250	0.02
251–350	0.025
351–450	0.04

FIG. 3-1. Circuit diagram for re-forming electrolytic capacitors.

c. *Leakage current.* This is normally considered instead of insulation resistance, which is very low in this type of capacitor. The leakage current varies directly with temperature, having quite a low value at $-40°C$; but at $85°C$, it has about three times the value of that at $25°C$. In addition, the leakage current increases with the applied load, being very high when the load voltage is first applied but falling rapidly immediately afterwards. After approximately one to five minutes, the leakage current tends to reach a stable value. For the purpose of comparing capacitors with different electrical ratings, leakage current can be normalized in terms of microamperes per microfarad-volt ($\mu a/\mu f$-volt), since it is a function of capacitance and voltage rating. This normalization is somewhat comparable to the ohm-farad product employed in evaluating paper and film capacitors.

d. Impedance. An increase in impedance occurs as the temperature is reduced; at $-40°C$, it is about five to seven times the 25°C value. At still lower temperatures, the increase is even greater. The impedance falls with an increase of frequency, so that a typical capacitor measured at 85°C will decrease from 20 ohms at 120 cps to 0.3 ohms at 10 kc/sec.

Since the dielectric film in an electrolytic is formed at rated voltage, little is to be gained from drastic voltage derating. For maximum reliability and long life, the working voltage should be no more than 80 per cent of full rating; thus surges can be kept within the full working voltage range. Surge voltage application should not be longer than 30 sec at intervals of 10 min. Because the dielectric film tends to form to any voltage at which it is held for any period of time, use of electrolytic capacitors should be avoided in circuits in which applied d-c voltage may vary over extended periods of time.

In the majority of metal-encased electrolytic capacitors, such as the types covered by specification MIL-C-62 (families 1, 2, and 3), the electrolyte cannot be completely isolated from the case. There is an indeterminate resistance between the negative terminal and the case (ground). In applications where the negative terminal of the capacitor is not at ground potential, the capacitor should be enclosed in an insulating sleeve.

Military specification MIL-C-62 covers the aluminum-foil dry electrolytic of the polarized type. This specification lists two characteristics which cover the temperature range of these capacitors as follows:

Characteristic	Temperature range*
C	-40 to 85°C
F	-40 to 65°C

* Temperature range should never be exceeded.

The so-called "computer grade" of electrolytics which are constructed of high-purity aluminum (99.99+ purity) exhibit superior characteristics, such as longer operating life, much longer shelf life (on the order of two years for temperatures of less than 40°C), and lower leakage current. Aluminum electrolytics are used for such applications as:

a. Bypass

b. Filtering

c. High-energy pulse storage

2. Nonpolarized aluminum electrolytics. Aluminum electrolytics exhibiting the same general characteristics as the polarized types can

be constructed by using oxide films of equal thickness on both the anode (positive) and the cathode (negative) films.   These capacitors are used principally as motor-starting capacitors and are covered by specification MIL-C-3871.

3. Tantalum electrolytics.   The recently developed tantalum electrolytic capacitors have many superior qualities when compared with the older aluminum types.   Tantalum electrolytics are superior in the following characteristics:

a. Greater capacitance to volume ratio

b. Expected shelf life of five to ten years because of greater film stability

c. Greater temperature range

d. Lower leakage current

e. Lower power factor

f. Longer life

In general, tantalum capacitors exhibit the characteristics shown in Table 3-6.

TABLE 3-6. GENERAL CHARACTERISTICS OF TANTALUM
ELECTROLYTIC CAPACITORS

Capacitor characteristic	At reduced temperature, −55°C	At elevated temperature, +85°C
Capacitance.................	Decreases	Increases
D-c leakage.................	Decreases	Increases
Equivalent series resistance....	Increases	Decreases

Several different types of tantalum electrolytic capacitors using different methods of construction with varying characteristics are available.

a. Foil type.   This capacitor is constructed in both plain (types CL34 and CL35 of MIL-C-3965) and etched-foil types (types CL24 and CL25 of MIL-C-3965).   It can also be made as either a polarized or nonpolarized unit.   It can operate from −55 to 85°C and, with a special double end seal (made of synthetic rubber and polytetrafluoroethylene), up to 125°C.

b. Sintered-slug type.   This capacitor is constructed in two basic configurations.   One is primarily a low-capacitance low-voltage unit (type CL44 of MIL-C-3965).   With the other configuration the capacitance value and voltage rating can be varied, since the capacitor consists of a number of separate cells (type CL15 of MIL-C-3965).   Each cell is a porous tantalum slug encased in an enclosure with the electrolyte. Type CL15 is capable of operating from −55 to 175°C with proper voltage derating. The rated voltage is based upon an 85°C ambient. Some of the major characteristics for these tantalum capacitors of different types of construction on a comparative basis are shown in Table 3-7.

TABLE 3-7. COMPARATIVE CHARACTERISTICS FOR TANTALUM ELECTROLYTIC CAPACITORS OF DIFFERENT TYPES OF CONSTRUCTION

Characteristic	Etched foil	Plain foil	Sintered slug*
Capacitance change			
At 85°C	+60%	+25%	+10%
At −55°C	−40% for 75-volt rating	−40% for 75-volt rating	−15% for 75-volt rating
	−55% for 15-volt rating	−45% for 15-volt rating	−35% for 10-volt rating
D-c leakage			
85°C	0.06 μa/μf-volt	0.2 μa/μf-volt	0.005 μa/μf-volt
25°C	0.01 μa/μf-volt	0.05 μa/μf-volt	0.001 μa/μf-volt
Impedance			
At −55°C	2,000 for 15-volt rating	2,200 for 15-volt rating	2,500 for 10-volt rating
In ohm-microfarads	1,500 for 75-volt rating	1,500 for 75-volt rating	1,500 for 75-volt rating

* Small low-voltage type (CL44 of MIL-C-3965).

The above types are covered by military specification MIL-C-3965. This specification gives the requirements for polarized and nonpolarized types. Characteristics in accordance with military specification MIL-C-3965 are shown in Table 3-8.

TABLE 3-8. CHARACTERISTICS FOR TANTALUM ELECTROLYTIC CAPACITORS IN ACCORDANCE WITH MILITARY SPECIFICATION MIL-C-3965

Characteristic	Operating-temperature range
B	−55 to 85°C
C	−55 to 125°C
D	−55 to 175°C

Tantalum capacitors are used in the same applications as aluminum electrolytics but only where superior shelf life, greater operating-temperature range and/or smaller size are required.

c. Solid electrolyte with tantalum-wire, etched-wire, or sintered-pellet anode. These subminiature capacitors have entirely different characteristics from the types with the liquid electrolyte. For the lower capacitance values up to approximately 0.1 μf, plain tantalum wire is employed as the anode; for higher values of capacitance, etched wire or sintered pellets are used. Manganese dioxide is used as the electrolyte with a copper counter electrode. These capacitors are very small. A typical unit of 4.7-μf capacitance value rated at 10 volts d-c would be ⅛ in. in diameter and ¼ in. long. These capacitors are available with the following characteristics:

1. Operating temperature range: −55 to 85°C (capable of operating at −80°C)

2. Working voltage: available up to and including 50 volts

3. Temperature coefficient of capacitance: approximately +600 ppm/°C

4. Dielectric absorption: comparable to oil-impregnated paper of the same rating

5. Impedance over the frequency range 10 kc/sec to 10 Mc/sec: essentially the same as for a paper capacitor of the same capacitance value

6. Dissipation factor: increases with temperature (the opposite of a paper capacitor) and will not exceed 0.05 at 85°C

7. Leakage current: increases with temperature and applied voltage. Leakage current therefore is usually given in microamperes per microfarad per volt. Leakage current for a 35-volt capacitor at 85°C would be approximately 0.175 μa

8. Capacitance tolerance: ±20 per cent for the lower voltage ratings, ±10 per cent for the higher voltage ratings.

This type of construction, using a solid semiconductor as electrolyte, eliminates one of the major deficiencies of the ordinary electrolytic capacitor, since the type of seal (to prevent loss of electrolyte) is no longer important. These capacitors are suitable for applications in transistor circuitry where larger values of capacitance and small size are required. This capacitor is covered by specification MIL-C-21720.

Air-dielectric Capacitors

Air-dielectric capacitors are used principally as laboratory standards of capacitance for measurement purposes. With precision construction and use of suitable materials, they can have a capacitance stability of 0.01 per cent over a number of years for large values of capacitance.

Vacuum and Gas-filled Capacitors

Vacuum capacitors are used primarily either as high-voltage capacitors in airborne radio transmitting equipment or as blocking and decoupling capacitors in high-voltage industrial and communications equipment. They are made in values from 1 to 5,000 pf for voltage

TABLE 3-9. SUMMARY OF SOME OF THE IMPORTANT CHARACTERISTICS OF FIXED CAPACITORS

Type of capacitor (military specification)	Closest tolerance in specification	Power factor (at 1 Kc/sec and 25°C) or Q (at 1 Mc/sec and 25°C)	Temperature coefficient (ppm/°C) characteristics where applicable	Insulation resistance (min at end of life test, megohms)	Length of life test MIL (spec)	Maximum capacitance variation after life tests	Maximum operating temperature for long life
Impregnated paper (MIL-C-25)	± 10 %	0.004–0.01	*	30 % of original specified req.	250 hr max amb & 90 to 190°C of rtd. volt. at 40°C depend on impregnant & watt-second group	10 %	85°C or 125°C‡ depending on impregnant
Metalized paper (MIL-C-18312)	± 10 %	0.005–0.015	*	⅓ of original specified req.	1000 hr at rtd. volts d-c	10 %	85°C or 125°C‡
Molded mica capacitors (MIL-C-5)	± 2 %	0.001–0.005	B—not specified C ± 200 ppm/°C D ± 100 ppm/°C E + 100 ppm/°C – 20 ppm/°C F + 70 ppm/°C – 0 ppm/°C	7,500	1,000 hr max amb 150 % of rtd. voltage	3 % or 0.5 pf, whichever is greater	85°C 125°C or 150°C‡
Glass dielectric (MIL-C-11272)	± 2 %	0.001	140 ± 25 ppm/°C	10,000	1,000 hr at 85°C at 150% of rtd. voltage	2 % or 1 pf, whichever is greater	85°C or 125°C‡
Vitreous enamel (none)	*	0.001	115 ± 25 ppm/°C	*	*	*	85°C
Ceramic temp. compensating (MIL-C-20)	± 1 %	1,000 min	+100 – 200 0 – 330 –30 – 420 –80 – 750 –150	1,000	1,000 hr 750 volts d-c +250 volts a-c (peak to peak, not to exceed 100 cycles)	3 % or 0.5 pf, whichever is greater	85°C
Ceramic general-purpose (MIL-C-11015)	+100 – 20	0.01 to 0.03 varies with temp., etc.	–1,500 varies non-linear	3,000	1,000 2x rtd. volts d-c	*	85°C or 150°C‡

Type	Tolerance	Dissipation factor	Temperature coefficient	7,500 or 50,000 (depends on type of seal)	250 hr & 1,000 hr at 750 volts for 85°C & 125°C units, respectively	3 % or 0.5 pf, whichever is greater	85°C or 125°C‡
Mica, button types (MIL-C-10950)	± 2 %	0.001–0.005	B—not specified D ± 100 ppm/°C				
Polystyrene film (MIL-C-19978)	± 5 %	4,000 min	−120 ± 30 ppm/°C	60 % of original specified req.	250 hr at 115 % of rtd. voltage at 85°C	6 % for values <0.05, 3 % for values >0.05	65°C (85°C)†
Polytetrafluoroethylene (MIL-C-19928)	± 5 %	5,000 min	*	60 % of original specified req.	250 hr at 115 % of rtd. voltage at 170°C	5 %	170°C (200°C)†
Polyethylene terephthalate (MIL-C-11978)	± 5 %	0.01 varies with temperature & frequency	Varies with temperature	60 % of original specified req.	250 hr at 50 % of rtd. voltage at 125°C	5 %	125°C (150°C)†
Aluminum electrolytic (MIL-C-62)	−10 + 150 (up to 50 volts) −10 + 100 (up to 350 volts) −10 + 50 (over 3,500)	0.02–0.35 (at 120 cps)	*	*	1,000 hr at rtd. voltage	10 %	65°C or 85°C‡
Tantalum electrolytic (MIL-C-3965)	± 2 %	0.02–0.2	*	*	2,000 hr at rtd. voltage		85°C, 125°C or 175°C‡
Tantalum solid-electrolyte (MIL-C-21720)	± 10 %	0.04–0.06 (at 120 cps)	+ 600 ppm/°C	*	1,000 hr at rtd. voltage	10 %	85°C
Precision-type air dielectric (none)	± 0.01	0.00001	+ 10	*	*	*	25°C

* Not applicable.
† Capacitors may be operated up to these temperatures with proper voltage derating and reduction in life expectancy.
‡ Different maximum operating temperatures specified for different characteristics.

49

ranges from 3,000 to 120,000 volts peak and with current rating from 14 to 500 (water-cooled) amp. Since the dielectric constant is essentially the same as for air, the capacitance-to-volume ratio is rather low. Gas-filled types are used for very high voltages—on the order of 250,000 volts. Clean, dry nitrogen may be used at pressures up to 150 psi (pounds per square inch). Capacitors are specifically designed for each application.

CHARACTERISTICS OF VARIABLE CAPACITORS

Variable capacitors may be grouped in five general classes—precision types, general-purpose types, transmitter types, trimmers, and special types, such as phase shifters.

Precision Variable Capacitors

These capacitors have been used many years primarily as laboratory substandards of capacitance in bridge and resonant circuits. Numerous measuring instruments have been designed around them. Various functions (laws) are available, and capacitances up to 5,000 pf can be obtained in one swing. Capacitance tolerances are on the order of one part in ten thousand. Long-term stabilities are possible under controlled conditions (e.g., for periods of several years, capacitance changes amount to less than 0.02 per cent).

General-purpose Capacitors

These units are used as tuning capacitors in broadcast receivers. They have been developed from large single capacitors to compact four- or five-gang units, which can have a standard capacitance tolerance of within 1 per cent or one pf to a stated function. The power factor of a modern air-dielectric variable capacitor, at 1 Mc/sec, varies from 0.03 per cent (at minimum capacitance setting) to 0.06 per cent (at maximum capacitance setting).

General-purpose capacitors are available in many functions, e.g., straight-line frequency, straight-line wavelength, straight-line percentage frequency, so that they can be used in test equipment and receivers of many types. The normal capacitance swing of this type is about 400 to 500 pf, but capacitors can be obtained in capacitance swing (in ranges) from 10 to about 600 pf.

Transmitter Capacitors

These types are similar in design to the general-purpose types but are designed for higher voltage operation. This is accomplished by increasing the space between the plates (vanes). The capacitance swing usually ranges up to about 1,000 pf. The edges of the plates are rounded and polished to avoid flashover, and special attention is paid to shape and mounting for high-voltage operation.

The most common functions are linear frequency and straight-line frequency (see Chap. 14). Special split-stator constructions are also used for push-pull circuits. Oil filling increases the capacitance and working voltages from two to five times, depending upon the dielectric constant of the oil used. High-voltage-gas variable capacitors for use in broadcast transmitters are constructed, using compressed nitrogen gas under pressures up to 2,000 psi.

A special type of transmitter capacitor is the vacuum variable. This capacitor is constructed with a bellows and can be obtained with capacitance variation from 10 to 2,000 pf in a single unit. Very high voltages and current ratings are also available. A typical unit has the following characteristics:

1. Capacitance variation: 2 to 500 pf
2. Peak voltage: 20 kv
3. Maximum current: 60 amp (rms)
4. Length: $9\frac{7}{8}$ in.
5. Diameter: $4\frac{3}{8}$ in.

These capacitors are very reliable, and the life is practically infinite as long as the seal is maintained.

Trimmer Capacitors

These capacitors are used primarily for coupling and tuning (e.g., coil trimming) at intermediate and radio frequencies. There are four main types:

1. Compression types (usually mica)
2. Air-spaced rotary types
3. Ceramic-dielectric rotary types
4. Ceramic-, glass-, or plastic-dielectric tubular or piston types

The capacitance range for rotary air-spaced types covers from about 3 to 145 pf. This range is affected by several capacitors, each covering a much smaller range—3.5 to 10, 6 to 75, 9 to 143 pf, etc. These capacitors are covered by military specification JAN-C-92.

Compression-type trimmer capacitors are smaller and cover a much wider capacitance range from 15 to over 3,000 pf, again in stages. A typical compression-type capacitor covers the range from 15 to 130 pf. This type of capacitor is not suitable for application in military equipment.

Ceramic-dielectric trimmer capacitors usually have a more restricted

capacitance range, from 1.5 to 7 pf with ranges from 7 to 45 pf, depending upon the temperature coefficient required.   These capacitors come
under military specification MIL-C-81, which lists the temperature
coefficients by characteristic, as shown in Table 3-10.

TABLE 3-10. CHARACTERISTICS FOR VARIABLE CERAMIC CAPACITORS
IN ACCORDANCE WITH MILITARY SPECIFICATION MIL-C-81

Characteristic	Trimmer capacitors, ppm/°C
A	NPO
B	−300
C	−500
D	−650

The piston or tubular types are used for fine adjustment of small
capacitance values.   The capacitance range is restricted.   Military
specification MIL-C-14409 specifies the requirements for the glass
types, which have the following characteristics:
  1. Temperature coefficient: ±100 ppm/°C
  2. Temperature range: −55 to 125°C
  3. Capacitance drift: ±0.04 pf
Two capacitor styles are listed in MIL-C-14409.   Several capacitors are required to cover the range from 0.5 to 30 pf.

CAPACITOR SELECTION

Reliable electronic equipment requires the selection and application
of high-quality electronic parts in applications for which they were
designed.   Many electronic-part failures can be attributed to improper
selection and application.   Care should be exercised in the use of the
individual military specifications for capacitors.   Though these specifications contain useful design information, they are primarily purchase
documents intended to define a product on a performance basis.   The
military specification defines only the minimum acceptable level or
value for any given parameter.   Since the military specifications for
electronic parts are performance documents, each manufacturer may
use different materials or processes.   This practice results in the manufacture of parts that often exceed the specification requirements by
varying amounts.   If the equipment is to be serviced in the field,
satisfactory operation should not be based upon the selection of capacitors with properties that exceed the specification requirements by a
wide margin.   Replacement parts, though they meet the requirements
of the specification, may not provide the necessary performance to
assure adequate equipment performance.

TABLE 3-11. SUMMARY OF SOME OF THE IMPORTANT CHARACTERISTICS OF VARIABLE CAPACITORS

Type	Capacitance function, law*	Approximate capacitance swing, pf	Power factor at 1 kc/sec and 25°C	Q at 1 Mc/sec and 25°C	Approximate oper. volts d-c at sea-level pressure	Temp. coeff., ppm/°C	Max oper. temp. for long life	Remarks
Single unit, precision	SLC	100–1,500	0.00001	—	1,000	+10 (best)	—	
Single unit, general-purpose	SLC and SLF	15–100 and 350–550	0.001	—	750	+120	—	
Multigang, general-purpose	SLC and SLF	15–100 and 350–550	0.001	—	750	+120	—	
Multigang, miniature, general-purpose	SLC	300–350	0.001	—	500	+150	—	
Trimmers, air-diel. vane type	SLC	3.5–145	—	250 min.	CI:850 C2:1,150 C3:1,400	+50–150	85°C	Covered by mil. spec. MIL-C-92
Trimmers, glass-diel. piston type	SLC	0.5–30	—	500 min.	500	±100	125°C	Covered by mil. spec. MIL-C-14409
Trimmers, ceramic dielectric	SLC	7–45	—	500 min.	500	Char. T-C / A NPO / B N300 / C N500 / D N650		Covered by mil. spec. MIL-C-81
Trimmers, mica compression	Non-linear	15–3,000	0.001	—	250–500	Poor	—	

* See Chap. 14.

53

Under performance specifications in which only the minimum acceptable value is defined, an important factor that is often overlooked is the slope of the curve of degradation of a parameter (e.g., capacitance) when subjected to a specific test (e.g., life). For long-term reliability, a capacitor with lower initial and final values (more gradual slope) may be superior to a capacitor with higher values but a greater rate of degradation.

Selection of a given type of capacitor for a particular circuit is often a compromise between the requirements of the electrical characteristics, the mechanical configuration, and available space. For any type of capacitor, three basic limiting considerations must be made: voltage, temperature, and size. Since capacitors find such widespread usage in all types of electronic equipment, the following procedure is outlined to aid the design engineer.

1. The designer should become quite familiar with the over-all environmental requirements for the system, so that he may be better able to determine the requirements for the individual capacitor. The following parameters should be determined for each capacitor:

    a. Operating-temperature range

    b. Minimum operating barometric pressure

    c. Shock (magnitude and drag time)

    d. Vibration (frequency and magnitude)

    e. Moisture present

    f. Any corrosive atmospheres

    g. Minimum life

2. Based upon a combination of the most severe conditions that may be encountered, each capacitor circuit application should be analyzed to determine limits for the following:

    a. Maximum capacitance variation

    b. Minimum insulation resistance

    c. Maximum leakage current

    d. Time constant (if applicable)

    e. Minimum Q (if applicable)

    f. Maximum applied d-c working voltage

    g. Maximum applied a-c working voltage

    h. Appearance of surges (if they appear, their peak value)

3. After the circuit is analyzed and the value for these parameters determined, consideration in selecting the capacitor should be given to each of the following:

    a. For maximum capacitance variation (stability):

        (1) Capacitance tolerance as specified by the specification

        (2) Capacitance variation with temperature (expressed either as

temperature coefficient or as percentage variation from value at 25°C)

    (3) Capacitance variation with voltage

    (4) Capacitance variation with frequency

    (5) Capacitance variation with shock and vibration

    (6) Capacitance variation with pressure

    (7) Capacitance variation with age

    (8) Retrace, after capacitance change

b. For minimum insulation resistance (ohm-farad product):

    (1) Value at maximum operating temperature

    (2) Value at maximum operating voltage

    (3) Value due to presence of moisture

c. For maximum leakage current:

    (1) Value at maximum operating temperature

    (2) Value due to presence of moisture

    (3) Value at maximum operating voltage

d. Time constant:

    (1) Importance of dielectric absorption

e. Minimum Q or power factor:

    (1) Value over what temperature range

    (2) Value over what frequency range

f. Applied d-c working voltage:

    (1) Value at maximum operating temperature

    (2) Value at minimum pressure

g. Applied a-c working voltage:

    (1) Value at maximum operating temperature

    (2) Value at minimum pressure

    (3) Value at operating frequency

4. Special attention should be given the mechanical construction to assure:

    a. Adequate seals

    b. Adequate corrosion protection

    c. Adequate construction for vibration and shock requirements

After these factors have been duly considered, a choice of capacitor can be made. Many times this choice will necessitate a compromise, since a capacitor capable of meeting all requirements will not often be available. Thus each characteristic should be carefully weighed against the corresponding requirement.

CHAPTER 4

THE MEASUREMENT OF CAPACITANCE

The precision measurement of capacitance over a wide frequency range is a complex subject to which a great many workers have devoted much attention over many years. This work is fully described in the literature, and a number of references to more detailed information are given in the Bibliography. Only a brief description will be given here, therefore, of the common methods of measurements of capacitance.

The impedance of any capacitor can be measured as though it consists of a pure capacitance C_s in series with a pure resistance R_s, or as a pure capacitance C_p in parallel with a pure resistance R_p. Usually the series measurements are made at low frequencies and the parallel measurements at high frequencies. The accuracy of the measurements depends (particularly at the higher frequencies) on the type of equipment used, the elimination of discontinuities of lead lengths between the unknown capacitor and the measuring equipment, stray coupling to the unknown capacitor, and the sensitivity of the detector. Measurements of capacitance may be generally classified into those carried out at low frequencies and those carried out at high frequencies.

LOW-FREQUENCY MEASUREMENTS

Since stray series impedances are small at audio frequencies, measuring equipment can be made extremely accurate by screening and by careful arrangements of components and with good evaluation of correcting terms. Great care may be required with these measurements. Precision measuring equipment usually consists of a bridge network which can give an accuracy of measurement of one part in a million for capacitance and 0.000005 for power factor (under the most favorable conditions). Many high-precision bridges use mutual-inductance ratio arms. Typical bridges are described briefly in the following paragraphs.

The Carey-Foster Bridge

This bridge gives series components C_s and R_s, and a simple circuit diagram is shown in Fig. 4-1. In this arrangement M is a standard mutual inductometer, Q is a fixed standard resistor, and R is the resistance of the self-inductance L. Let R_s = resistance of unknown capacitor C_s. Then

$$C_s = \frac{M}{QR} \qquad \text{at balance}$$

and capacitor resistance $R_s = Q\,\dfrac{L}{M} - 1.$

In practice the capacitance of the leads to the unknown capacitor is usually measured and subtracted from the value obtained with the

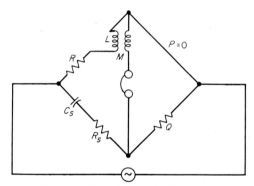

FIG. 4-1. Carey-Foster bridge circuit.

unknown capacitor in circuit. The range of capacitance measurement of this bridge is up to about 10 μf, and an accuracy of better than one part in ten thousand can easily be obtained.

The Schering Bridge

This bridge also gives series components C_s and R_s, and a simple diagram of the circuit is given in Fig. 4-2. In this circuit, C_2 is a standard fixed capacitor, C_s is an unknown capacitor to be measured, and R_s is the unknown series resistance of the capacitor C_s. Then

$$C_s = \frac{R_3 C_2}{Q} \qquad \text{and} \qquad R_s = \frac{Q C_3}{C_2} \qquad \text{at balance}$$

and $\qquad\qquad \tan\theta = \omega R_3 C_3 = \omega C_s R_s$

where θ is the loss angle, and ω is $2\pi \times$ frequency of supply.

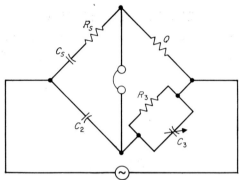

FIG. 4-2. Schering bridge circuit.

This bridge is of the highest precision and has wide applications. Modified forms are used for most measurements of capacitors at audio frequencies, including measurements at voltages up to 100 kv.

General Types of Bridges

Bridges are also made in similar designs to the high-precision bridges mentioned above, but using lower-grade components and construction. Accuracies are of the order of 0.1 to 1.0 per cent. There are many designs and variations of bridges of this type, with similar accuracies,

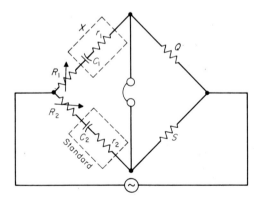

FIG. 4-3. Series-resistance bridge circuit.

which are in general use. A typical series-resistance bridge circuit is shown in Fig. 4-3.

In this bridge arrangement Q and S are fixed known resistors, and we may write $P = R_1 + r_1$ and $R = R_2 + r_2$. C_2 is a standard capacitor, and C_1 is the capacitor under measurement. Then

$$C_1 = \frac{C_2 S}{Q}$$

so that $\qquad \dfrac{C_1}{C_2} = \dfrac{S}{Q} = \dfrac{R}{P} \qquad$ at balance

then $\qquad C_1(R_1 + r_1) = C_2(R_2 + r_2)$

and $\qquad \omega C_1 R_1 - \omega C_2 r_2 = \omega C_2 R_2 - \omega C_1 r_1$

that is, $\qquad \tan\theta_1 - \tan\theta_2 = \omega C_2\left(R_2 - \dfrac{S}{Q}r_1\right)$

This bridge gives the impedance in series terms but requires the power factor of the standard capacitor C_2 to be known in order to obtain the power factor of the unknown capacitor C_1. Typical measurement accuracies with this bridge are 0.2 per cent for capacitance and 1 to 2 per cent for resistance.

Substitution Methods

A most useful method at low frequencies is the substitution for the unknown capacitor of an accurately known capacitor. This method does not give the resistive term but can give the capacitance to 0.01 pf. It has the advantage that the only accurate equipment needed is the standard variable capacitor, although a sensitive detector is also required. The method is limited to about 100 kc/sec, depending on the frequency characteristics of the standard capacitor and the stability of the apparatus.

Small capacitances can be measured by noting the change in frequency of a tuned circuit (oscillator) when the unknown capacitor is placed in parallel with the circuit capacitance. If the frequency is above about 10 Mc/sec, great care may have to be taken to avoid introducing errors due to stray capacitance and small inductances.

The Wagner Earth Connection

The Wagner earth connection is of great value in accurate bridge measurements, since it can improve the sensitivity of a bridge by minimizing earth capacitance effects, such as capacitance to the bridge case.

A circuit employing a Wagner earth connection is given in Fig. 4-4. Capacitors C_2 and C_4, in series, shunt the supply and do not affect the bridge itself.

At balance the points C and D of the bridge are at the same potential, but, because of C_1 and C_3, are not at earth potential. Since the detector itself is often coupled by stray capacitances to earth, a current may flow through the detector when the bridge is balanced.

The procedure is first to balance the bridge as well as possible, switch the detector to the midpoint of Z_A and Z_B, and balance with these two impedances. Since this midpoint is at earth, point C will

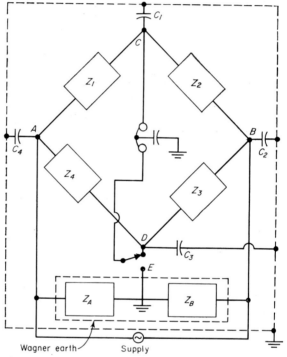

FIG. 4-4. Circuit employing Wagner earth connection.

also be at earth potential, and D is brought to earth potential by final balancing.

HIGH-FREQUENCY MEASUREMENTS

Transformer Bridges

Transformer bridges, which are mainly a postwar development, are now in use covering the frequency range 15 kc/sec to 250 Mc/sec. Above 50 Mc/sec the bridges are designed mainly for the measurement of cable impedances, but by suitable arrangement of the bridge terminals they can be used for measuring small capacitances. The higher-frequency bridges are capable of measuring poor power factors only where the effective parallel resistance is between 10 ohms and 10 kilohms. The accuracy of the capacitance measurements is 1 to 2 per cent, or 0.5 pf, and of the resistance measurement 1 to 2 per cent, or, measured as a conductance, 0.025 millimhos. It is, therefore, not possible to obtain an accurate value except for a poor capacitor.

Transformer bridges have the advantages of covering a wide frequency range and ease of measurement, and can measure inductance in terms of negative capacitance. The results are always in parallel terms.

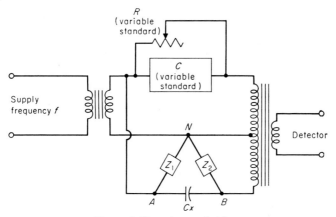

Fig. 4-5. Transformer bridge.

A typical circuit diagram is shown in Fig. 4-5. The unknown capacitance is usually connected across terminals A and B. With three-terminal components, N is used, but only the capacitance between A and B is measured, since the impedance Z_1 is directly shunting the supply, and Z_2 is shunting the detector. The detector usually consists of a communication-type receiver, and the supply is a modulated oscillator.

Q Meters

General-purpose Q meters can be used to measure capacitance to an accuracy of approximately 5 per cent up to about 50 Mc/sec. They can be modified to use external variable standard capacitors and voltmeters so that measurements can be made to an accuracy of 2 per cent up to about 20 Mc/sec. Above this frequency, stray capacitances and inductances introduce large errors. The Q meter is, however, an extraordinarily versatile instrument, for it is capable of making almost any impedance measurement over a range from about 50 kc/sec to 200 Mc/sec. Q meters can measure almost any impedance at an accuracy depending on the quality of the equipment. (The operation of a Q meter is described in the section on the measurement of power factor, page 66.)

The Hartshorn and Ward Dielectric Test Set

This equipment is an extremely accurate high-frequency apparatus and consists of a very carefully designed Q meter covering the frequency range 10 kc/sec to 100 Mc/sec. It is specifically designed for measuring flat disk dielectrics or liquid dielectrics, but suitable jigs and terminal arrangements permit other components to be measured. The principle of the equipment is shown in Fig. 4-6.

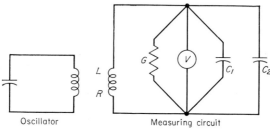

Oscillator   Measuring circuit

FIG. 4-6. Basic diagram of Hartshorn and Ward dielectric test set.

The oscillator is inductively coupled to the tuned circuit L, R, and C_2. The unknown capacitance is C_1, and C_2 is an accurately calibrated variable capacitor. When C_1 is added to the tuned circuit, C_2 is adjusted to bring the circuit back to resonance, and the change in C_2 is the value of the added capacitance. The conductance G of the tuned circuit, with and without C_1, is measured by the reactance variation method, from which the resistance of C_1 is determined. The accuracy of measurement is 1 per cent and the capacitance range is 0 to a few hundred pf. The power-factor range is down to 0.0001.

Twin-T Bridges

Twin-T bridges are often used for measurements up to 50 or 100 Mc/sec, with an accuracy of about 5 per cent. A simple diagram of a twin-T bridge is given in Fig. 4-7.

Two T sections are connected in parallel. For null indication the sum of the transfer impedances of the two T sections must be zero. The susceptance is measured by the change in the capacitor C_B (directly in picofarads). The conductance is measured by the change in the capacitor C_G, calibrated in microhms. R is a straight wire resistor, whose residual inductance at radio frequency is compensated by a trimmer capacitor which is adjusted to give essentially zero effective reactance over the range of the bridge.

Twin-T bridges are now being designed for accurate measurements up to 150 or 200 Mc/sec. By paying detailed attention to symmetry it is possible to extend the range, and a simple Wheatstone bridge has

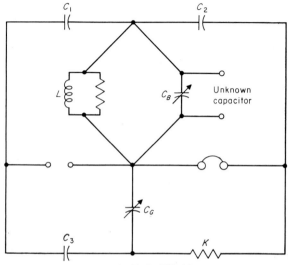

FIG. 4-7. Twin-T bridge.

been designed in Germany which is reported to cover the frequency range 0.1 to 1,000 Mc/sec (see Bibliography).

Measurements above 200 Mc/sec

Above about 200 Mc/sec, Lecher-wire (i.e., standing-wave) measuring apparatus is used, and this can give reasonably accurate results, but, in general, small capacitors are not often used at these frequencies, since the stray capacitances in circuits can introduce large errors. At frequencies higher than 200 Mc/sec, interest is generally centered on measurement of dielectric properties of materials.

METHODS OF MEASUREMENT OF THE PROPERTIES OF DIELECTRIC MATERIALS

Methods of measurement of capacitance from low frequencies up to about 200 Mc/sec have been described, and these can be used to assess the dielectric properties of materials up to these frequencies. Above these frequencies coaxial line, waveguide, and resonant cavities are used, and the Bibliography gives a number of references to work in this

field. Very brief descriptions of the principles of these three methods
are given below.

Coaxial-Line Method

For approximately 200 to approximately 1,000 Mc/sec, coaxial lines
are used, modulated c.w. being injected into a slotted coaxial line along
which a probe (which is connected to a calibrated amplifier) can travel,
as shown in Fig. 4-8. This line is terminated in a coaxial section in
which the dielectric used is the material to be investigated, and the
standing waves set up in the slotted line when this is terminated
(usually by an open circuit or a short circuit, but sometimes by other
convenient reactances) are measured on the amplifier.

The standing wave is specified by the ratio of minimum to maximum voltages and by the position of voltage maxima and minima
in relation to the end of the line.

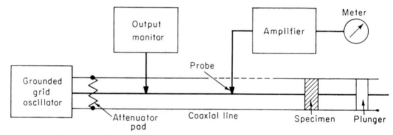

FIG. 4-8. Coaxial-line measurement of dielectric properties.

If the slotted line is terminated by purely resistive load, the voltage
maximum or minimum will occur at the end of the measuring section,
the maximum occurring if the resistance is high compared to the
characteristic impedance of the line, and the minimum if the resistance
is low.

The purely reactive load will lead to an apparently infinite standing-
wave ratio, while if the load is perfectly matched to the line, there is
no reflection, and consequently no standing wave is observed.

If the magnitude and phase of the standing-wave ratio have once
been determined, the nature of the terminating impedance is expressed
in terms of the characteristic impedance of a line by the following
formula:

$$Z_i = \frac{Z_0[Z_i + jZ_0 \tan \theta]}{Z_0 + jZ_i \tan \theta}$$

where Z_i = input impedance
Z_0 = characteristic impedance
θ = electrical length of test specimen (number of wavelengths)

According to whether the section under investigation is open or short-circuited, or otherwise terminated, the impedance which it presents will differ. From the impedances found with two different terminations the propagation constant and impedance of the specimen can be found by means of the formula above. This is most conveniently done with the help of the Smith Circle diagram. For details of this calculation, reference should be made, for instance, to the paper by Willis Jackson and Huxley [*J. Inst. Elec. Engrs.* (London), vol. 91, pt. III, p. 105, 1944] on the solution of transmission-line problems. Other references are contained in the Bibliography.

Waveguide Method

For frequencies of approximately 1,000 to approximately 3,000 Mc/sec, the method of measurement may be as follows. The coaxial

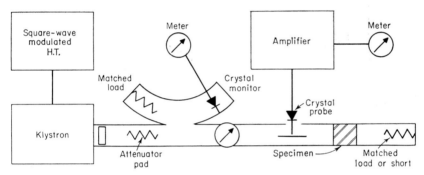

FIG. 4-9. Waveguide method of dielectric measurement.

lines are replaced by waveguides, in which the fundamental processes are essentially as described above. The schematic diagram of the apparatus is shown in Fig. 4-9. A point to be remembered is that in the waveguide the wavelength is longer than its value in free space because of wall-to-wall reflections, the difference depending upon the frequency and the guide dimensions. Under certain conditions the wave will not be propagated and is said to be cut off. The filled section, however, will be worked under conditions far removed from cutoff, and the propagation conditions will be almost exactly as in an infinitely extended medium. Bearing these corrections in mind, the essential calculations are similar to those described for coaxial-line methods.

Resonant Cavities

From approximately 3,000 Mc/sec upward, resonant cavities can be used. Essentially, oscillations are set up in a completely enclosed cavity of simple shape, and their rates of decay determined when a body of the material under investigation is introduced as an absorbing material. The most convenient form of cavity is cylindrical, and a cylindrical sample is placed on the axis. Decay of the oscillations is determined from the bandwidth of the cavity used as the termination, in a manner precisely similar to that discussed with Q meters at lower frequencies (page 61).

In the case of very-loss-free materials the specimen may be allowed to fill a good deal of the cavity, but the method can be applied to

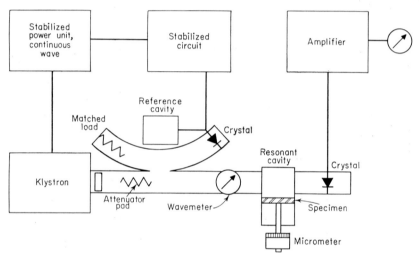

FIG. 4-10. Resonant-cavity method of dielectric measurement.

materials with a relative high loss provided that the specimen is small. A diagram of the apparatus is given in Fig. 4-10.

THE MEASUREMENT OF POWER FACTOR

In the series bridges described in the previous paragraphs, the power factor is equal to $2\pi frC$, where r is the series resistance. This is calculated directly from the readings of C and r on the bridges.

A parallel bridge differs from the series bridge in that the resistance shunts the capacitance instead of being in series with it. In this case the power factor is equal to $\frac{1}{2}\pi fRC$, where R is the parallel resistance.

A Q meter can also be used. In this method the circuit is first tuned to resonance without the unknown capacitor in circuit and then retuned with the capacitor in parallel with the tuning capacitor, as shown in Fig. 4-11.

The resonance curve gives a measure of the capacitance, and also the loss of the capacitor and the power factor can be calculated from the height and sharpness of this curve. The change in capacitance from the resonance point is taken at 0.707 of the peak voltage (Fig. 4-12).

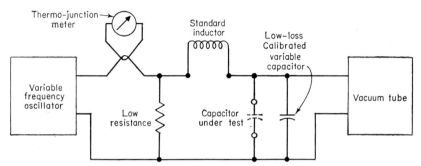

FIG. 4-11. Schematic diagram of Q meter.

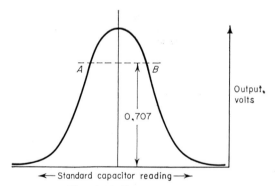

FIG. 4-12. Resonance curve.

If C is capacitance and ΔC is the change in capacitance (or half the width AB), then

$$Q = \frac{C}{\Delta C}$$

and

$$\text{Power factor} = \frac{1}{Q} = \frac{\Delta C}{C}$$

If the capacitor has very low losses, a correction is necessary to allow for the losses in the measuring circuit, and the width of the bandpass curve without the unknown capacitor is subtracted from the width of the curve with the capacitor in circuit.

THE MEASUREMENT OF TEMPERATURE COEFFICIENT
OF CAPACITANCE⌋

The temperature coefficient of capacitance α of a capacitor is defined by the formula

$$\alpha = \frac{\Delta C}{C \Delta t}$$

If ΔC and C are expressed in the same units of capacitance, and Δt is in degrees centigrade, this may be expressed as

$$\alpha = \Delta C \times \frac{10^6}{C \Delta t} \quad \text{ppm}/°\text{C}$$

Increases of Δt and ΔC are taken as positive.

The equation implies linearity over the range of Δt, and thus a statement of the value of α should strictly be accompanied by a statement of the value of Δt over which it is calculated. All measurements are usually made at a frequency of 1 Mc/sec.

TABLE 4-1. RANGE OF TEMPERATURE COEFFICIENTS IN
MILITARY SPECIFICATIONS

Type of capacitor	Range of temperature coefficients, ppm/°C
Mica	−200 to +200
Ceramic, tubular	0 to +100
Ceramic, tubular and disks	−30 to −750
Glass	+115 to +155
Vitreous enamel	+103 to +131

Temperature-coefficient measurements are usually required on mica, ceramic, vitreous-enamel, glass, polystyrene, polytetrafluoroethylene, and air-dielectric capacitors. Typical ranges of values covered in military specifications for capacitors are shown in Table 4-1.

The tolerance on temperature-coefficient measurement at this time varies with the military specification. These specification requirements are listed in Table 4-2.

The measuring equipment must have an accuracy greater than the tolerances listed in Table 4-2. Great difficulty is experienced in measuring capacitors with very low capacitance values, particularly those under 10 pf. Modern measuring equipment is capable of measuring capacitance changes due to temperature with an accuracy in excess of 0.015 pf over the temperature range −55 to 125°C.

In temperature-coefficient measuring equipment the thermal and electrical requirements are quite distinct. The requirement is to

TABLE 4-2. TOLERANCE ON TEMPERATURE COEFFICIENT FOR
SEVERAL MILITARY SPECIFICATIONS

Specification(s)	Tolerance on temperature coefficient
MIL-C-5, MIL-C-11272, MIL-C-10950...	±0.025% of nominal capacitance +0.05 pf. Tolerance on temperature at each step required to be $T + 2°C$ $- 0$
MIL-C-20............................	±0.025 pf (for capacitance values above 100 pf). Tolerance on temperature at each step required to be $T + 0$ except for those in excess $- 2$ of 25°C, then $T +2$ -0

measure the capacitance change ΔC of a fixed capacitor when its temperature is changed by a known amount. Although bridge methods could be used, the general method is to use resonant-circuit methods.

The resonant circuit forms the oscillatory circuit of a tube, as shown in Fig. 4-13. If C_1 is the capacitor under test, then a small change in its value ΔC_1 can be measured either in terms of the change in oscillator frequency or by altering the value of the parallel capacitor C_2 to keep the frequency constant. The general method is to substitute C_2 for C_1 by means of a switch and to adjust the value of C_2 until the oscillator

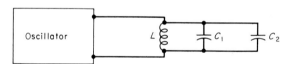

FIG. 4-13. Capacitor substitution method of temperature-coefficient measurement.

frequency equals that obtained with C_1 in circuit. Under these conditions $C_1 = C_2$. This measurement is repeated at different temperatures. A typical measuring equipment of this type is shown in Fig. 4-14.

The outputs of the two oscillators O_1 and O_2 are combined at A, the resultant signal is rectified, and the frequency difference is available at B. Oscillator O_2 may be set to the frequency of measurement (usually 1 Mc/sec), and oscillator O_1 adjusted to a slightly different frequency to produce a beat note at B. This beat note is in turn combined with the output of a stable 1,000-cps oscillator via a demodulator, and a further beat note is produced which can be fed to a cathode-ray oscillograph. By this means a change of about 2 or 3 cps can be detected in the original 1 Mc/sec frequency, i.e., a change of frequency of O_2 of about 2 or 3 parts in 10^6.

The capacitor to be measured is placed in an oven and connected across the oscillatory circuit of O_2, and the frequency of O_1 is adjusted for zero beat at C. The capacitor being measured is then replaced by a standard capacitor having micrometer adjustment. The standard capacitor is adjusted until zero beat is again obtained. The oven is heated (to say 65°C), and the above process is repeated. This will give a new reading on the standard capacitor. The change of reading of this capacitor equals the change of capacitance of the capacitor under test, and if the temperature rise of the capacitor is measured, the temperature coefficient can be calculated as described.

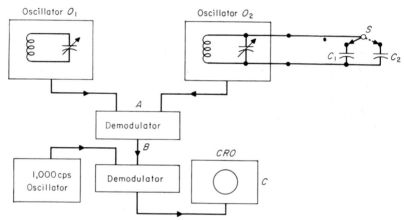

FIG. 4-14. Apparatus for temperature-coefficient measurement.

Measurements for capacitors in accordance with the military specification are made at the temperature extremes, as well as at a number of intermediate points. Capacitance and temperature are measured and recorded at room temperature. The capacitor is then lowered to either −55°C or the next temperature step specified in the governing military specification, and the capacitance measurement at that temperature is recorded when two successive readings taken at 5-min intervals at that temperature indicate no change in capacitance. Reference frequency for the measurements is usually 1.0 Mc/sec. This procedure is repeated for the seven to nine temperature steps as specified in the governing specification to cover the temperature range from −55°C to the high test temperature. Then the temperature coefficient is calculated as follows:

$$\text{Temperature coefficient } \alpha = \frac{(C_2 - C_1) \times 10^6}{C_1(T_2 - T_1)} \qquad \text{ppm/°C}$$

where C_1 is capacitance at the reference temperature (25°C), C_2 is capacitance at the test temperature, T_1 is room temperature (25°C), and T_2 is test temperature.

THE MEASUREMENT OF CAPACITANCE AND TEMPERATURE COEFFICIENT OF VARIABLE CAPACITORS

To measure the capacitance of variable capacitors, similar apparatus to that described for measuring fixed capacitors is used. The capacitance is usually measured with the rotor set at 0° and 180°, although

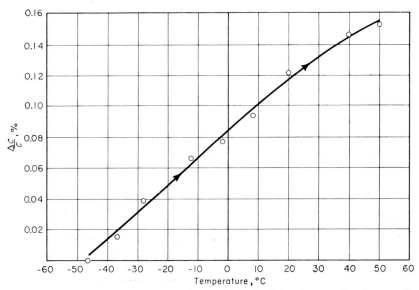

FIG. 4-15. Variation of capacitance of a variable air-dielectric capacitor from −50 to +50°C.

measurements are sometimes required at 0, 15, 35, 70, 105, 140, and 180°, depending upon the function (law).

Temperature-coefficient measurements are also performed in a manner similar to those described for fixed capacitors. Greater care should be taken in temperature-stabilizing the variable capacitor in view of its greater mass. Results of typical measurements on a radio-receiver type of variable capacitor of 2 to 256 pf over a temperature range of −50 to 50°C are shown in Fig. 4-15.

Linearity of temperature coefficient, drift, and cyclic behavior are important. Linearity is ascertained by determining the capacitance-temperature relationship using relatively small temperature increments. Cyclic measurements are made by repetitive measurements

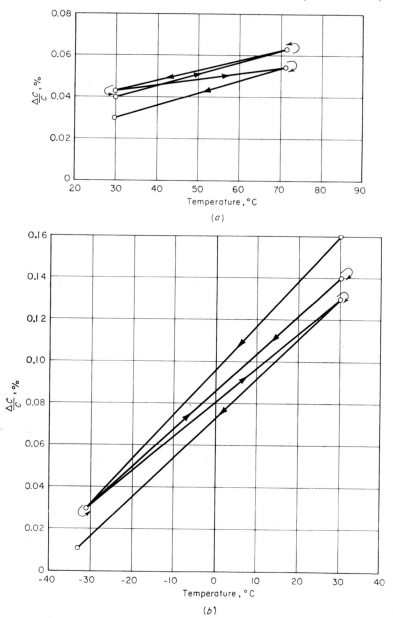

FIG. 4-16. Cyclic variations of capacitance (a) above and (b) below room temperature.

and the behavior of the capacitor above and below room temperature to end points of the operating temperature range. An example of such behavior is shown in Fig. 4-16 for temperatures up to 70°C and down to -30°C.

The capacitor is maintained at each temperature for about a half hour to avoid any variation in capacitance measurement as a result of undue stresses between parts of the capacitor with different coefficients of thermal expansion. Also, silica gel should be placed in the testing chamber to ensure that the capacitor is in a moisture-free atmosphere at low temperatures.

Many capacitors exhibit noncyclic-temperature characteristics during the first two or three thermal cycles. In such cases the tests must be repeated until consistent results are obtained over several cycles. Noncyclic behavior may be due to internal changes in the dielectric material, or relative movement of the electrodes due to differential expansion and contraction.

THE MEASUREMENT OF CAPACITANCE OF TRIMMER CAPACITORS

Where small changes in capacitance are to be measured, as in a trimmer, many difficulties arise, particularly at radio frequencies.

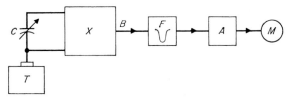

Fig. 4-17. Temperature-coefficient measurement of trimmer capacitors.

For example, if a trimmer capacitor has a capacitance of 30 pf and it is assumed that a variation of one part in 10^5 will affect the stability of the circuit, the change of capacitance which has to be measured is 0.0003 pf. This requires apparatus of extremely high precision and stability. Resonance methods are generally used, and a block diagram of typical measuring equipment is shown in Fig. 4-17.

The capacitor C under tests is connected across a tuned circuit of an oscillator in a reactance meter X. This circuit consists of two precisely matched high-frequency (h-f) oscillators whose outputs are combined in a demodulator with their audio-frequency (a-f) difference appearing at B. This output is connected to a tuned amplifier-detector, consisting of a sharply resonant bandpass filter F, an amplifier A, and a rectifier meter M. The frequency at B is adjusted to coincide with the resonant frequency of the filter F.   A change in the capacitance of C will cause a corresponding change of frequency B, and the output meter reading will fall because of the increased attenuation of the filter.   This decrease will be a measure of the amount of change in the capacitance of C.

For maximum sensitivity the oscillator frequency should be as high as conveniently possible, using C as the bulk of the tuning capacitance and thus producing the maximum change of heat frequency at B for a given variation of C.   The resonant frequency of the filter should be as low as possible, thus giving the greatest change in attenuation for a given change in frequency.   The practical limit of sensitivity is

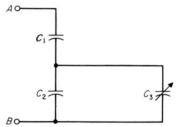

Fig. 4-18. Calibration by capacitor substitution.

determined by the inherent stability of the apparatus; with an oscillator at 4 Mc/sec and the filter tuned to 120 cps, representing optimum sensitivity, it is possible to detect a capacitance change of about one part in 10^6.   Calibration of the meter reading can be carried out by substituting for C a capacitance which can be varied by a known amount, as shown in Fig. 4-18.

If C_1 is approximately equal to the capacity of the trimmer to be measured, and C_2 is comparatively large, then a very small change in total capacitance between A and B may be produced by varying C_3 by an amount which is large enough to be mechanically convenient. Values of C_2 can be chosen to give over-all variations in capacitance of one part in 10^3, 10^4, 10^5, or 10^6.

For checking or measuring the function of shaft rotation vs. capacitance, the capacitance is checked at various angular settings and the results plotted.   The mechanical accuracy and stability of the whole apparatus must be of a high order.

PART 2

FIXED CAPACITORS

CHAPTER 5

GENERAL INFORMATION ON FIXED CAPACITORS

There are two main sets of specifications in general use in the United States today: those prepared by the Department of Defense (the military series) for military electronic parts and those prepared by the Electronic Industries Association (EIA) for commercial electronic parts. [EIA was formerly the Radio, Electronic and Television Manufacturers Association (RETMA).] The Aircraft Industries Association (AIA) and the International Electrotechnical Commission (IEC) have issued a limited number of specifications, which are also available.

UNITED STATES SPECIFICATIONS

Department of Defense Specifications

Specifications for fixed capacitors published by the Department of Defense are as follows:

MIL-C-5:   Capacitors, fixed, mica-dielectric
MIL-C-20:   Capacitors, fixed, ceramic-dielectric (temperature compensating)
MIL-C-25:   Capacitors, fixed, paper-dielectric, d-c (hermetically sealed in metallic cases)
MIL-C-62:   Capacitors, fixed, electrolytic (d-c, aluminum, dry-electrolytic, polarized)
MIL-C-91A: Capacitors, fixed, paper-dielectric (nonmetallic cases)
MIL-C-3871:   Capacitors, fixed, electrolytic (a-c, dry-electrolytic, nonpolarized)
MIL-C-3965:   Capacitors, fixed, electrolytic (tantalum)
MIL-C-10950:   Capacitors, fixed, mica-dielectric, button styles
MIL-C-11015:   Capacitors, fixed, ceramic-dielectric (general-purpose)
MIL-C-11272:   Capacitors, fixed, glass-dielectric

MIL-C-11693: Capacitors, feed-through, radio-interference reduction, paper-dielectric, a-c and d-c (hermetically sealed in metallic cases)

MIL-C-14157: Capacitors, fixed, paper-dielectric, d-c, high reliability (hermetically sealed in metallic cases)

MIL-C-18312: Capacitors, fixed, paper-dielectric, metalized-paper
(Navy)   construction, d-c, hermetically sealed in metallic cases

MIL-C-19978: Capacitors, fixed, plastic-dielectric
(Navy)

MIL-C-21720: Capacitors, fixed, solid-electrolyte, tantalum
(Ships)

Except the Navy specifications, the above specifications are obtainable from the Armed Services Electro Standards Agency (ASESA), at Fort Monmouth, N.J.

Navy Department specifications are obtained from the Commanding Officer, Naval Aviation Supply Depot, 5801 Tabor Ave., Philadelphia 20, Pa.

EIA Specifications

Specifications published for the use of the electronics industry by the EIA are as follows:

REC-107A: Capacitors, fixed, ceramic-dielectric, classes 1 and 2

RS-165:   Capacitors, fixed, ceramic-dielectric, classes 1 and 2 (1,000–75,000-volt rating)

RS-171:   Capacitors, fixed, ceramic-dielectric, high voltage, class 2

RS-154:   Capacitors, fixed, dry electrolytic, for general use

TR-140:   Capacitors, fixed, dry electrolytic, special quality

RS-153:   Capacitors, fixed, mica, molded types

TR-109:   Capacitors, fixed, mica, potted types

TR-113A: Capacitors, fixed, paper-dielectric, metal encased, d-c applications

RS-164:   Capacitors, fixed, paper-dielectric, nonmetallic, tubular types

These specifications are obtainable from the Electronic Industries Association, Engineering Office, Room 650, 11 West 42d Street, New York 36, N.Y.

AIA Specifications

Specifications for use by the aircraft industry are published by the Aircraft Industries Association. They are:

NAS 700: Capacitors, fixed, stacked-dielectric, miniature
NAS 701: Capacitors, fixed, rolled-foil, miniature

These are obtainable from the Aircraft Industries Association of America, Inc., 610 Shoreham Building, Washington 5, D.C.

IEC (ASA) Specifications

The International Electrotechnical Commission is an international body located in Switzerland, which through the standards agencies of the various countries (American Standards Association in the United States) coordinates and issues industrial standards on electronic parts. With regard to capacitors, the IEC has issued one specification, Publication 80, dated 1956, Specification for Fixed Paper Capacitors for Direct Current.

Additional IEC capacitor specifications are planned and are now in the draft stage:

Color code for ceramic-dielectric capacitors
Electrolytic capacitors
Specification for Type 1A and 1B ceramic-dielectric capacitors
Specification for aluminum electrolytic capacitors for general-purpose application

IEC specifications are published by the Central Office of the IEC, 30 Route de Malagnon, Geneva, Switzerland. They are obtainable in the United States from the American Standards Association, 70 East 45th Street, New York 17, N.Y.

BRITISH SPECIFICATIONS

British specifications on fixed capacitors may also be of interest and are given below. The United Kingdom has two main sets of specifications in general use today: those prepared by the Radio Components Standardization Committee (RCSC) for use by the military (equivalent to the U.S. military (MIL) specifications) and those prepared by the Radio Industry Council (RIC) for use by commercial electronic industries (equivalent to our EIA specifications).

RCSC Specifications

RCG 130:   Guide on capacitors, fixed

RCG 131:   Specification for capacitors, fixed, paper-dielectric (d-c rated)

DEF 5132:   Specification for capacitors, fixed, mica-dielectric

DEF 5133-1: Specification for capacitors, fixed, ceramic-dielectric with specified capacitance temperature coefficients (normal dielectric constant)

DEF 5133-2: Specification for capacitors, fixed, ceramic-dielectric (high dielectric constant)

RCS 134A: Specification for capacitors, fixed, electrolytic (not suitable for use below −30°C)

RCS 134B: Specification for capacitors, fixed, electrolytic (with tantalum electrode)

RCS 136:   Specification for capacitors, fixed, paper-dielectric, metalized (d-c rated)

RCS 137:   Specification for capacitors, fixed, plastic-film dielectric (d-c rated). Suitable only for temperatures from −30 to +60°C

RCL 131:   List of standard capacitors, fixed, paper-dielectric

DEF 5135:   Specification for capacitors, fixed, vitreous-enamel and glass-dielectric

RCL 134A: List of standard capacitors, fixed, electrolytic (not suitable for use below −30°C)

RCL 134B: List of standard capacitors, fixed, electrolytic (with tantalum electrode)

RCL 136:   List of standard capacitors, fixed, paper-dielectric, metalized

RCL 137:   List of standard capacitors, fixed, plastic-dielectric (suitable only for temperatures of −30 to +60°C)

These specifications are obtainable from the Radio Components Standardization Committee, 77/91 New Oxford Street, London, W.C.I., England.

RIC Specifications

RIC/131: Capacitors, fixed, paper-dielectric, tubular, foil

RIC/132: Capacitors, fixed, mica-dielectric, stacked, foil

RIC/133: Capacitors, fixed, ceramic-dielectric, Grade I

RIC/134: Capacitors, fixed, electrolytic

RIC/136: Capacitors, fixed, paper-dielectric, tubular, metalized

RIC/137: Capacitors, fixed, mica-dielectric, metalized

These specifications are obtainable from the Radio Industry Council, 59 Russell Square, London, W.C.I., England.

FIXED-CAPACITOR SYMBOLS

Symbols which are in general commercial and military use listed in standard MIL-STD-15A, Electrical and Electronic Symbols, are given here:

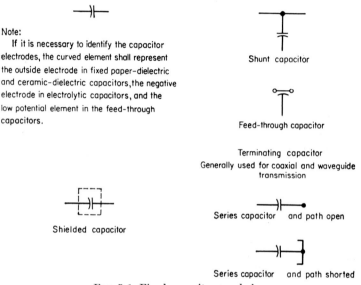

Note:
  If it is necessary to identify the capacitor electrodes, the curved element shall represent the outside electrode in fixed paper-dielectric and ceramic-dielectric capacitors, the negative electrode in electrolytic capacitors, and the low potential element in the feed-through capacitors.

Shunt capacitor

Feed-through capacitor

Terminating capacitor
Generally used for coaxial and waveguide transmission

Shielded capacitor

Series capacitor   and path open

Series capacitor   and path shorted

FIG. 5-1. Fixed-capacitor symbols.

PREFERRED OR STANDARD TYPES AND VALUES

All types and values which are contained in the military specifications are considered standard (preferred) for new designs by part or all of the individual military departments. Several military bureaus have issued supplementary documents with restrictive listings of the styles and values contained in the military specifications. Notable among these is the Navy standard MIL-STD-242, Electronic Equipment Parts (Selected Standards).

The present standardization program of the military departments, under the management of the Office of Assistant Secretary of Defense for Research and Engineering, is directed toward the development and issuance of a series of military standards listing all electronic parts which are considered standards (preferred) for new design for all three departments.

The standard values for all small fixed capacitors except the non-tubular paper and electrolytic types, in accordance with either the military or EIA specifications, must follow the preferred number series listed in the EIA general standard GEN-102, Preferred Values.

Because the electronics industry has a practice of applying ± 5 per cent, ± 10 per cent, and ± 20 per cent tolerance on electronic parts, the Electronic Industries Association adopted a series of preferred values based upon $\underline{24}/\overline{10}$, $\underline{12}/\overline{10}$, and $\underline{6}/\overline{10}$.

COLOR CODES

Colors for Color Codes

Unless otherwise indicated in the specific military electronic-part specification, the colors for color coding used in military specifications are defined by standard MIL-STD-174, Colors for Coding Electronic Parts. Colors used for color coding in accordance with EIA specifications are covered by EIA standard GEN-102.

Paper-dielectric Capacitors

Paper-dielectric capacitors which are constructed in accordance with the existing military specifications [MIL-C-25, MIL-C-91, MIL-C-14157, and MIL-C-18312(Navy)] are required to be marked with

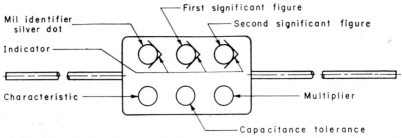

Fig. 5-2. Standard code for molded-paper capacitors in accordance with specification MIL-C-91.

type designation, capacitances, rated voltage, and the manufacturer's name or symbol. If space does not permit, the capacitance and rated voltage may be omitted. Table 5-1 gives the MIL-C-91 color code.

Commercial types are usually marked with capacitance, rated voltage, manufacturer's type number, and manufacturer's name.

Molded-paper capacitors, in accordance with specification MIL-C-91, may be marked with a color code as shown in Fig. 5-2 if insufficient

TABLE 5-1. COLOR CODE FOR MOLDED-PAPER CAPACITORS IN ACCORDANCE
WITH SPECIFICATION MIL-C-91

Color*	Capacitance		Capacitance tolerance, %(±)	Characteristic
	First and second significant figures	Multiplier†		
Black...........	0	1	20 (M)	A
Brown..........	1	10	—	E
Red.............	2	100	—	—
Orange..........	3	1,000	30 (N)	—
Yellow..........	4	10,000	—	—
Green...........	5	—	—	—
Blue............	6	—	—	—
Purple (violet)....	7	—	—	—
Gray............	8	—	—	—
White...........	9	—	—	—
Silver...........	—	—	10 (K)	—

* The MIL identifier shall be a silver dot.

† The multiplier is the factor by which the first two significant figures are multiplied to yield the nominal capacitance.

space prohibits full markings as specified above.   The colors shall be in the form of six dots arranged in two rows of three dots each with an indicator to show the order in which they are to be read.

Mica-dielectric Capacitors

Mica-dielectric capacitors (molded axial-lead types), under military specification MIL-C-5, must be marked with type designation, capacitance, working voltage, and manufacturer's name or symbol, or with color code to denote these characteristics.

The commercial types in accordance with EIA specification RS-153 follow the same color code.   (First six dots only.)

The military color code for mica capacitors consists of nine dots arranged in three rows of three with an arrow indicator to show in which direction the dots are to be read, as shown in Fig. 5-3.   The color code used for the dots is given in Table 5-2.

All button mica-dielectric capacitors, in accordance with specifi-

TABLE 5-2. COLOR CODE FOR MICA CAPACITORS IN ACCORDANCE WITH SPECIFICATION MIL-C-5

Color	Characteristic†	Capacitance		Capacitance tolerance, % (±)	D-c working voltage	Operating temperature range	Vibration grade
		First and second significant figures	Multiplier*				
Black	—	0	1	—	—	(M) −55 to +70°C	(1) 10–55 cps
Brown	B	1	10	—	—	(N) −55 to +85°C	—
Red	C	2	100	2 (G)	300	—	(3) 10–2,000 cps
Orange	D	3	1,000	—	—	(O) −55 to +125°C	—
Yellow	E	4	—	—	500	—	—
Green	F	5	—	5 (J)	—	(P) −55 to +150°C	—
Blue	—	6	—	—	—	—	—
Purple (violet)	—	7	—	—	—	—	—
Gray	—	8	—	—	—	—	—
White	—	9	—	—	—	—	—
Gold	—	—	0.1	—	—	—	—
Silver	—	—	—	10 (K)	—	—	—

* The multiplier is the factor by which the two significant figures are multiplied to yield the nominal capacitance.
† The characteristic is a single letter which indicates the relative stability of the capacitor with temperature change.

84

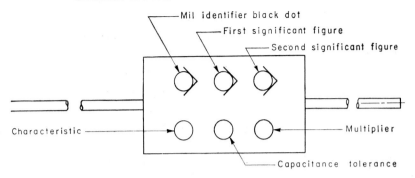

- Mil identifier black dot
- First significant figure
- Second significant figure

Characteristic ————————— Multiplier

Capacitance tolerance

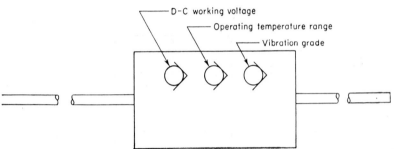

- D-C working voltage
- Operating temperature range
- Vibration grade

FIG. 5-3. Standard code for molded-mica capacitors in accordance with specification MIL-C-5.

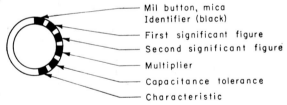

- Mil button, mica Identifier (black)
- First significant figure
- Second significant figure
- Multiplier
- Capacitance tolerance
- Characteristic

FIG. 5-4. Standard code for button-mica capacitors in accordance with specification MIL-C-10950.

cation MIL-C-10950, are marked by color coding. The colors are shown in the form of six dots arranged clockwise, as shown in Fig. 5-4. For colors used in standard code see Table 5-2. These capacitors are available only in characteristics *C* and *D*.

Glass Capacitors

Glass-dielectric capacitors for military use in accordance with requirements of specification MIL-C-11272 shall be marked either with the type designation or color code.   The color code is the same as shown for molded-mica capacitors (first six dots only).   These capacitors are available only in characteristic *C*.

Ceramic-dielectric Capacitors

Temperature-compensating-type ceramic-dielectric capacitors in accordance with specification MIL-C-20 can be marked either with type designation, capacitance tolerance, and temperature coefficient,

TABLE 5-3. COLOR CODE FOR CERAMIC CAPACITORS IN ACCORDANCE WITH SPECIFICATION MIL-C-20

Color	Charac- teristic*	Nominal capacitance, $\mu\mu f$		Capacitance tolerance	
		First and second significant figures	Multi- plier†	For nominal capacitances greater than 10 $\mu\mu f$, %	For nominal capacitances of 10 $\mu\mu f$ or smaller, $\mu\mu f$
Black..............	C—(0)	0	1		±2.0 (G)
Brown.............	H—(−30)	1	10	±1 (F)	
Red...............	L—(−80)	2	100	±2 (G)	±0.25 (C)
Orange...........	P—(−150)	3	1,000		
Yellow............	R—(−220)	4			
Green.............	S—(−330)	5		±5 (J)	±0.5 (D)
Blue..............	T—(−470)	6			
Purple (violet).....	U—(−750)	7			
Gray.............		8	0.01		
White............		9	0.1	±10 (K)	±1.0 (F)
Gold.............	A—(+100)				

* The characteristic is a two-letter symbol identifying the nominal temperature coefficient and the envelope for the temperature-coefficient tolerance, respectively. However, the characteristic band or spot identifies only the nominal temperature coefficient.

† The multiplier is the factor by which the two significant figures are multiplied to yield the nominal capacitance.

or with a color code consisting of five bands, as shown in Fig. 5-5. The standard color code is shown in Table 5-3.   Commercial types under EIA specification RS-165 use the same color code.

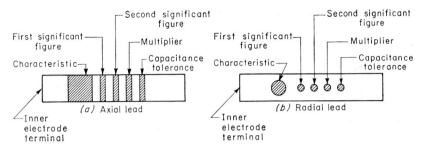

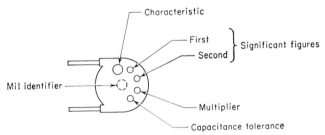

FIG. 5-5. Standard code for ceramic capacitors in accordance with specification MIL-C-20.

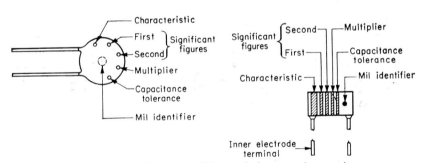

FIG. 5-6. Standard code for disk or tubular ceramic capacitors.

General-purpose ceramic capacitors (disk or tubular) meeting marking requirements of specification MIL-C-11015 may be marked with type designation, characteristics, capacitance, and manufacturer's name or symbol, or with a color code if required by shape or limited space, as shown by Fig. 5-6. The standard color code is shown in Table 5-4.

TABLE 5-4. COLOR CODE FOR CERAMIC CAPACITORS IN ACCORDANCE WITH SPECIFICATION MIL-C-11015

Color	Temperature range and voltage-temperature limits*	Nominal capacitance		Capacitance tolerance, %
		Significant figure	Multiplier†	
Black...............	—	0	1	±20 (M)
Brown..............	AW	1	10	±10 (K)
Red.................	AX	2	100	
Orange..............	—	3	1,000	
Yellow..............	—	4	—	$\begin{cases} +80 \ (X) \\ -20 \end{cases}$
Green...............	CZ	5		
Blue................	—	6		
Purple (violet)........	—	7		
Gray...............	—	8		
White..............	—	9		

* The operating temperature range and the voltage-temperature limits are identified by two letters. The first letter indicates the operating temperature range, and the second letter indicates the voltage limits or allowable capacitance variation at specified temperatures, both with and without rated voltage applied.

† The multiplier is the factor by which the two significant figures are multiplied to yield the nominal capacitance.

CHAPTER 6

PAPER- AND MICA-DIELECTRIC FIXED CAPACITORS

In this chapter we shall consider in more detail the construction and behavior of various types of paper-dielectric capacitors (impregnated, metalized, castellated, and pressurized types) and the various mica-dielectric capacitors (stacked, silvered, etc.).

IMPREGNATED-PAPER CAPACITORS

Fixed tubular impregnated-paper capacitors are constructed by rolling paper insulation between metal electrodes. The electrodes are usually aluminum, but may be tin or copper. The paper is made

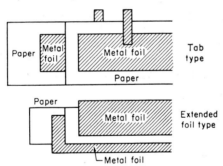

FIG. 6-1. End-connection contacts to foils.

specially as capacitor tissue and is carefully dried and impregnated in wax or oil. End-connection contacts to the metal-foil electrodes are of two kinds, the tab type or the extended-foil type, represented in Fig. 6-1. The construction of a typical metal-cased tubular capacitor is shown in Fig. 6-2.

The paper is used in thicknesses which lie between 5 microns (0.0002 in.) and 25 microns (0.001 in.), and the foils used are about 0.00025 in. thick. The paper is usually made from vegetable fiber which has been chemically "digested" in strong alkali, resulting in cellulose in fibrous form. This pulp is then rolled into paper through warm rollers. All papers contain carbon particles, which can project

89

right through, particularly in the thinnest papers; metal impurities
are also present at times. For this reason the minimum number of
papers used is two, but there may be more, depending on the voltage
rating and other characteristics of the capacitor being made. "Shives"

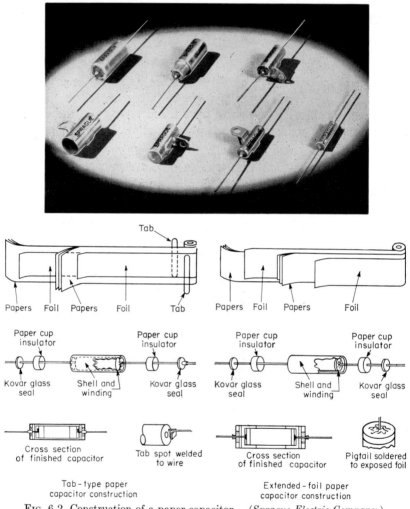

Fig. 6-2. Construction of a paper capacitor. (*Sprague Electric Company.*)

or hard spots occasionally occur, which will not take impregnation
and which may contain impurities affecting the life of the capacitor.
The working stress of impregnated paper as a dielectric is 15 to
25 volts per micron.

The actual breakdown or ultimate strength is about 150 volts per micron, giving a safety factor of six. The voltage across one unit of foil and paper should never exceed 3 kv. A new paper is hydroscopic and contains from 5 to 7 per cent of moisture. After drying, therefore, vacuum impregnation with synthetic fluids or oils, mineral oils, paraffin waxes, or petroleum jelly is necessary to fill up the voids left between the cellulose fibers of the paper. As these voids or air spaces are effectively in series with the cellulose, the effect of impregnation is to increase the dielectric constant, the power factor, and the dielectric breakdown strength of the dielectric material.

Impregnants of higher dielectric constant, such as chlorinated naphthalene and chlorinated diphenyl, result in a capacitor of smaller size when compared to an equivalent design using mineral oil. Chlorinated naphthalene can be used for capacitors with voltage ratings of 200 to 300 volts for operation in ambients up to 55°C. At higher temperatures failures may occur through deterioration of the paper as a result of its being attacked by hydrochloric acid, formed from hydrogen generated by electrolysis and chlorine from the impregnant. In the United Kingdom, to inhibit this deterioration the inclusion of a stabilizer such as azobenzene has been suggested by reason of its ability to accept hydrogen. Results from many tests which have been made show that long lives under d-c voltage stress at high temperatures, previously obtainable only with nonpolar impregnants such as petroleum jelly, are possible with chlorinated naphthalene impregnants if 5 per cent azobenzene is added.

Chlorinated-diphenyl-impregnated capacitors have a dielectric constant which is dependent on both frequency and temperature. The life expectancy of this type of capacitor under higher temperatures (90°C) and d-c voltage stress has been considerably increased by the work done by D. A. McLean and L. Egerton (see Bibliography). This increase was accomplished by prebaking the paper for many hours at a high temperature with an air environment and then adding a small amount (one-half of 1 per cent) of anthraquinone dissolved in the chlorinated diphenyl. It is essential to maintain scrupulous cleanliness in the manufacture of these capacitors as chlorinated diphenyl is a powerful solvent and may absorb impurities from such materials as rubber and copper (unless heavily plated).

Castor oil can be used where the temperature range is restricted (−25 to +65°C) or where considerable variation in capacitance is allowable at low temperatures. Since the dielectric constant is comparatively high at low frequencies, the capacitor will be smaller than an equivalent design using mineral oil as the impregnant.

Mineral oil is generally used for temperature ranges from −55 to 105°C where good capacitance stability with a variation in temperature is required. Silicon fluids, polyesters, or polyisobutenes are generally used for wider temperature ranges (−55 to +125°C). Capacitors impregnated with these materials have good capacitance stability with a variation in temperature.

The use of one sheet of polyethylene terephthalate in lieu of one sheet of paper has been found to provide a capacitor with higher insulation resistance and better life characteristics. This laminated type of construction for paper capacitors will see greater and greater usage.

General Characteristics of Impregnated-paper Capacitors

Capacitance Tolerances. The final capacitance of the manufactured capacitor may vary through causes such as variations in the following:

1. Thickness of the paper used (may be ±10 per cent)
2. Density of the paper
3. Smoothness of the paper surface
4. Amount of metal foil used
5. Tension of winding
6. Characteristics of the impregnant used

The over-all tolerance of typical impregnated-paper capacitors is usually not better than ±10 per cent.

Breakdown Voltage. There is a large difference between d-c and a-c breakdown voltages and the a-c conditions are discussed on page 94 under The Behavior of Paper-dielectric Capacitors on Alternating Current. The maximum d-c or a-c voltage which may be applied decreases with increase of temperature, e.g., at 125°C it may be only half the breakdown voltage at room temperature. In general, the losses in an impregnated-paper capacitor increase with increase of voltage, while the breakdown voltage decreases with increase of temperature. The ultimate breakdown strength of wax-, oil-, and jelly-impregnated capacitors also depends a great deal on the time of application of the voltage. If the rate of increase of voltage is 50 volts/min, the stress required to break down a good-quality capacitor paper is about two million volts d-c per centimeter at room temperature; at 50°C it is one and a half million volts per centimeter, and at 80°C approximately one and a quarter million. On alternating current the peak breakdown voltage would be slightly less. With a steady voltage (either d-c or a-c) applied for 24 hr at room temperature, the stress required to break down the capacitor would be about half a million volts per centimeter.

Temperature Coefficient. The temperature coefficient depends to a large extent on shape, mechanical construction, and the impregnant the capacitor has. Because of the large variation in capacitance at low temperatures for paper capacitors, capacitance variation from the value at 25°C is usually expressed in per cent, and the temperature-coefficient notation as such is not used. If capacitors are designed for application over a limited temperature range, this notation is sometimes used. The tubular construction wound on a rigid former is the most satisfactory type mechanically, since the cylinder is an inherently rigid shape. The flat construction (where the cylinder has been pressed flat) usually has a higher temperature coefficient and may be noncyclic. The temperature coefficients for both types of construction vary from +100 to +200 ppm/°C over a restricted temperature range of +20 to +60°C.

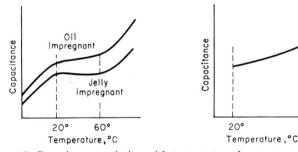

Fig. 6-3. Capacitance variation with temperature for paper capacitors.

The temperature coefficient is largely dependent on the impregnant, and in some cases it is nonlinear because the impregnant changes viscosity with temperature. Mineral-oil impregnants are slightly positive over the temperature range +20 to +60°C, while petroleum jelly is slightly negative over the same range. Figure 6-3 shows typical variations of capacitance with temperature for these types.

Dielectric Constant. For capacitors impregnated with oil, wax, or jelly, the dielectric constant is usually between 3.4 and 4.5. For a tubular capacitor where little winding pressure is used, the dielectric constant would be about 3.5. It is dependent also on the density of the paper; using heavy pressure and dense paper, the dielectric constant would be about 4.5. The dielectric constant rises slowly with increase of temperature and falls slowly with increase of frequency.

Power Factor or Loss Angle. For oil-, wax-, and jelly-impregnated capacitors, power factor is also mainly dependent on the density of the paper; at 60 cps it lies between 0.0015 and 0.005 for temperatures between 25 and 65°C. The power factor decreases with increasing temperature and then rises again. At high temperatures the loss depends chiefly on the moisture impurities in the dielectric. The shape and position of the power-factor temperature curve also vary with frequency. The power factor increases slowly with increase of frequency (the increase is rapid above 10 kc/sec) but may fall again if the temperature is high—i.e., at high frequencies the maximum power factor occurs at a lower temperature.

Insulation Resistance or "Resistivity." The insulation resistance of all paper-dielectric capacitors falls rapidly with increase of temperature, so that doubling the temperature may result in the insulation resistance dropping to one-tenth of its original value. It depends critically on the moisture and impurity contents of the materials in the capacitor, and the effectiveness of the sealing is therefore of

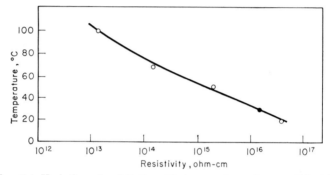

Fig. 6-4. Variation of resistivity with temperature of paper dielectric.

importance. Variations in value of over 1,000 to 1 are common between samples of commercial capacitors. Accurate measurements of resistivity must eliminate false readings due to surface leakage, and the graph in Fig. 6-4 shows the variation of resistivity with temperature, the conduction current in the paper being measured some time after all absorption current has ceased. Conventional readings taken without guard rings and without great precautions may result in measurements at least ten times lower than these figures.

The results of some measurements showing the variation of insulation resistance with temperature for typical paper-dielectric capacitors are given in Chap. 2.

The Behavior of Paper-dielectric Capacitors on Alternating Current. When an alternating voltage is applied to a capacitor, the metal foils are alternately positive and negative, which causes attraction for one another. This introduces mechanical stress, in addition to electrical stress. The tendency of the plates to come closer together, as the voltage is increased, increases the capacitance. This produces a marked effect on capacitors impregnated with oil or liquid filling. The effect is less on those impregnated with jellies and comparatively small on those with viscous or solid impregnants.

The maximum peak a-c voltage which should be applied to a tubular impregnated-paper capacitor is limited to about 350 volts. This is because some air bubbles are always left in the impregnated paper, even after vacuum impregnation at 0.5 mm of mercury for 50 hr. On alternating current, these bubbles ionize, glow discharge takes place, and the surrounding paper is burned. With alternating current, this occurs on each cycle, and is therefore serious. On direct current, it occurs only at the moments of switching on and off, although ionization will occur with steady direct current if the voltage is high

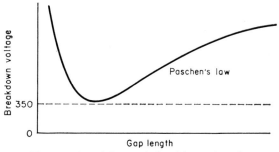

FIG. 6-5. Breakdown of air with gap length.

enough. There are two approaches to this problem—either the vacuum can be increased still more during impregnation (which is expensive) or the air can be prevented from ionizing by reducing the voltage across the air bubbles. If a curve is plotted of breakdown voltage against gap length in air, the Paschen's curve of Fig. 6-5 results.

It is seen that there is a definite minimum voltage below which breakdown does not take place, regardless of gap length. This is about 350 volts for air (for neon it is about 120 volts). Ionization is not, however, synonymous with breakdown. In air, ionization can occur continuously and stably, as for example in high-temperature (h-t) lines and cables. In a capacitor it is the ionization in air voids which reduces the life, owing to local overheating. The peak voltage across the capacitor elements should, therefore, never be more than 350 volts on alternating current. Capacitors for operation at higher a-c voltages are specially made, using series sections and oil impregnation free from voids. In practice, a factor of safety is provided by the fact that the discharge requires a voltage slightly higher than 350 volts to actually strike.

As the frequency is increased the maximum alternating voltage which a capacitor will withstand becomes very much reduced. This reduction is greater for the higher capacitance values. This is partly the result of the excessive heating when larger currents flow at high frequencies, the current being proportional to $E/X_c = E\omega C = E2\pi fC$, and partly the result of the greater damage from discharges at the higher frequencies.

The Behavior of Paper-dielectric Capacitors at Radio Frequencies. The tubular types of paper capacitor are the only ones likely to be used in r-f circuits, and the inductance of such a capacitor is taken as

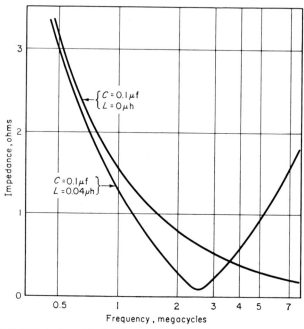

FIG. 6-6. Effect of residual inductance on impedance of 0.1 μf capacitor.

equivalent to that of a straight length of 20 swg copper wire equal in length to the capacitor, including connecting wires. This inductance will be between 0.01 and 0.05 μh. In r-f filters, the self-inductance of the capacitor may be used to resonate at some particular frequency, and the reduction in impedance under such conditions is shown in Fig. 6-6.

Metalized-paper Capacitors

One side of the impregnated paper tissue can be sprayed with metal, or metal can be evaporated onto it. This has the advantage that the electrode is as thin as possible, and when rolled the capacitance for a given volume is higher than that of the normal foil-and-paper types. With the exception of a small distance from one edge, the entire width of one side of the paper can be metalized, leaving a narrow band of unmetalized tissue along one edge of its length. The actual width of this band is determined by the working voltage of the capacitor. The most important property of this type of capacitor, apart from its small size, is its property of self-healing under slight excess voltage. If the voltage across the capacitor is gradually raised, a value will be reached at which sparking occurs, and if the voltage is maintained at this value, the sparking will be only momentary. This sparking occurs at points of dielectric weakness in the paper, and the thin metal film is evaporated from these spots without damaging the paper. With aluminum film the high temperature will produce aluminum oxide, which is itself a good insulator. The electrical strength of the paper dielectric will therefore be restored almost immediately. The voltage can then be increased to a higher value when further momentary sparking will occur. A point is finally reached when sparking becomes continuous and breakdown occurs. The maximum voltage at which this self-healing action may occur without detriment to the properties of the capacitor is the life *test voltage* and is approximately 1.4 times the working voltage. The maximum short-term voltage (applied for less than 60 sec) which can be applied without destroying the capacitor is termed the *spark voltage* and is approximately two times the working voltage. Care must, therefore, be taken to avoid continuous voltage overloading in this type of capacitor.

More recent types of metalized-paper capacitors use a lacquered-paper dielectric tissue on which aluminum or zinc has been evaporated in a vacuum. In several types a laminated structure of paper and polyethylene terephthalate, each with an evaporated metalized film, has been used. The paper tends to hold the impregnant, and higher insulation and better life characteristics result. The evaporated coating is extremely thin, and is of the order of 0.000004 in. The metalized dielectric tissue is passed between metal rollers, across which the working voltage of the capacitor is applied to remove any weak points, as described previously. The two dielectric tissues are superimposed, so that the metalized edge of one dielectric tissue lies over the unmetalized edge of the other, and the dielectric tissues are then wound into a roll. As the unmetalized part of the dielectric tissue serves as an insulator between the two electrodes, no other dielectric tissue is required for voltage ratings below 200 volts. For higher voltage ratings, additional dielectric tissues are added as required. Each end

of the roll is then sprayed with copper to enable the edges to be connected and the terminations attached.   The construction of a typical
tubular metalized-paper capacitor is shown in Fig. 6-7.

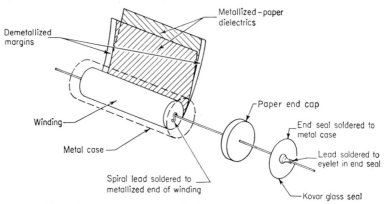

FIG. 6-7. Construction of tubular metalized paper capacitor.

Castellated Metalized-paper Capacitors

Another development is the "castellated" technique originally
developed in the United Kingdom by A. H. Hunt, Ltd.   This technique
uses one paper to provide the dielectric tissue and both electrodes.   A
castellated insulating track along the aluminized paper is produced as
shown in Fig. 6-8.

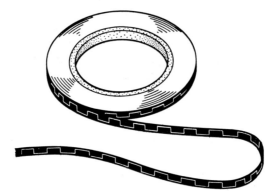

FIG. 6-8. Castellated metalized paper.   (*A. H. Hunt, Ltd.*)

It is arranged that each metal tongue corresponds to an exact cir-
cumference; as the diameter of the winding increases, the tongue
length increases.   This method produces an extremely compact capacitor.   The internal construction of such a capacitor is shown in Fig. 6-9,

General Characteristics of Metalized-paper Capacitors

The insulation resistance of this type of capacitor (with the exception of some of the laminated types using polyethylene terephthalate) is considerably lower than that of an equivalent foil and paper capacitor. With the working voltage applied, the insulation resistance at 25°C is on the order of 250 ohm-farads. The working temperature range is between −55 and +85°C for the wax-coated petroleum-jelly-impregnated capacitors. The newer types using laminated construction of paper and polyethylene terephthalate have much higher insulation resistance. These mineral wax-impregnated hermetically sealed

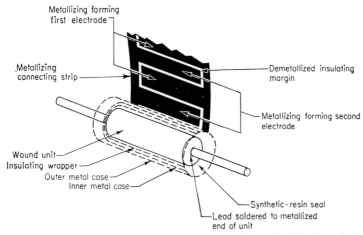

Fig. 6-9. Construction of castellated paper capacitor. (*A. H. Hunt, Ltd.*)

metallic tubulars are capable of operating over a temperature range of −55 to 125°C without voltage derating. The insulation resistance at rated voltage is on the order of a product of 2,000 ohm-farads at 25°C and 100 ohm-farads at 85°C. Capacitance tolerances are on the order of ± 10 per cent. The power factor at 25°C and 1 kc/sec varies from 0.005 to 0.015. The self-inductance is low and approximately equivalent to that of a solid piece of metal of the same size and shape as the capacitor.

Pressurized Paper-dielectric Capacitors

Large paper-dielectric capacitors are used for power-factor correction in industrial electric systems. It is possible by pressurizing these large capacitors to increase the working voltage considerably and still maintain their reliability. Breakdown is usually caused by ionization of voids in the paper tissue, resulting in overheating and carbonization at these spots with consequent failure of insulation. The voltage at which breakdown occurs in air is given by Paschen's curve, shown on page 95. The curves in Fig. 6-10 show the increase in working a-c voltages by pressurizing, for different thicknesses of paper.

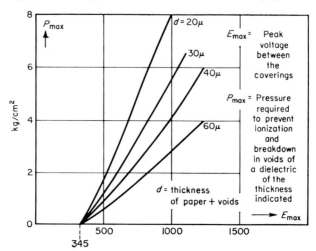

FIG. 6-10. Increase in working voltage obtained by pressurizing. (*Philips Ltd., Eindhoven.*)

MICA-DIELECTRIC CAPACITORS

Mica occurs naturally, mainly in India (Bengal and Madras), Canada, and South America. It is found in laminated masses which are capable of being split or separated into sheets. This property of cleavage is due to the particular molecular structure and is the most important property of mica for electrical usage. For use in capacitors it is usually split down to about 0.002 in.; below this, wastage may become serious. It is possible by special laboratory techniques to split to about 0.00001 in. Although there are many types of mica, only the most common are mentioned here. The qualities of each type may vary widely.

Muscovite (White Mica). This is the most common form. Much of it is colorless and transparent. It has the greatest mechanical strength and a maximum working temperature of about 500°C. At temperatures above 600°C, it begins to calcine. It is widely used for electrical insulation.

Ruby Mica (Rose-colored Mica). A variety of muscovite. The best dielectric properties obtainable in mica are found in high-quality ruby mica. Widely used for insulation and particularly for capacitor dielectrics.

Phlogopite (Amber Mica).   Softer than muscovite but with a higher maximum working temperature (900 to 1,000°C).   Often used in armature construction.   Dielectric properties inferior to those of good muscovite.

Biotite (Iron Mica or Black Mica).   Electrical properties are inferior to muscovite, but it is used for general insulation.

Vermiculite.   This name covers a group of hydrous silicates occurring as decomposition products of the micas.   They are mainly hydrated silicates of aluminum, iron, and magnesium.   When heated slowly they exfoliate and open into long wormlike threads.

TABLE 6-1. ELECTRICAL PROPERTIES OF MICA

Origin	Resistivity, ohm-cm $\times 10^{12}$	Dielectric constant, K	Disruptive strength, volts/mm
Bengal.............	15–133	2.5–7.0	50,000– 80,000
Madras............	7–118	2.8–7.0	40,000–120,000
Canada............	0.44– 22	2.9–3.0	70,000– 90,000
South America.....	37– 40	5.8–6.0	40,000– 90,000

The electrical properties of mica vary according to the place of origin and are approximately as shown in Table 6-1, although it should be remembered that these figures depend on the dryness of the specimen and on the method of testing.

The power factor of mica varies considerably, from 0.02 to 0.0002, but can be as low as 0.00005 if specially selected and dry.   The specific gravity varies from 2.7 to 3.2.   It should be borne in mind that the insulating value of mica deteriorates with heat (commencing, with poor specimens, at about 400°C), as a result of delamination due to dehydration.   Mica, being a natural material, also contains impurities which vary according to the source of supply.   In processing mica for capacitors and for other uses, a number of terms are used which are defined below.

Crude mica is the crude crystals or "books" as extracted from the mine.

Cobbing is the process of removing dirt, rock, and mine scrap from crude mica.

Rifting is the process of splitting cobbed mica into sheets of suitable thicknesses.

Full-trimmed mica is rifted mica trimmed on all sides with all cracks and cross grains removed.

Half-trimmed mica is rifted mica trimmed on two sides only.

Blocks of mica are 0.007 in. minimum thickness, full-trimmed.

Book-form splittings are in the form of individual books or bunches, each book comprising consecutive splittings obtained from the same piece of block mica. Book-form splittings are generally dusted with mica powder to offset residual cohesive forces.

Trimming or *dressing* is the process of removing major flaws in rifted mica. Trimming may be accomplished by fingers, sickle, knife, shear, or guillotine, and the mica is called thumb-trimmed mica, sickle-trimmed mica, etc.

Thins are knife-dressed mica plates, at least 0.002 in. but less than 0.007 in. in thickness.

Scrap mica is the name given to byproducts obtained in the course of processing different grades of mica.

Hard mica is mica which does not show any tendency to delaminate when slightly flexed or distorted with thumb pressure. Thick pieces of this mica will give an almost metallic sound when tapped or dropped on a hard surface.

For use in capacitors, the full-trimmed mica is graded for size and quality by visual examination; it falls into blocks varying from 1 in. square or less to a maximum of about 5 to 6 in. It is usually tested electrically in two ways—testing for conducting particles or pinholes by a form of high-frequency spark, and testing the Q of the mica.

It is also examined for imperfections, such as spots, stains, cracks, hairlines, holes, and air inclusions. As a capacitor dielectric, the ASTM specification D.748/52T divides mica into three classes: *Class C1* block mica or mica film has the highest Q value obtainable for mica (a minimum of 2,500 at 1 Mc/sec in capacitors) and is suitable for use with all sizes and types of silver and foil electrodes in high-stability tuned circuits as well as transmitter capacitors. *Class C1* mica also has the highest Q obtainable in the a-f range—a minimum of 1,000 at 1 kc/sec. *Class C2* is suitable for general use and has a minimum Q of 1,500 at 1 Mc/sec in capacitors. The temperature rise in transmitter types will be higher than for *C1* mica capacitors. *Class C3* block mica and mica film has the lowest Q value—200 at 1 Mc/sec in capacitors—and is suitable for use in foil-electrode molded and clamped-type capacitors.

Stacked-mica Capacitors (Stacked Foil and Mica)

Mica, prepared as described above, is tested and cut to the required size. The sheets are then interleaved with electrodes of brass, tin, or copper foil, and the assembly is held together in a clamp to maintain rigidity of the foils.   The construction of a typical stacked-mica foil capacitor is shown in Fig. 6-11.

The lead-out contacts are usually attached by spot-welding, which also connects the foils of similar polarity where a number of foils are attached.   It is essential that a reliable, noisefree contact be made to the foils.   The assembly is then often molded in a plastic case to protect it from mechanical damage and as a partial seal.   Some units are then wax-treated to minimize moisture penetration and also to reduce leakage across the surface.

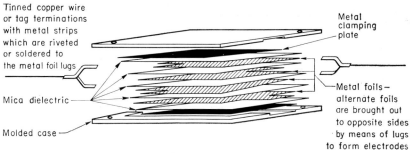

Tinned copper wire or tag terminations with metal strips which are riveted or soldered to the metal foil lugs

Mica dielectric

Molded case

Metal clamping plate

Metal foils— alternate foils are brought out to opposite sides by means of lugs to form electrodes

FIG. 6-11. Construction of a stacked-mica capacitor.   (*Aerovox Corporation.*)

Other methods of sealing the mica stack are either encapsulating with an epoxy resin or impregnation with a high-melting-point wax only.

The type of encasing employed for mica-dielectric capacitors is important, as the dielectric leakage and temperature limitations of encasing materials often restrict the performance of the capacitor. Both stacked- and silvered-mica capacitors are very susceptible to the effects of moisture, and the power factor will increase severely if moisture is allowed to penetrate the case.   As the dielectric constant of water is high (approximately 80) comparatively small quantities will lower the insulation resistance, increase the power factor, and increase the capacitance.   Thorough protection by sealing is therefore essential. Various plastic and other materials have been and are being used, among them the following:

1. Wax
2. Molded loaded phenol formaldehyde (bakelite, etc.)
3. Molded loaded and unloaded epoxy resins

Apart from molecular penetration through the encasing material, moisture penetration occurs along the lead-out wires. For a good seal, therefore, the material must either "wet" the metal, or a ceramic or glass casing with end-soldered joints must be used.

The main use of stacked-mica capacitors is as coupling capacitors, etc., in r-f circuits, because of their low inductance and low power factor. They are capable of carrying appreciable r-f currents and are, therefore, used as transmitter capacitors. There is no intrinsic upper frequency limit for stacked-mica capacitors, but lead lengths, leakage over casing, etc., usually set practical limits (page 24). Difficulty is sometimes experienced in specifying temperature coefficients accurately owing to the method of construction and the changes in quality of the mica now being mined, but the total variation with temperature of the element, uncased, can be specified within narrow limits. Most mica capacitors produced commercially have appreciable mechanical pressure applied to the dielectric. This may arise from the clamping of the stacked unit during assembly and/or the process of molding. Measurements show that the effect of pressure is to increase both the temperature coefficient and the absolute capacitance of the capacitor. As the pressure varies with temperature, owing to the relative thermal expansions of the various materials used in construction, the complete capacitor exhibits a complex and nonlinear variation of capacitance with temperature.

Precision sealed mica-dielectric capacitors have been used at room temperature as substandards for many years. The performance of such capacitors was summarized by C. G. Garton in 1946 (see Bibliography).

As an example of the stability of precision mica capacitors, the British National Physical Laboratory took a 20-year-old capacitor, dried it in a desiccator at 65 per cent rh for one year and sealed it in a brass case fitted with glass-to-metal seals. After sealing, the capacitance remained constant at 10,054 pf ± 0.2 pf over a test period of 10,000 hr. The power factor before sealing was 0.0006 and, after drying and sealing, was reduced to 0.0001, remaining constant at that value (see Bibliography). Commercially produced mica substandards, such as type 505, manufactured by the General Radio Company, are available with an accuracy of ±0.5 per cent or ±3 pf

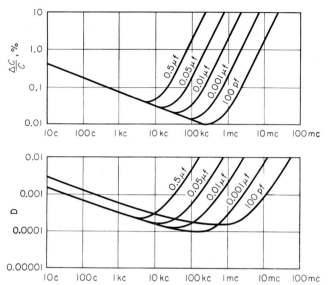

Fig. 6-12. Change in capacitance and dissipation factor with frequency for a precision mica capacitor. (*General Radio Company.*)

(whichever is larger). The variation of capacitance and dissipation factor with frequency for such a capacitor are shown in Fig. 6-12.

Silvered-mica Capacitors (Metalized-mica Capacitors)

Silvering the mica sheets has the advantage of eliminating voids between sheet and foil and results in improved stability and reduced size. The mica sheets are tested and cut to size in a similar manner to that for stacked-plate types. A silvering solution is prepared, consisting of silver oxide powder in lavender oil, and a coat is applied on the clean mica surface. The sheets are then fired in an oven at about 400 to 500°C. This volatilizes the oil and reduces the oxide to silver. Methods of placing the silvering paste on the mica plates vary; squeegeeing through a silk-screen pattern or offset printing methods can be used, the mica plates being held in suction clips during the process. The plates are usually silvered asymmetrically on both sides and over the ends, and stacked alternately (see Fig. 6-13). Leads are soldered on to each end of the stack, although generally small pieces of brass foil are interleaved to make better contact with the silver electrodes (Fig. 6-13). Each capacitor can be accurately adjusted to the required value by removing small areas of the silver.

The process of manufacture is very similar to that described for stacked-mica electrodes. The required number of silvered-mica sheets (for the total capacitance needed) is placed in a special clamp with foil connections making contact with the silver film. This clamp has a window through which a portion of the film may be removed to adjust the capacitance. Terminal wires are soldered to the foils and the unit

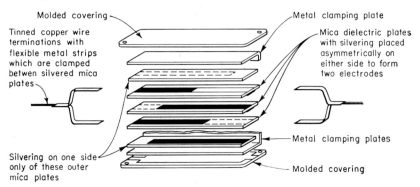

FIG. 6-13. Construction of a silvered-mica capacitor.

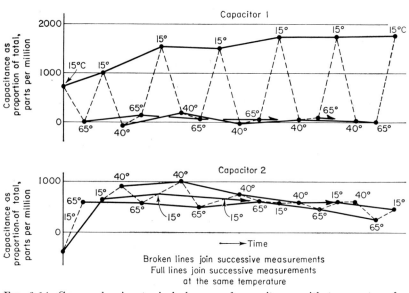

Broken lines join successive measurements
Full lines join successive measurements
at the same temperature

FIG. 6-14. Curves showing typical changes of capacitance with temperature for silvered-mica capacitors.

is then impregnated, usually with wax, to keep the molding material from affecting the silver. The unit is then molded, using loaded phenol-formaldehyde, or other similar material, such as is used for stacked types. The construction of a typical capacitor is shown in Fig. 6-13.

Capacitors are made to tolerances of ± 20, ± 10, ± 5, ± 2, and ± 1 per cent, with a minimum of 5 pf.   The variation of capacitance with temperature for typical capacitors is shown in the curves of Fig. 6-14. Typical temperature-coefficient measurements on molded silvered-mica capacitors are shown in Fig. 6-15.

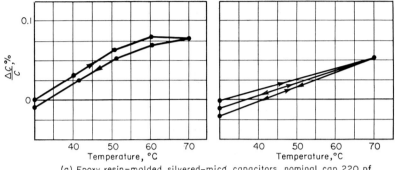

(a) Epoxy resin—molded silvered-mica capacitors, nominal cap 220 pf

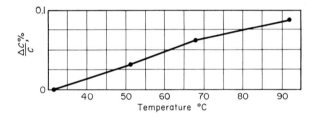

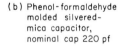

(b) Phenol-formaldehyde molded silvered-mica capacitor, nominal cap 220 pf

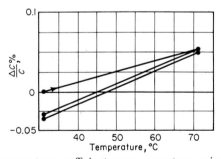

FIG. 6-15. Typical temperature-coefficient measurements on mica capacitors.

An effect known as *scintillation*—random variations in capacitance which cause frequency jumping—has been observed on silvered-mica capacitors (and also on silvered-ceramic types) when these capacitors are used in tuned circuits.   This is due mainly to the applied voltage jumping across spasmodically from the main silvered area to small islands of silvering isolated from the main area.   When the silver is properly applied, as the result of improved silvering techniques, this effect should not occur.

For experimental purposes, chemical silvering on mica is possible, and one method will be described. The surface of the mica is cleaned in organic solvents, and the mica is washed in water. It is then activated by immersion in 10 per cent stannous chloride solution, to which is added 15 per cent hydrochloric acid (in water). After washing in running water the mica is immersed in a mixture of 70 per cent formaldehyde solution, 30 per cent methyl alcohol. The solution is then drained off and the silvering is effected by immersion in the following solution (for 250 ml). One gram of silver nitrate is dissolved in 50 ml distilled water, and ammonia is added until the brown precipitate first formed redissolves. The solution is then made up to 150 ml. To this, just before use, is added a solution of 6.0 g of Rochelle salt (sodium potassium tartrate) in 100 ml distilled water. Silvering takes about 20 min.

Since the silver film imposes a limit on the current rating of the capacitor, silvered-mica capacitors are used only as power capacitors where superior temperature coefficients are required.

In the past, difficulty has been experienced with silver-ion migration on silvered-mica capacitors constructed prior to 1946 when these capacitors were operated with high d-c voltage stress, high ambients, and high humidity. The construction techniques now being used by the industry provide a better moisture seal than those employed prior to 1946. To minimize the possibility of ion migration, the d-c voltage stress should be kept as low as possible by derating.

Synthetic Mica

Synthetic mica is being manufactured in increasing quantities in the United States. During the Second World War, Germany produced small quantities in a pilot plant. Synthetic mica can be made from a mixture of the following approximate proportions:

Aluminum oxide (Al_2O_3)..........	11.5 per cent
Magnesium oxide (MgO).........	32.7 per cent
Sand (SiO_2)...................	30.7 per cent
Cryolite (K_2SiF_6)...............	25.1 per cent

The materials, being only technically pure, are preheated in electric furnaces to 900°C and then transferred to a special porcelain crucible in a main gas-fired furnace. The process of heating to melting point at 1,300°C and cooling to 900°C takes 7 days, including 3 days allowed for crystallization by temperature gradient, cooling at approximately

10 degrees per hour.   The actual time of crystallization is 5 to 6 hr, but a safety factor of at least 500 per cent is allowed.

The Properties of Synthetic Mica.   Synthetic mica is a phlogopite but, unlike natural micas, has no water in its composition.   It is, therefore, stable nearly to its melting point of 1,300°C—the natural micas begin to give off water at about 400 to 500°C.   It is more difficult to split than natural mica but has similar cleavage planes. The material is harder than natural muscovite, which in turn is harder than natural phlogopite.   Flexibility is much the same, and the characteristics favor punching.   The power factor compares favorably with natural mica.   The surface resistivity is of the order of ten to one hundred times that of natural mica, because of the comparative purity. At high temperatures synthetic mica tends to absorb gas, rather than give it up; it is therefore singularly free from noise and is useful in making mica bridges for transmitting tubes.   It was originally developed for this purpose.   Synthetic mica is being manufactured in three principal forms:

a. Glass-bonded mica

b. Reconstituted sheet mica

c. Hot-pressed mica

Glass-bonded mica, using finely powdered natural mica with a lead borate glass binder, has been produced for many years.   Substitution of the synthetic-mica crystals improves all properties, particularly refractoriness and machinability.   It has greater high-temperature stability, since it does not release water vapor.

Reconstituted sheet mica is made from small mica flakes with a silicon binder.   The temperature breakdown of this material, using natural mica, varies from 1,200 to 1,400°F.   When this sheet is formed using synthetic-mica crystals, no breakdown is shown at 1,500°F.

Hot-pressed mica is a dense, ceramiclike dielectric made by hot-pressing synthetic mica into a homogeneous block.   Electrical and mechanical properties vary with the formulation of the synthetic-mica powder.

Mica Paper

Methods have been developed of manufacturing mica paper in long sheets of even thickness.   Sheets are made from flake mica by a process somewhat resembling the making of paper.   The muscovite mica is first shredded into flakes, heated to a critical temperature, then immersed in a solution of sodium bicarbonate, and finally drained and saturated with a weak solution of hydrochloric or sulfuric acid.   The mica is then washed and agitated, and treated as paper pulp through a paper-making machine. Bonded mica paper is made by impregnating mica paper with silicone resins. The power factor is higher than for natural mica, and it is essential that the material be kept free from water. These papers are manufactured in several thicknesses in a range from 1 to 2 mils.

The unbonded mica paper has an average dielectric strength of approximately 800 volts/mil. The 60-cycle power factor is about 0.0006 at 25°C and 0.0015 at 100°C. For two silicone-impregnated plies of this mica paper (resin content approximately 25 per cent of impregnated mica paper), the 60-cycle power factor is approximately 0.02 at 25°C. The minimum average dielectric strength of the silicone-impregnated material is 2,000 volts/mil.

Integrated-mica Sheet

Another process, that of producing sheets of integrated mica, is made possible because of the principle that the natural adhesive forces in thin, freshly split flakes of mica are high enough to bond layers of flakes together to form a single sheet. No binder is used and the sheet possesses most of the electrical properties of the natural micas from which the flakes were split originally. All of the four main types of natural mica—muscovite, phlogopite, biotite, and vermiculite—as well as synthetic mica can be integrated. The mica is first split into a thickness of less than 4 microns by means of a disintegrator which uses high-velocity water jets (or heat) to split open the mica pieces. Water chambers are used to carry the disintegrated mica along and are arranged so that the thin flakes settle onto a belt, which passes over a vacuum plate that keeps the flakes in place until the water is extracted. The resulting sheet is then dried. To overcome its fragility, it is dipped in a solution containing 6 per cent silicone resin.

The electrical properties of integrated mica are uniform; the difference in dielectric constant between integrated mica and the material from which it is made is not more than 10 per cent—in most cases less than 5 per cent. The power factor depends to some extent on the impregnant; for use in capacitors, impregnation with polystyrene or similar materials having low power factor results in a material with a power factor at 1 Mc/sec of about 0.0009. When made in the laboratory with distilled water, a power factor can be obtained as low as 0.0003. The dielectric strength of integrated mica averages about 400 volts/mil for the unimpregnated material in a thickness of 0.01 inches. The material is highly hydroscopic and the small percentage of silicone resin assists in preventing water absorption. It is possible to soften the material by subjecting it to saturated steam or heavily moistened air so that it can be rolled, disked, or formed to make complicated parts. After the mica has been formed, it is dried out and impregnated.

Mica-paper Capacitors

Several industrial concerns have announced recently the availability of mica-paper capacitors for use where high ambient temperatures are encountered. Two types of construction are used: the stacked-plate type, similar to that used for ordinary mica capacitors, and the rolled type, similar to that used for paper or plastic-film capacitors. While the rolled type of construction has been used for some capacitors constructed for jet-engine ignition systems, the stacked-plate structure is now used in commercial types. They are available in hermetically sealed metal rectangular cases or in molded epoxy cases, and they are also uncased. Typical characteristics for the hermetically sealed capacitors are as follows:

Capacitance value: 0.01 to 4 μf
Voltage rating (WVDC): 150 to 10 kv
Minimum Q: 1,000 at 25°C
Power factor: 0.005 maximum at 25°C, 0.03 maximum at 315°C
Dielectric absorption: Less than 0.1 per cent after 10-sec discharge
Capacitance tolerance: 10 per cent
Operating temperature range: −55 to 315°C
Insulation resistance: 10,000 ohm-farads at 25°C, 4 ohm-farads at 315°C
Capacitance variation: 3 per cent maximum at 315°C

Usually silicone resin is used as the impregnant for the structure. When subjected to radiation, the only observable effect was a slight change in the capacitance value. Although the power factor did not change, insulation resistance improved.

Mica-dielectric-transmitter Capacitors

The principal requirements for a transmitter capacitor are:
1. High r-f power-handling capacity
2. High d-c voltage rating
3. Low internal inductance
Mica-transmitter capacitors are used primarily for decoupling in circuits where the radio frequency is usually not higher than 30 Mc/sec. They are also used in modulators. Because of their low power factor and high breakdown strength, mica power capacitors have advantages

in applications where high-voltage rating and high-capacitance values are required. The capacitor element usually consists of a clamped stack of selected mica sheets and tin-foil electrodes. If silvered-mica construction is used, the current rating must be reduced by 50 per cent (see Table 6-2). All connections are soldered to ensure high current

FIG. 6-16. Typical mica-transmitter capacitors. (*Cornell-Dubilier Company.*)

ratings. The stacks may then be mounted in a pot of porcelain and filled with wax to prevent the ingress of moisture. The capacitor is usually made up as a series combination, the arrangement depending

TABLE 6-2. TYPICAL CHARACTERISTICS FOR POT TYPE OF
MICA-TRANSMITTER CAPACITORS

Military style*	Maximum peak working voltage available for style	Rated current† in amperes at frequency of:			
		3 Mc/sec	1 Mc/sec	0.3 Mc/sec	0.1 Mc/sec
CM75	6,000	16	16	12	6.2
CM80	10,000	16	13	8.2	3.6
CM85	20,000	16	15	8.2	3.9
CM90	30,000	16	15	10	5.1
CM95	35,000	33	36	20	5.6

* In accordance with military specification MIL-C-5.

† When these capacitors are constructed using silvered-mica, characteristics *D, E,* and *F* of MIL-C-5, the rated current has to be reduced by 50 per cent.

upon the working voltage required. The maximum capacitance and working voltage therefore are interdependent for each capacitor. Typical characteristics for the pot-type mica-transmitter capacitor are shown in Table 6-2.

Capacitance values of mica-transmitter capacitors are obtainable up to about 0.1 μf, depending upon the voltage and current rating required. Sizes range from approximately 2½ in. high and 3¼ in. in diameter (center of mounting holes) for the CM75 to 10 in. high and 4 in. in diameter (center of mounting holes) for the CM95. Transmitter-type mica capacitors are also made in molded-plastic rectangular cases for the lower-voltage ratings. These are shown in Fig. 6-16.

Fig. 6-17. Mica assembly for a transmitter capacitor (pot type). (*Aerovox Corporation.*)

The mica assembly for a typical pot-type transmitter capacitor is shown in Fig. 6-17.

Mica-dielectric (Button-type[1]) Capacitors

Button mica-dielectric capacitors are generally used for high-frequency feed-through applications. Two different types of construction are manufactured: the hermetically sealed types and the encapsulated or impregnated types. These capacitors consist of a series of stacked silvered-mica disks connected in parallel, through which the high potential terminal is connected in the center of the stack and encased in a silver-plated brass case. The metal case forms the other electrode by making connection around the entire outer edge of the other silver electrode. The unit is then impregnated with wax, encapsulated with a polyester or hermetically sealed. The latter type of construction uses glass feed-through terminals.

[1] Registered trademark of the Erie Resistor Corporation.

The insulation resistance after moisture for the impregnated and encapsulated types is erratic and is of the order of 100 to 500 megohms. The hermetically sealed types have consistent insulation-resistance values in excess of 2,000 megohms. This type of design permits the current to fan out in a 360° pattern from the center terminal which maintains low internal inductance. This, coupled with the use of heavy and short terminals to provide the minimum amount of external inductance, provides a design with low inductance suited for vhf and uhf applications.

CHAPTER 7

CERAMIC-, GLASS-, AND VITREOUS-ENAMEL-
DIELECTRIC CAPACITORS

Ceramic materials have been used for many years as electrical insulators. They are able to withstand severe working conditions because they are vitrified by firing at temperatures of the order of 1,200°C. Being completely inert they will withstand their rated working voltage indefinitely and retain their shape and physical characteristics under normal conditions.

CERAMIC CAPACITORS

Low-loss Low-dielectric-constant Ceramic-dielectric Types

As the materials are naturally-occurring minerals they contain impurities. Therefore, after they have been finely ground, intimately mixed, and compressed into tough but suitable shapes they are calcined at a temperature below the fluxing or melting point, which is sufficient to oxidize any organic matter and reduce to oxides any carbonates, chlorides, or sulfates present. The resultant mass or body is then reground. The calcined finely ground "body" is mixed with water and binding or emollient matter (such as gum or oil) and mechanically reduced to a smooth stiff paste from which pressure moldings and extrusions into capacitor bodies can be made. A carefully controlled drying sequence follows until ultimately the capacitors are fired in a controlled atmosphere (generally oxidizing) at temperatures between 1,200 and 1,400°C until vitrification occurs, ensuring nonporosity.

Capacitors are usually made in either tubular or disk shapes but can also be made as flat plates. The construction of a typical uninsulated tubular capacitor is shown in Fig. 7-1.

Low-loss capacitors are usually made from steatite (more commonly known as talc), which has a dielectric constant of approximately 8. This is fluxed with one of the feldspars, or preferably an alkali-free flux, such as witherite ($BaCo_3$).

115

FIXED CAPACITORS

The ceramic-dielectric material is in the form of a tube and the capacitor is formed by metalizing part of the internal and external surface of the tube. This is usually done by brushing on a silvering solution and firing, or sometimes by dipping the tube (suitably masked) into a silvering solution. Firing to reduce the silver solution to metal is usually carried out at about 700 to 800°C. If the silvering process is not done carefully, scintillation can occur, and for this reason all brushing, cleaning, etc., is carefully controlled throughout the manufacture. Poor silvering may also affect the temperature coefficient.

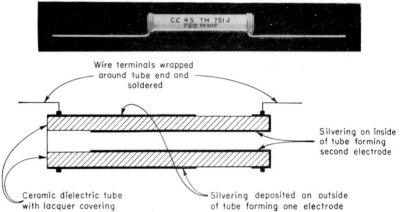

Fig. 7-1. Construction of uninsulated ceramic capacitor. (*Erie Resistor Company.*)

The capacitance of a tubular capacitor can be calculated from the formula

$$C = \frac{0.0241 l \kappa}{\log (D/d)} \times 10^{-6} \qquad \text{microfarads}$$

where l = overlapping part of metalizing, mm
D = outer diameter of tube, mm
d = inner diameter of tube, mm
κ = dielectric constant of ceramic material

It can be seen from this formula that the capacitance of a tubular capacitor is independent of the diameter of the tube, provided the ratio between inner and outer diameters remains the same; the capacitance depends only on the tube length and length of silvering. In contrast with the capacitance, the breakdown voltage of a tubular capacitor varies with the wall thickness of the tube. The general characteristics of a steatite-base capacitor are given below:

κ at 1 Mc/sec: 5 to 7
tan δ: 0.001

Temperature coefficient: varies from $+100$ to $+120$ ppm/°C

Frequency range: approximately 100 cps to 200 Mc/sec

Maximum temperature of operation: approximately 150°C (usually limited by covering and solder connections)

Minimum temperature of operation: no intrinsic limit

Breakdown voltage: approximately 500 volts (depending on size)

Medium-dielectric-constant Ceramic-dielectric Capacitors

The medium-dielectric-constant dielectrics now in use are all based on titania (titanium dioxide, TiO_2) or its derivatives, the alkaline-earth titanates ($M.TiO_3$). Titania is very widely distributed, occurring in a mineral form as rutile, anatase, and, less frequently, as brookite: in combination it occurs chiefly as ilmenite and perovskite. Its refining, however, is a matter of considerable difficulty.

The general physical properties of all the resulting dielectrics are very similar, and their method of preparation follows the ordinary ceramic methods, previously described, in oxidizing atmospheres. The processing is, however, more difficult, owing to the danger of partial reduction and the need for accurate temperature control.

The materials are extremely hard, refractory, and chemically inert. Electrically, they are fairly good insulators, but the breakdown voltage is low compared to that of mica, and conduction becomes serious at temperatures of 150°C or more. Their main use is in capacitors.

The exceptionally high dielectric constant of titania in all its three mineral forms was first noticed by Schmidt in 1902. For rutile he found a dielectric constant of 170 parallel to the crystal axis and 80 perpendicular to it; values were low for anatase, which also belongs to the tetragonal crystal system; for brookite, which is rhombohedral, he gave a dielectric constant of 80.

His values were confirmed by Eucken and Buchner in 1934, who studied the temperature dependence of the dielectric constant, using sections of large single crystals, again of mineral origin. They concluded that for rutile the dielectric constant parallel to the axis passes through a minimum near room temperature; perpendicular to the axis, the minimum occurs at -100°C. It is not certain that this would occur in pure materials (as opposed to those of mineral origin). For anatase they found that the dielectric constant along the axis increases steadily with the temperature from -100 to $+100$°C. No observations were made on brookite, or on anatase perpendicular to the axis. Since these measurements were made on mineral samples, the part played by impurities remains uncertain. In 1935, French workers, using highly compressed masses of chemically pure titania, confirmed the very high values observed by Schmidt and by Eucken and Buchner (allowing for the incomplete space-filling of the compressed mass, and for the random orientation of the particles). The high dielectric constant of titania was thus established, and shortly afterward it was marketed in a number of forms.

There is a change of capacitance with temperature of the order of -800 ppm/°C for TiO_2. The power factor is usually less than 0.0003 at radio frequencies. The high dielectric constant persists up to the highest radio frequencies. The loss, with titania only, increases at lower frequencies, being of the order of one or two per cent at 1 kc/sec and becoming very large at a few hundred cycles per second, but with suitable additions the loss can be made much smaller.

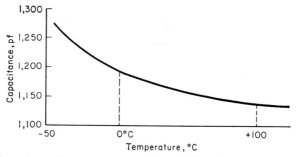

FIG. 7-2. Capacitance/temperature curve for medium-dielectric-constant ceramic capacitors.

The addition of increasing amounts of barium oxide first lowers the dielectric constant, then raises it, at the same time changing the sign of the temperature coefficient. Low-loss and linear characteristics persist until the proportions of the mix are almost equimolecular, so that up to these proportions, barium-titanium oxide behaves as a normal dielectric of very high dielectric constant, showing no evidence of hysteresis. Titania-calcium oxide mixtures behave similarly, and useful dielectrics can be made with compositions approximating to calcium titanate (dielectric constant, about 150, temperature coefficient, 1,200 ppm/°C). Magnesia-titania mixtures give lower dielectric constants, that for compositions approximating to magnesium titanate being 14 to 16, with a positive temperature coefficient.

Using suitable mixtures of titania and the alkaline earths already mentioned, the temperature coefficient can be controlled, giving small capacitance values for positive temperatures, through zero, to high values for temperatures below zero, and these dielectrics are used mainly in temperature-compensating capacitors for communication receivers, etc.

For capacitors with medium dielectric constants (70 to 100) the shape of the capacitance/temperature graph is shown in the typical curve of Fig. 7-2.

High-dielectric-constant Ceramic-dielectric Capacitors

The main advantage of this type of capacitor is the possibility of obtaining a large capacitance in a small volume. Dielectric constants of 1,000 to 5,000, or more, are realizable, but with certain limitations.

The methods of manufacture follow principles similar to those already described. For dielectric constants of this order, barium titanate (pure or with the barium partly replaced by other metals) is used. This material is exceptional in showing a Curie point and associated ferroelectrical properties. If ultra-high values of dielectric constants are required free from hysteresis, they can be obtained

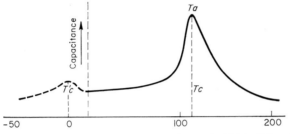

FIG. 7-3. Dielectric-constant/temperature curve for typical high-dielectric-constant ceramic capacitor.

reliably only by working above the Curie point. They will have a large negative temperature coefficient, but their total range of usefulness may well be considerable. By choosing compositions which give Curie points at very low temperatures it is possible to produce reliable materials with usefully large dielectric constants, giving a reasonably linear change with temperature over normal operating temperatures, and relatively low loss.

The equimolecular mixture of barium oxide and titania, having the composition $BaTiO_3$ (barium titanate) has entirely different properties from the medium-dielectric-constant titania and related dielectrics. The dielectric constant varies with temperature in the manner shown in Fig. 7-3. There is a very large peak at a certain temperature T_a (around 110 to 120°C) at which a value of at least 9,000 may be attained. Above this, the dielectric constant falls according to the Curie law:

$$\kappa = \frac{a}{T - T_c}$$

where a = constant

T = actual temperature, °C

T_c = temperature, Curie point

T_a differs only slightly from T_c. Below T_a, the dielectric constant drops abruptly to a relatively low value, usually of the order of 1,000 to 1,500, at which it remains constant down to a second Curie point T_c' at approximately 0°C and then falls off.

The most important electrical change is that hysteresis (see page 122), with greatly increased loss in strong fields, sets in below T_c but is absent above it. Hence, below this the dielectric constant and power factor can be defined only for vanishing field-strength.

The temperature T_c' previously referred to is often termed the lower Curie point. It corresponds to a second change of crystal structure; it does not correspond to any very marked changes in the electrical properties, and hysteresis in particular is unaffected.

The Curie temperature of barium titanate is approximately 120°C. It is lowered if some of the barium is replaced by strontium; for 70:30 (Ba:Sr) titanate it is at 0°C, and for a 40:60 mixture it is at −120°C, and within this range the Curie point temperature falls linearly with the composition. If, instead of replacing barium by strontium, the proportion of titania is reduced in the $BaOTiO_2$ mixture, the Curie point is lowered and may even be split. Other materials, such as calcium mixes, can also be added to lower the Curie point. The substitution of lead for some of the barium raises the Curie point.

At the Curie point, a number of important physical changes occur. The crystal lattice, cubic at high temperatures, passes to a tetragonal form, one edge of the elementary cube being extended and the other two contracted, while the whole structure undergoes a slight shear. The precise ionic displacements involved are not yet known, and considerable research is being done on this problem.

The effect of these changes is reflected in the final capacitor, as shown in the typical capacitance/temperature curves for commercial capacitors of values 1,500 pf (K = 3,000) and 1,000 pf (K = 1,250) in Fig. 7-4.

The peak of the curve can be moved along the temperature axis by varying the mix, and many attempts have been made to flatten the curve by adding various materials, chiefly to the barium-strontium series of titanates. The effects of these additions vary. For instance magnesium lowers the power factor, broadens the dielectric-constant peak, and lowers the temperature at which it occurs. Zirconium behaves similarly, but it does not affect the power factor. Tin has less

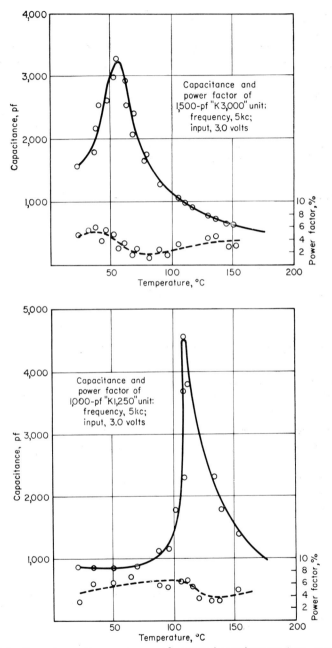

FIG. 7-4. Capacitance/temperature and power-factor/temperature curves for $K = 1,250$ and $K = 3,000$ ceramic capacitors.

broadening effect than zirconium. Lead shifts the peak to higher temperatures.

Constant endeavors are being made in the United States and the United Kingdom to achieve a reasonably flat curve by combinations of additives of this type. The shape of these curves indicates that when specifying a required capacitance it is best to specify a minimum capacitance, particularly for decoupling and other purposes, so that temperature variations will increase the capacitance and not reduce it.

A typical curve for a good, modern high-dielectric-constant capacitor is shown in Fig. 7-5, from which it can be seen that over the range 20 to 100°C the curve is sensibly flat.

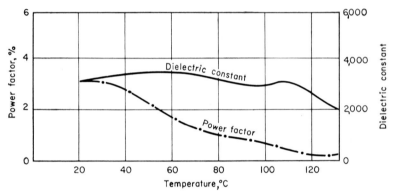

Fig. 7-5. Dielectric-constant/temperature and power-factor/temperature curves for typical high-dielectric-constant dielectric. (*Steatite and Porcelain Products, Ltd.*)

Over a wider temperature range, capacitors have been made, with κ equal to 3,000, which have the capacitance/temperature characteristics shown in Fig. 7-6.

The effect of a large d-c bias on the capacitor is to reduce its capacitance and to flatten the capacitance/temperature curve. The amount is dependent on whether the capacitor is operated above, below, or at its Curie point. A typical graph of the effect of d-c bias on capacitance is shown in Fig. 7-7. The variation of capacitance with temperature at differing applied voltages takes the form of the curves shown in Fig. 7-8.

Hysteresis Losses, etc., in High-dielectric-constant Capacitors. High-dielectric-constant capacitors are ferroelectric at room temperatures; i.e., the charge and voltage are not linearly related, but a hysteresis loop is described during a charging cycle, resembling the magnetization loop for iron. The ferroelectric properties place severe limits on the use of such materials as dielectrics. These properties

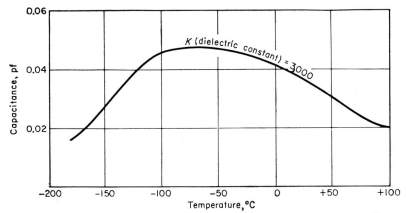

FIG. 7-6. Capacitance/temperature curve for K or $(E) = 3,000$ capacitor.   (*Plessey Company, Ltd.*)

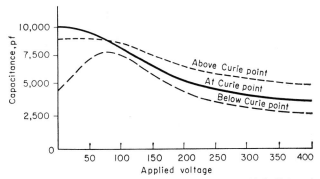

FIG. 7-7. Variation of capacitance with applied voltage for high-dielectric-constant capacitor.

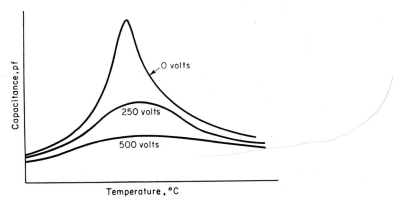

FIG. 7-8. Variation of capacitance with temperature at different voltages for high-dielectric-constant capacitor.

can be most clearly understood from Fig. 7-9, which is drawn for a general case.

Under large voltage swings, the curve $ABCD$ is described in the sense shown. The energy dissipated per cycle is equal to

$$\int V \, dQ$$

where V = applied voltage
    Q = charge

that is, to the area enclosed by the loop. Hence, to large alternating voltages, the unit is highly dissipative, and energy is lost. Moreover, it produces considerable harmonic distortion. For small alternating

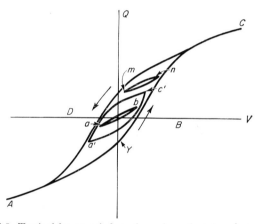

FIG. 7-9. Typical hysteresis loop for a ferroelectric substance.

voltages, the capacitor is "normal," although the power factor is poor, possibly about 1 per cent. Operation is then along the narrow loop ab, as in the diagram. Further increase of the voltage would make this curve tend to cross the boundary of the hysteresis loop, which is physically impossible, and a path such as $a'c'$ must be described. Hence the loss increases severely at this stage. It will be seen from Fig. 7-9 that the polarization does not vanish with the field: a certain remanent polarization y still exists. This does not produce an external field under static conditions, as it is neutralized by surface charges, but in applications which require similarity in the behavior of two elements, this value plays an important part. Under large fields, the behavior of a high-dielectric-constant capacitor has no counterpart with that of ordinary capacitors, and for other than small voltages it becomes exceedingly complex. The behavior may be summarized as follows:

(a) *Superposed a-c and d-c fields.* So long as the d-c field is not large enough to saturate the element, and the alternating emf is less than the coercive field, it is clear that during the first charging half-cycle, a path such as *mn* in Fig. 7-9 will be obtained. The limiting alternating voltage and the incremental capacitance and power factor are not very much affected by the d-c field, although the capacitance falls slowly as the bias increases.

For larger alternating voltages, a hysteresis loop must be described, unless the bias is so large that the total field never falls below the saturating voltage. For such fields, the only effect of the d-c bias is to shift the entire figure along the voltage axis.

(*b*) *Superposed a-c fields of different frequencies.* For small fields, the element acts as a normal capacitor. If a high-frequency field of small amplitude is imposed on a low-frequency field of much larger amplitude, the normal hysteresis loop is described. Using a CRT display, the varying speed of the light spot causes intensity modulation of the trace, when the two frequencies are simply related, as shown in Fig. 7-10*a*.

If, however, the amplitude or the frequency of the high-frequency component is increased, so that, during part of its cycle, dV/dt changes sign, this is no longer the case, for the hysteresis loop can be described in only one sense. Consequently, a path such as Fig. 7-10*b* appears on the CRT display. These simple examples show the complexity of the effects which may arise in nonlinear capacitors.

The quantities described above are also temperature-sensitive: the hysteresis loop becomes narrower with rise of temperature, eventually vanishing at the Curie point. Above this point the substance behaves almost as a normal dielectric with a very high dielectric constant, the dielectric constant falling with further increase of temperature. Simple mixes with a high barium content cannot be used in this state, owing to the large conduction loss, but modern commercial materials, with no marked Curie points, give a much better performance in respect to power factor and conductivity at high temperatures.

It will be seen, therefore, that where high d-c bias or large a-c fields are involved, or where wide temperature ranges are required, great care should be taken in the use of high-dielectric-constant capacitors.

Creep in High-dielectric-constant Capacitors. A phenomenon which has recently become associated with high-dielectric-constant capacitors is known as "creep." This is a change in internal resistance with time, which becomes marked at high temperatures, i.e., over 100°C. It is a separate effect from normal high-leakage currents. The increase of leakage current over 100°C may be quite serious.

According to studies made by the Linden Laboratories (Pennsylvania

State College) under Signal Corps sponsorship, considerable improvement in the leakage current as well as other parameters can be obtained by the use of additives. The stability of a dielectric can be characterized by the independent parameters:

    a. Voltage stress (volts/mil)

    b. Life (hours)

    c. Temperature (C°)

To be usable, a material should have minimum values of 30 volts/mil and 1,000 hr, respectively, for (*a*) and (*b*) above. Using these values

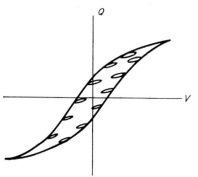

(*a*)
Small high-frequency signal imposed on large low-frequency signal

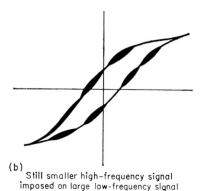

(*b*)
Still smaller high-frequency signal
imposed on large low-frequency signal

FIG. 7-10. Hysteresis loops for high-dielectric-constant capacitors with superposed a-c fields.

for (*a*) and (*b*), the Linden Labs were able to raise the value for (*c*) from approximately 150 to 275°C. With additional effort of this kind, extension to 300°C seems feasible.

This development work was based upon the hypothesis that the degradation process of titanate dielectrics is an electrolytic process and that the movable ions are the empty positions in the oxygen lattice, which are called *anion vacancies* (AV). While this hypothesis cannot be proved definitely, conclusions drawn are consistent with experimental facts.

If the bodies could be made homogeneous and if formation of AV at the anode and disposal of AV at the cathode would occur at the same rate, nothing harmful would happen. The result would be that only a small ionic current would be superimposed on the predominantly electronic current of the sample. The harmful effect of AV movements comes from the fact that the bodies are not homogeneous.

The method of stabilization employed is to introduce electron donors into the dielectric to achieve a drastic reduction in the AV concentration. The donor has to be chosen with care so as to have the proper valency and concentration range. Using this method, parameters such as resistivity with time (at 325°C), loss (tan δ) with temperature, and decrease in dielectric constant with temperature for K2,000 and K6,000 (BaTiO$_3$ bodies) were all improved. A great reduction in rate of aging for the K2,000 body was also achieved for:

a. Loss (tan δ) from 23 to 2.5 per cent/decade

b. Dielectric constant from 5.7 to 1.0 per cent/decade

Types of High-dielectric-constant Capacitors

The majority of the high-dielectric-constant types are constructed in either the disk or the tubular types by methods similar to those described for the manufacture of the low-loss ceramic tubular, plate, and disk types. Standoff capacitors, both insulated and uninsulated types, are made to save space and achieve more efficient decoupling. These capacitors have a high resonant frequency due to the low inductance, which makes them particularly suitable for vhf applications. The resonant frequency for a specific type of construction is a function of lead length and capacitance value. The shorter the lead length and the lower the capacitance value, the higher the resonant frequency. As an example, a typical unit of 300 pf with a lead length of 0.2 in. would have a resonant frequency of approximately 80 Mc/sec.

Standoff capacitors are also available with the temperature-compensating series of dielectrics (medium dielectric constant) for use in r-f tuned circuits. The range of capacitance values is more restricted because lower dielectric-constant materials are used. The construction of such typical capacitors is shown in Fig. 7-11.

Feed-through capacitors are also made in which the capacitor becomes an integral part of the metal chassis through which it projects, simplifying grounding (earthing) problems at radio frequencies. Lead inductance is virtually eliminated because the physical size is small and the inductance is in series with the inner electrodes. A typical construction is shown in Fig 7-12.

Disk types, either encapsulated or sealed in a ceramic case, are made in miniature and subminiature sizes for use in applications where their small size adapts them for wiring directly across the required points. Such an application is used in an intermediate-frequency (i-f) strip where short lead lengths are desirable. All these types are generally used for bypassing in low-power r-f circuits.

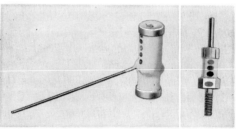

Fig. 7-11. Typical standoff-type ceramic capacitors. (*Erie Resistor Company.*)

For capacitance values larger than can be produced with either the tubular or the disk types, flat types are being made. Machines have been developed capable of producing very thin films by band-casting processes similar to that described below.

The ceramic mix, prepared as described previously, is passed through an extruding hopper on to a stainless-steel belt, which is slowly moving at a few feet per minute. The ceramic "slip" is very carefully prepared and ball-milled for at least 24 hr. Thorough mixing and ball-milling is essential where thin films are required, and the material is

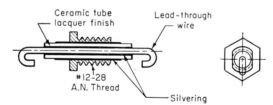

Fig. 7-12. Construction of feed-through ceramic capacitor.

usually passed through a 300-mesh sieve, chemical cleanliness being maintained throughout the whole process. The slip is fed into an extruding hopper over the moving belt and leveled on the moving belt by a doctor bar. It then passes through a drying oven where it is dried sufficiently to be removed from the belt and cut into suitable sections. The sections are then fired on zircon or similar plates with

4- or 5-hr preheating, an hour at the maximum temperature, and a 3- or 4-hr cooling.

In other methods a small bottomless box, with a "gate" in the trailing side, contains the slip. This box is drawn along a glass plate, leaving behind a thin layer of slip, the thickness of the layer being controlled by the depth of the gate and the speed of drawing. The movement of drawing must be absolutely constant in speed; films as thin as 0.005 cm have been drawn by this method.

The main difficulty in the manufacture of these thin, fragile flat plates is curling or warping, which precludes their assembly as stacked capacitors. They are usually silvered by paste-silvering methods and fired in the stacked form, palladium and platinum pastes being used to withstand the high temperatures. The electrode leads are then soldered on to the ends, the stacks being preheated sufficiently to avoid cracking by thermal shock.

Another method used for making thin films, which enables the construction of very small low-voltage capacitors, is the technique used on Cerafil[1] capacitors. In this technique the dielectric material is extruded to form a rod which is used as a substrate. This is done to assure that the base material will have the same physical properties as the thin dielectric film. The substrate is then placed in a holder and dipped in solutions of palladium, the dielectric material, and the silver to form alternate layers or thin films of these materials. The distance the substrate is dipped into each solution is accurately controlled to allow the first electrode to extend beyond the dielectric film for termination purposes. The necessary drying, baking, or firing operation(s) are performed between these dippings as required. Lead attachment to the two film electrodes is made. The capacitor is then encapsulated in a loaded phenol-formaldehyde material. For larger capacitance values, these units are assembled in bundles prior to encapsulating.

Ceramic-dielectric Transmitter Capacitors

Ceramic capacitors are designed for use in medium-power oscillator and transmitter circuits. Their high stability and small size, compared with an air-dielectric capacitor, make them suitable for use in tank and matching circuits, but they are equally useful as bypassing, blocking, or coupling capacitors. A very valuable feature is their ability to withstand high voltages without deterioration.

Where high voltages are used, voltage gradients at the edges of the electrodes can be very troublesome. For working voltages over 3.5,

[1] Registered trademark of the Aerovox Corporation.

kv capacitors are provided with a glazed-ceramic rim, which reduces the voltage gradient at the edges of the electrodes and avoids corona losses that can lead to premature breakdown. The shape and position of the electrodes are determined by the rim, and no adjustment of capacitance is possible, as grinding off the metalizing would negate the very careful design for maximum-voltage stress loading. Standard tolerances are ±10 per cent, but ±5 per cent can be made. The electrodes consist of coatings of fired-on silver of adequate thickness and high conductivity, capable of withstanding a high current loading.

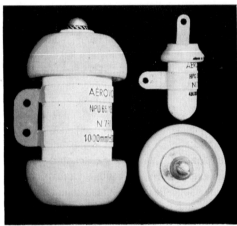

Fig. 7-13. Typical examples of ceramic transmitter capacitors. (*Aerovox Corporation.*)

The terminal lugs are soldered to the electrodes, the contacts being made sufficiently large to prevent local overheating on full-load current.

The plate type of construction is used for the lower kilovolt-ampere ratings, while the pot type of construction is used for the higher kilovolt-ampere ratings. For applications requiring higher voltage, higher current, or higher power than is available for a single capacitor, the capacitors may be connected in a bank in series or series-parallel combinations. For the higher kilovolt-ampere ratings (pot type), the dielectric is in the form of a heavy ceramic tube with carefully designed glazed ceramic sheds at each end. This open tubular construction allows either free-air ventilation or forced-air cooling if higher power-handling capability is required. Characteristics of a typical plate-type capacitor manufactured in the United States are shown in Table 7-1.

Typical capacitors of the above-mentioned constructions are shown in Fig. 7-13.

TABLE 7-1. CHARACTERISTICS OF CERAMIC PLATE-TYPE CAPACITOR

(a) Capacitance value: 25 pf ±10 per cent
(b) Voltage rating (d-c and h-f peak): 5,000
(c) Current rating: 5 amp
(d) Temperature coefficient (over range −40 to +75°C): N030 $^{+30}_{-45}$ ppm/°C
(e) Insulation resistance (500 volts d-c at 25°C): greater than 50,000 megohms
(f) Q at 1 Mc/sec: 1,125
(g) Capacitance at 1 Mc/sec: 25.06
(h) Capacitance drift (−40 to +75°C): 0.019 pf
(i) Dielectric strength: 7,500 volts
(j) Temperature rise at rated current (0.32 amp) at 1 Mc/sec: 7.5°C
(k) Insulation resistance at 105°C (after 1,000 hr at 105°C at maximum rated voltage): greater than 50,000 megohms

Bentonite

Bentonite clay, which is chemically similar to mica, is found in many parts of the world. It is possible to make dielectric film out of bentonite-clay derivatives. The advantages of such a film are:

a. High dielectric strength
b. Low dielectric absorption
c. Mechanical and electrical stability over a wide temperature range

Dielectric strengths on such a film that can be made in the United States are consistently obtainable on the order of 10,000 volts per mil when 1-mil samples are measured between ball electrodes under oil. This test voltage is a peak voltage of 60 cps.

The material is brittle, incompressible, and behaves much like a piece of glass of comparable thickness. The base film will show a degradation in power factor when exposed to moisture. In the United States, a bentonite cast film (Amplifilm[1]) is manufactured with the characteristics shown in Table 7-2.

The present field of application is for high-voltage pulse capacitors (used sometimes as part of pulse-forming networks) and high-voltage filter capacitors for radar modulators and indicators. The characteristics for such capacitors are shown in Table 7-3.

These capacitors are constructed by the use of heavy copper electrodes, stacked with the dielectric film and then banded together under high temperature and pressure with a thermoplastic resin. When they are used in applications other than oil-filled, as when encased in an encapsulate, care must be taken to avoid ionization (corona).

[1] Registered trademark of Aircraft-Marine Products Company.

TABLE 7-2. CHARACTERISTICS OF BENTONITE CAST FILM

(a) Thickness: 0.5 mil ±0.1 mil
(b) Temperature coefficient of capacity (over temperature range −55 to +125°C): 0.015 per cent per °C
(c) Dielectric constant over the temperature range −55 to +125°C: 4.3
(d) Power factor at 25°C: 1 kc/sec = 0.0023
                         1 Mc/sec = 0.0017
(e) Insulation resistance: 10^{15} ohm-cm
(f) Dielectric strength (from −55 to −175°C):
                         1 mil sheet = 5,000 volts/min
                         2 mil sheets = 4,000 volts/min
(g) Chemical stability: stable to 250°C
(h) Corona resistance: good
(i) Physical properties: insoluble, inelastic, and incompressible

TABLE 7-3. CHARACTERISTICS OF HIGH-VOLTAGE FILM CAPACITORS

(a) Capacitance range: 25 to 100,000 pf
(b) Capacitance tolerance: ±5 per cent
(c) Voltage rating (−25° to +125°C): 0 to 9,000 volts pulse, 0 to 11,500 direct current
(d) Dissipation factor (25°C and 60 cps): 0.35 per cent average, 0.5 per cent maximum
(e) Insulation resistance: at   25°C = 100,000 ohm-farads
                    at 125°C =   50 ohm-farads
(f) Capacitance variation with frequency 1 kc/sec to 10,000 kc/sec: ±1 per cent
(g) Capacitance variation with temperature −55 to 125°C: ±3 per cent

                                      (Aircraft-Marine Products Company)

GLASS-DIELECTRIC CAPACITORS

Glass has been described as a "supercooled liquid solution" and also as "an inorganic product of fusion which has cooled to liquid conditions without crystallizing." There are many types and varieties in use—it has been estimated that, at the moment, 500 to 600 varieties of glass are available. Domestic and commercial glass consists fundamentally of silica in the form of sand fused into a translucent mass by the assistance of fluxing oxides, whose purpose is to lower the melting point of the mixture. The properties of the fundamental base can be adapted to special requirements by the inclusion of one or more of many oxides and certain halides, e.g., the addition of alumina improves the mechanical strength, litharge varies the optical characteristics, and boric oxide increases the resistance to thermal shock. These and other effects can be obtained by skillful mixing of the ingredients used in making glass.

Glass which has been subjected to heat and work cools in a condition of strain; if it is reheated to a temperature approaching, but less than, the softening point, it will lose this strain and become annealed. The temperatures between which this phenomenon occurs are referred to as the annealing *range*—there is no fixed temperature at which a glass suddenly becomes soft or molten. For practical purposes, the "softening point" is regarded as the temperature at which the glass may be deformed without cracking.

Glass maintained at a high temperature for an extended period may suffer molecular and atomic regrouping and become crystalline and devitrified. The melting point of silica varies according to the form in which it is used, but will generally be between 1,600 and 1,700°C. This is an inconveniently high temperature for commercial working, and the common practice is to reduce the fusing point very considerably by the inclusion of the oxides (generally in the form of carbonates) of the alkali metals. These alkali-metal silicates or glasses are not stable or durable in themselves, being freely attacked by the mildest chemicals, and are frequently soluble in water. It is, however, easy to include a quantity of lime or magnesia in order to obtain the necessary durability, without sacrificing the conveniently low softening temperature.

Low-power-factor glasses having suitable characteristics, such as low temperature coefficient, have been developed for use as capacitor dielectrics. In general, for electrical purposes the glass should contain little or no alkali-metal oxides in the primary base (silica). A considerable amount of the glass used for electrical work has boric oxide as a flux and is referred to as a *boro-silicate* glass.

The lowest-power-factor glass known is the pure vitreous silica which has a quoted value tan δ = 0.000115. Glasses of the boro-silicate type containing 4 per cent or less of alkali-metal oxides have a tan δ of the order of 0.005 to 0.007 at 1 Mc/sec, with a dielectric constant of 4.18. The power factor of glass generally increases with increasing temperature, increasing more rapidly with temperature for low frequencies than for high frequencies. The following results (from Hoch) are representative of the values obtained on a Pyrex chemical-resistance glass at 500 kc/sec.

Degrees, C	Loss angle, tan δ	Dielectric constant, κ
20	0.0042	4.9
74	0.007	5.0
125	0.012	5.0

The dielectric constants of glass mixtures range from about 3.7 (for a pure silica glass) up to 18 or 20, fairly high dielectric constants being obtained in glass containing the oxides of lead, potassium, and silicon. There is a tellurium glass with κ equal to 26 and a low loss-angle.

For capacitors at high frequencies, the glass used will generally contain one of the heavy metals (barium, strontium, or lead) as oxides and will have low alkali-metal content. If an alkali metal is used, it should preferably be potassium. Glasses made in this manner can give fairly high dielectric constant with reasonably low power factor. Boro-silicate glasses now being made show relatively low values of temperature coefficients of power factor, dielectric constant, and resistivity and are also characterized by low coefficients of thermal expansion, of the order of 3.2 to 4.0 $\times$ 10^{-6}. They have a high surface stability to chemical and atmospheric attack and good thermal stability. Temperature coefficients are positive and decrease at the higher frequencies.

The dielectric strength of glass is high, decreasing with increase of temperature and frequency, and as the time of application of the potential increases.

Construction and Behavior of Glass-dielectric Capacitors

Glass capacitors have many advantages, including wide temperature range of operation ($-55°$ to $+200°C$), low power factor, high insulation resistance, and high breakdown strength, comparing favorably with mica, particularly at high temperatures. The variation of capacitance with temperature is repeatable or cyclic, and the spread of temperature coefficient is very small.

There are two methods by which such glass capacitors can be made, depending upon the quantities to be produced. In either method, the flexible glass ribbon is extruded in a continuous process. Then the capacitors are constructed in either of two ways:

1. Cut the glass to size and hand-stack the foil and glass.

2. Or feed the glass ribbon and foil into an automatic stacking machine.

The glass ribbon and the metal foils are stacked, alternate pieces of the foil being extended beyond opposite ends of the glass plates. The terminals are then attached to the aluminum foils (electrodes) by spot-welding the overhanging tips of foil to a silver-plated or tinned-brass wire. The capacitor assembly is placed between two thicker plates, of similar glass, sufficiently large to provide enough overhang on both the sides and ends. The entire assembly is placed in an oven where it is fused into a monolithic block.

Aluminum is used for the electrodes. Copper cannot be used owing to the formation of cupro-cupric oxide. Silver gives difficulty as a result of diffusion with the formation of yellow-silver silicate at temperatures above 600°C.   Gold can be used, and gold foil is available in thin sheets.   The capacitor assembly may be fired in air when gold foil is used, but an atmosphere of nitrogen is required for the aluminum foil.

An important feature of the glass capacitor is that the casing material can be made of the same low-power-factor glass.   The capacitor need not be encased in plastic or other materials with higher dielectric losses.   Typical glass capacitors are shown in Fig. 7-14.   This design, however, has several deficiencies.   Since the glass did not wet the lead material, a moisture path existed.   This was sealed with a silicone oil, which proved erratic under certain conditions.   Recently, the Corning Glass Works released their new "fusion" sealed capacitor.   This

FIG. 7-14. Typical glass capacitors.   (*Corning Glass Works.*)

design has welded lead connections, hot-tinned copper-clad nickel-iron leads, and a bead structure that provides a true glass-to-metal hermetic seal.

The variation of capacitance with temperature is shown in Fig. 7-15, and the temperature coefficients of capacitance, derived from the curve of Fig. 7-15, are given in Fig. 7-16.

The volume resistance, as for most inorganic insulating materials, decreases approximately exponentially with an increase of temperature.   A typical glass capacitor rated at 10,000 pf and 300 volts d-c would have an insulation resistance in excess of 50,000 megohms at 25°C, which would decrease to approximately 1,150 megohms at 175°C.   The variation of Q with temperature and capacitance that can be expected is shown by the graphs in Fig. 7-17.

Experimental glass capacitors have been constructed for use as mica replacements for medium- and high-power types.

The basic construction of the medium-power types for replacement of mica MIL-C-5 types, CM45 through CM70, is similar to that of

the axial-lead types previously described.   Internal series construction
(shielding foil) is used to achieve high-voltage units.   Several sections
are sealed together in parallel using a "solder glass" to facilitate manufacture, e.g., in achieving capacitance tolerance, etc.   The terminal
lugs are attached by means of a form of "housekeeper" seal which
provides electric contact to the active foils.   Additional foils may be
used, if necessary, to remove the heat to the lugs, hence to the chassis.

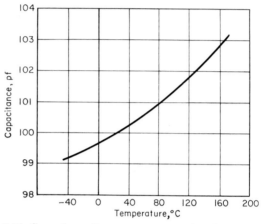

Fig. 7-15. Capacitance/temperature curve for glass capacitor.

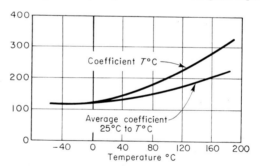

Fig. 7-16. Temperature-coefficient/temperature curve for glass capacitor.

Two types of capacitors composed of several parallel sections span two
decades of capacitance.   Seven or eight types of sections are used for
the lower-voltage ratings.   A similar number are used for the higher-
voltage ratings.   The introduction of corona on the low-capacitance
units is a limiting factor, and the use of an additional series dielectric
for each 300 volts of radio frequency is required.

It is not necessary to limit the maximum operating temperature of
these capacitors to 85°C (70°C ambient, plus 15°C rise) as they are

satisfactory for use at temperatures up to 125°C (ambient, plus rise). The exception to this rule would be applications where the temperature coefficient or dielectric loss would be the limiting factor.

These capacitors have very low self-inductance; therefore, the self-resonant frequency is much higher than for mica capacitors. A self-resonance frequency of 100 Mc/sec is reached for a capacitance value

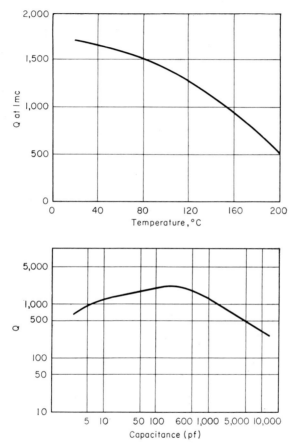

Fig. 7-17. Variation of Q with temperature capacitance for glass capacitor. (*Corning Glass Works.*)

of 800 pf, compared to 100 pf for a mica capacitor. This characteristic makes these capacitors more suitable for higher-frequency applications.

The high-power types, for the replacement of mica MIL-C-5 types, CM75 through CM95, were constructed by building up stacks in series or series-parallel combinations of the medium-power types. These were then encased in wax in a typical enclosure used for the CM75 through CM95 types. Owing to the high-current ratings, sheet-copper connections were used for the series and series-parallel connections.

VITREOUS-ENAMEL OR GLAZE-DIELECTRIC CAPACITORS

Capacitors have been made in which layers of vitreous enamel are alternated with layers of electrode metal (squeegeed through

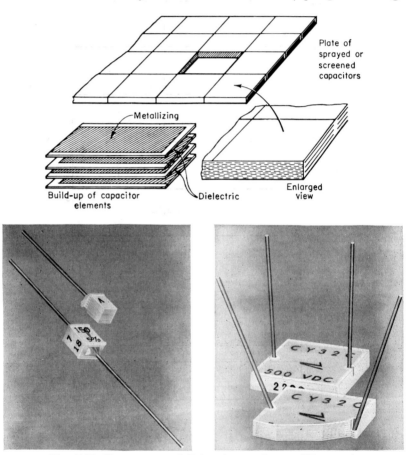

FIG. 7-18. Vitreous-enamel-dielectric capacitors. (*Vitramon.*)

suitable masks), with semidrying between each spraying. The dielectric enamel is a mixture of suitable consistency for spraying, consisting of silica, alkali oxides, and fluorides, with lead and other oxides. Many capacitors are made at once by using a large area and cutting up as shown in Fig. 7-18. The masking is arranged so that the silver electrodes are overlapped alternately at each end of the unit. The capacitors are then fired and leads attached.

The characteristics of capacitors produced in this way are good. They have a positive temperature coefficient of approximately 115 ppm/°C. They can be rated for operation at 500 volts and have a capacity of the order of 0.01 μf/in.[3]. Leakage current is negligible up to 150°C, and they can be used at 85°C continuously. Their performance is comparable to that of mica capacitors through the range of radio frequencies, and they withstand climatic conditions well. Their retrace characteristics are good.

Recently, the Sprague Electric Company has developed a new line of capacitors using the same constructional techniques with other ceramic materials, such as high-K and temperature-compensating compositions.

In the United Kingdom, a vitreous-enamel capacitor, under the trade name Vitricon, has been produced by the Welwyn Electric Laboratories. The technique of manufacture is different, being intermediate between that of glass working and ceramics and is comparable to enameling techniques used in producing wire-wound resistors.

In producing the vitreous-enamel capacitor, the foils are coated with a frit compounded from the dielectric enamels and are glazed before assembly. The glazed foils are stacked to produce the desired capacitance value and then fused together under pressure, forming a compacted mass of alternate layers of metal and dielectric. After the terminals are attached, the entire assembly is given a further coat of enamel to seal it off completely from the atmosphere.

A number of formulations for the dielectric enamel are available and offer various combinations of characteristics. For example, a dielectric constant can be obtained up to 120 with a controllable temperature coefficient and a power factor of 0.003, or better. At the other end of the range, a dielectric constant of approximately 20 can be produced with a zero temperature coefficient and a power factor of 0.0005. Any combination may be produced within these limits. The dielectric enamel has a melting point between 500 and 600°C.

The working range in most formulations is at least 200°C, and in others it may be as high as 250°C. The limit of working temperature is set arbitrarily, not because there is danger of destruction of the unit but because of the fall of the insulation resistance with increasing temperature.

The enamels are so chosen that the coefficient of expansion of an enamel matches exactly that of the foil with which it is used, and in consequence there is little strain in the capacitor when it is subjected to a wide temperature variation; thus they are suitable for use at extremely high and low temperatures, and can withstand a considerable degree of thermal shock.

The dielectric enamels are not especially resistant to moisture, and it is mainly for this reason that a further coat of enamel which is more moisture-resistant is provided. The resulting capacitor unit will withstand 100 climatic cycles without deterioration of insulation resistance, this remaining of the order of 10^{12} ohms. As an example of the resistance to load and high temperature, such capacitors have withstood 1,000 hr at 150°C with an applied d-c load 50 per cent greater than normal.

MAGNESIUM SILICATE CAPACITORS

Experimental stick-type capacitors have been made by the Philips Company in Holland in which a central metal electrode is inserted into a magnesium-silicate tube with an outer metal tube fitted. This assembly is heated and drawn down like wire until the required diameter is obtained. The length of "stick" is cut off according to the capacitance required. A small portion of the outer tube is cleaned off at the ends and connections made to the electrodes.

Experimental capacitors produced are about $1\frac{3}{4}$ in. long by $\frac{1}{32}$ in. in diameter with a capacitance of approximately 100 pf.

CHAPTER 8

CAPACITORS WITH PLASTIC DIELECTRICS

POLYSTYRENE-FILM CAPACITORS

The most important property of the polystyrene-film capacitor is its extremely high insulation resistance. These capacitors also have extremely low dielectric absorption, so that they are able to store an electric charge and to deliver it completely when required. This property is of value in such applications as:

R-f tuned circuits
Precision-timing circuits
Integrating circuits
High-Q tuned circuits
Laboratory standards
Long-time-constant circuits

The percentage of absorption, compared with other dielectrics, is shown in Table 2-2.

The power factor is low—about 0.0005 at 1 kc/sec. The capacitance stability is good, and the temperature coefficient is from -100 to -200 ppm/°C. There is a slight change in temperature coefficient at about room temperature, as shown in Fig. 8-1.

The main disadvantage for military use is the limited range of temperature over which the capacitor may be used—it should not normally be operated over 65°C, although some low-capacitance types can be operated up to 85°C. The properties of polystyrene are as follows:

Power factor (tan δ) (up to 10^9 cps).......... 0.0002 to 0.0005
Dielectric strength, 0.003 in. thickness........ 3,000 volts/mil
                    0.002 in. thickness........ 4,000 volts/mil
Dielectric constant (up to 10^9 cps)............ 2.5 to 2.7
Surface resistivity........................ 10^{16} ohms/cm^2
Volume resistivity........................ 10^{17} to 10^{19} ohms/cm^3
Specific gravity............................ 1.05
Tensile strength............................ 11,000 psi
Elongation at break
  (room temperature)...................... 4 per cent
Coefficient of linear expansion.............. 0.00001 per °C
Softening temperature..................... Approximately 85°C

141

Polystyrene is soluble in benzene, toluene, and xylene; its chemical formula is $(C_6H_5{-}CH{-}CH_2)_n$.

For use in capacitors the polystyrene film must be extruded flat and free from pinholes, and many difficulties have been overcome in fulfilling this requirement. Film for capacitors is made from polystyrene granules by extruding a heated tube of polymer, which is then spread out and stretched in two directions at right angles and cooled in the stretched state. The cooling rate is carefully controlled and air jets are commonly used. After this process the molecular chains of the

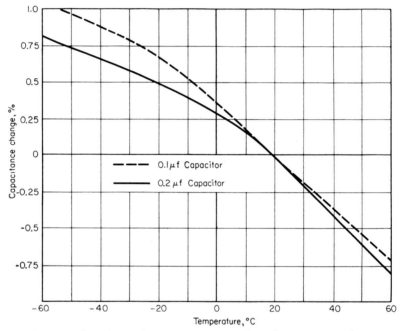

FIG. 8-1. Capacitance/temperature curves for polystyrene capacitors.

polystyrene lie predominantly in the plane of the film, and at normal temperatures the arrangement remains "frozen-in" indefinitely. This orientation will, however, rapidly relax at a temperature between 90 and 100°C, and if the film is not constrained in some way it will contract in its own plane and become thicker, thus reducing the capacitance.

To allow for this possibility, during manufacture heat treatment above the relaxation temperature can be applied after the film has been wound with aluminum-foil electrodes (Fig. 8-2). This ensures that the film contracts firmly into contact with the electrodes, eliminates voids or spaces between the electrodes, seals the ends of the winding, and results in a stable capacitor.   Capacitors made in this way are often referred to as "shrunk" capacitors.   Great difficulty may be experienced during winding because the films acquire static charges which collect extraneous dust particles, and these embed themselves in the film, causing shorts and consequent failures.   One method of overcoming this difficulty is by the use of a high-voltage transformer connected to a metal comb with the teeth facing the film and with a flat earthed metal plate mounted under the comb.   Such a winding arrangement for plastic film capacitors is shown in Fig. 8-2.

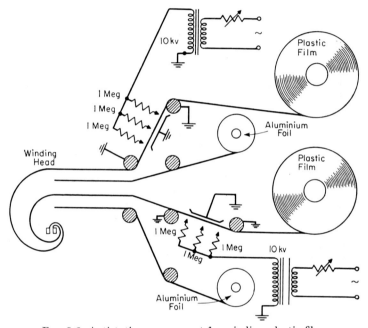

Fig. 8-2. Antistatic arrangement for winding plastic films.

There are several alternative and better arrangements.   One is to enclose the winding machine in a transparent case, as shown in Fig. 8-3. Another and more practical way is to air-condition and control the concentration of dust particles in the room in which the winding machines are operated.   Such a room is illustrated in Fig. 8-4.   More than one polystyrene film is usual, to increase voltage strength, and the metal foil used is almost invariably aluminum, although tin has been used.   The contact between the metal foil and the lead-out foil is most important and in some cases welded joints are made to ensure perfect contact.   It is essential that chemical cleanliness be maintained throughout the manufacture of this type of capacitor, and it is par-

FIG. 8-3. Enclosed film-winding machine used for making experimental plastic-film capacitors. (*Sprague Electric Company.*)

FIG. 8-4. Typical air-conditioned rolling room for plastic-film capacitors. (*Sprague Electric Company.*)

ticularly important that contamination of the film by grease, oils, or even dandruff from the operator's hair should be avoided. It is essential for high Q, low power factor, and high insulation resistance that the rolled capacitor be thoroughly dried prior to hermetically sealing in the can. Construction details in general are similar to those used for rolled-paper capacitors.

CELLULOSE-ACETATE

Cellulose-acetate, although inferior in electrical characteristics to polystyrene, has been used for certain specialized capacitors. Polyethylene terephthalate is now used in many of the applications in which cellulose-acetate was previously used. The losses for cellulose-acetate are lower than for paper but rise to a high value at approximately 100 Mc/sec. The power factor is slightly higher than that for paper, i.e., 0.01 to 0.03 at 25°C and 1 kc/sec, while the dielectric constant from 3.0 to 4.0 decreases with frequency up to about 1 Mc/sec. Cellulose-acetate does not offer any marked advantage over paper and, therefore, was never used in great quantity. The techniques for the manufacture of paper-dielectric capacitors were well known and paper was readily available. In view of the recent developments and large-scale use of polyethylene terephthalate, the future use of cellulose-acetate will be even more restricted.

POLYTETRAFLUOROETHYLENE (TEFLON[1]) CAPACITORS

Teflon is an excellent high-temperature material and a promising dielectric, having electrical characteristics similar to polystyrene at ordinary temperatures, but capable of operating, and retaining these electrical properties, up to about 200°C. There are two methods of producing thin films suitable for experimental capacitors—by shaving film from the solid roll and by casting. The main defect in the shaved film is the large number of pinholes, and it is also very difficult to produce films of a thickness below 0.002 in. A process of casting has been developed in which a highly polished metal surface is coated with a colloidal aqueous dispersion of Teflon, force-dried, and sintered until a continuous film is formed. When cold, the film is stripped off. Films made in this way have fewer pinholes than the shaved film. Low breakdown points experienced may not necessarily be due to pinholes or voids, as foreign particles may be carbonized at the sintering temperature.

Several metalizing processes have been developed, and considerable

[1] Registered trademark for E. I. du Pont de Nemours & Company.

work is now being carried on by industry. Appreciable development on metalized Teflon capacitors has been done by the Balco Research Laboratories under Air Force sponsorship. Theoretically, metalized capacitors offer a 4:1 size reduction over capacitors of the same configuration, capacitance value, and voltage rating. This is important with Teflon capacitors, since because of the low dielectric constant, the capacitors in general have a poor capacitance-to-volume ratio. This size reduction is realized as follows:

a. Halving the number of layers of dielectric material produces approximately a 2:1 size reduction. This is possible since the inherent self-healing property of the metalized film permits clearing of the dielectric faults and thus eliminates the need for doubling the dielectric thickness to protect against dielectric failures.

b. Halving the distance between the plates produces a 2:1 increase in capacitance. This is in accordance with the inverse dielectric-thickness law where the capacitance is doubled when the distance between the electrodes is halved and all other parameters remain constant.

To ensure adequate performance of metalized Teflon the electrode material should meet the following requirements:

a. Metal should be thin enough to permit vaporization and self-healing action.

b. Metal should bond well to Teflon.

c. Metal film and bond should not become degraded at maximum operating temperature (200°C).

d. Metal film should not degrade electrical characteristics of Teflon film (chemical reaction).

e. Metal film should have high electrical conductivity.

f. Metal should be easily evaporated.

g. Metal oxides (if it is a metal that oxidizes) should not affect capacitor performance.

According to investigations by the Balco Research Laboratories, aluminum most nearly fits all these requirements. Copper forms an oxide rapidly which reacts with Teflon at elevated temperatures. Silver is good in all respects except that its oxide results in a low Q. During the vacuum deposition process it is important that the thin films not be stretched, since stretching the film in excess of 1 per cent will cause its electrical resistance to increase greatly.

It was found that the impregnation of metalized Teflon capacitors with silicon fluids lowers the insulation resistance, increases the temperature coefficient of capacitance, increases the dielectric absorption but improves the voltage breakdown.

The use of two metalized layers (both electrodes) of Teflon has been found to present difficulty, since Teflon lacks rigidity and thus presents a serious termination problem. This difficulty has been overcome by the development of a composite structure, using one metalized electrode and one plain-foil electrode with one sheet of clear Teflon. Sprayed metal on the ends of the roll were used for lead attachment. A clearing voltage of twice rated voltage was used. For these experimental capacitors the following tentative voltage ratings were chosen:

Thickness of metalized Teflon	Tentative voltage ratings
¼ mil	50–100
⅜ mil	200–300
½ mil	300–400

For capacitors constructed with the above techniques, the temperature coefficient remains consistently negative and varies from -72 to 224 ppm/°C. The capacitance stability averages from 1 to 2 per cent, with the uncased units proving superior.

TABLE 8-1. TYPICAL PARAMETERS FOR METALIZED TEFLON CAPACITORS

Capacitance value		Voltage rating, 200°C	Power factor		IR	Construction
25°C	200°C	Volts d-c	25°C	200°C	25°C	
0.2562	0.2520*	200	0.50	0.82	1×10^{14}	Two layers (1 layer, ¼-mil metalized Teflon and 1 layer, ¼-mil clear Teflon)
0.3168	0.3076*	800	0.02	0.06	4.8×10^{13}	Two layers (1 layer, ½-mil metalized Teflon and 1 layer, ½-mil clear Teflon)

* After 1,000-hr-load life test.

POLYETHYLENE TEREPHTHALATE (MYLAR[1])

Mylar, a polyester material (known as Melinex in the United Kingdom) makes an excellent dielectric, comparable to paper but with the advantage of higher insulation resistance and slightly higher operating temperature (around 150°C).

Mylar can be used either alone or in combination (interleaved) with

[1] Registered trademark of E. I. du Pont de Nemours & Company.

paper or other plastic films. When used alone it is usual to impregnate the film with polystyrene, mineral oil, silicone fluid, or some other fluid to fill the pinholes. It is made in several thicknesses. Films of $\frac{1}{4}$, $\frac{1}{2}$, and 1 mil in the electrical grades are currently available.

It is possible to metalize by silvering or vacuum-metalizing with aluminum or zinc. The dielectric strength is a function of the film thickness. Considerable work has been done to try to determine, for example, whether one $\frac{1}{2}$-mil film is superior to two $\frac{1}{4}$-mil films when

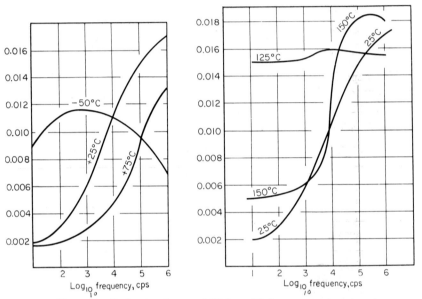

FIG. 8-5. Change in dissipation factor of Mylar with frequency at various temperatures. (*E. I. du Pont de Nemours & Company.*)

wound into a capacitor. Results so far have not been conclusive. While dielectric strength on normally used thicknesses is good, it becomes very good when the film is 0.001 inches thick.

A film 0.001 in. thick will withstand an instantaneous voltage of 4000 volts/mil. In order to make full use of this property it is essential to prevent a-c corona, as this results in dielectric fatigue. It has been found that the film is attacked to some extent in air by corona at 300 to 400 volts rms. Therefore, when high-voltage capacitors are used, they should be effectively sealed and perfectly impregnated to prevent internal corona.

It is important to remember that the material is temperature- and frequency-sensitive. At low frequencies the dielectric constant is comparable with that of paper but at high frequencies it becomes comparable with that of polystyrene. At the changeover frequency the losses are higher and at room temperature this frequency occurs near 1 Mc/sec.

The variation of dissipation factor and dielectric constant with frequency is shown by Figs. 8-5 and 8-6.

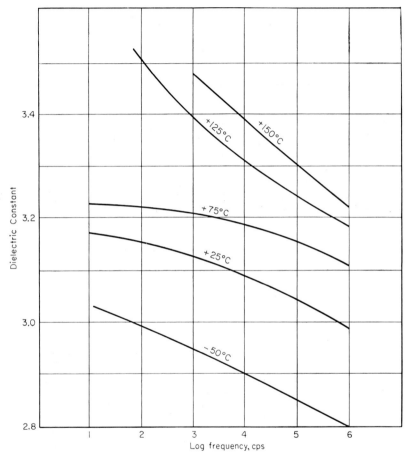

Fig. 8-6. The change in dielectric constant of Mylar with changes in temperature and frequency. (*E. I. du Pont de Nemours & Company.*)

One of the most important properties of Mylar is its extremely high insulation resistance at high temperatures as compared with paper. This is shown in Fig. 8-7.

Another important advantage that Mylar has over kraft paper is that of very low moisture absorption upon exposure to normal room ambients (less than 0.5 per cent during water-immersion test). Under

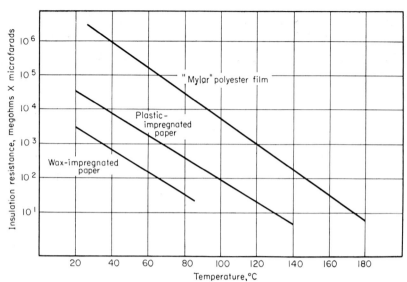

FIG. 8-7. Insulation resistance/temperature curves for paper and Mylar film at high temperatures. (*E. I. du Pont de Nemours & Company.*)

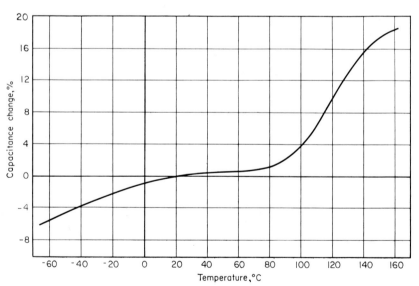

FIG. 8-8. Capacitance variation with temperatures for a typical Mylar capacitor.

the same conditions, kraft paper may absorb up to 6 per cent by weight.   Any remaining moisture in a paper-foil capacitor is a major contributor to early failure of the unit.   Even after a thorough vacuum

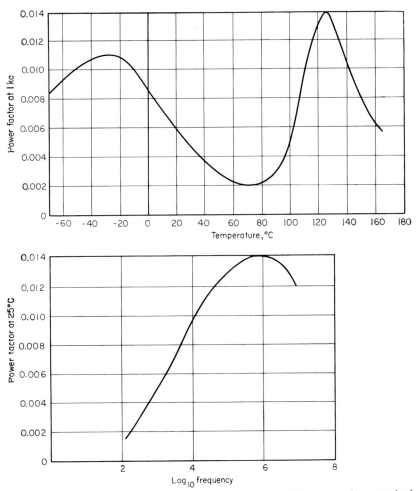

FIG. 8-9. Variation of power factor with temperature and frequency for a typical Mylar capacitor.

drying, the paper may retain more than 0.1 per cent of its absorbed moisture by weight.

The variation in capacitance of a typical Mylar capacitor over the temperature range −60 to 160°C is shown in Fig. 8-8, while the change of power factor with temperature and frequency is illustrated in Fig. 8-9.

IRRADIATED POLYETHYLENE

It is possible to increase the upper temperature limit of polyethylene without greatly affecting its electrical properties by exposing it to beta or gamma radiation. Polyethylene possesses very low losses at all radio frequencies and a low dielectric constant, but it is softened at about 70°C (depending to some extent on its composition) and melts at about 120°C. It is attacked and swollen by many organic solvents and hydrocarbon oils. When the polymer is submitted to gamma radiation, all these properties are modified to a degree dependent on the dosage. Mild dosage produces slightly greater heat resistance through some cross-linking mechanism, but increasing the dose renders the material more amorphous than crystalline, so that it does not soften or melt until temperatures over 200°C are reached. At the same time the dielectric properties are slightly degraded, and the polyethylene is discolored from opaque white to yellow. In this condition it is not attacked by solvents and oils. This change is thought to occur when the molecular chains of the polymer are cross-linked to a greater or lesser degree, according to the dosage, and hydrogen is liberated and partial oxidation takes place. Experiments are proceeding to introduce this material into capacitors, but difficulties are experienced in producing a finished capacitor, as it is not possible with present techniques to irradiate, at reasonable cost, enough film for winding as a capacitor. It is also not possible to irradiate the assembled capacitor, as the aluminum foil would absorb radiation. Additional development of this material may improve its properties.

CHAPTER 9

ELECTROLYTIC CAPACITORS

It is nearly 70 years since the first electrolytic capacitor was made in Germany and nearly 90 years since the principle was first noticed. The outstanding advantage of the electrolytic capacitor is its large capacitance/volume ratio.

PLAIN-FOIL TYPES

The large capacitance arises from the very thin film of dielectric used—of the order of 10^{-5} cm (a few millionths of an inch). The method of making this thin film is by anodic oxidation. Certain

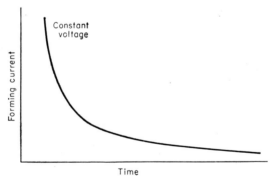

Fig. 9-1. Forming current for constant voltage for an electrolytic capacitor.

metals, notably aluminum, tantalum, vanadium, magnesium, bismuth, and antimony, are readily coated with a film of dielectric by an electrolytic "forming" process. If an aluminum electrode is placed in a solution of ammonium borate and a constant voltage applied, the initial current will be high, but it will drop gradually as the dielectric film forms, as shown in Fig. 9-1.

The forming process consists of the deposition of a thin film of aluminum oxide on the surface of the plate. In modern practice, the anode foil enters a tank of electrolyte with a constant voltage applied and passes through the tank until the required thickness of film is produced.

The film is extremely strong. A stress of 100 volts across a film of 10^{-5} cm represents a dielectric strength of ten million volts per centimeter. This is beginning to approach the theoretical strength predicted by the ionic theory of crystals. This strength has never otherwise been approached in practice. The maximum capacitance obtainable with a given anode surface area is inversely proportional to the voltage used in the forming process—i.e., the film thickness depends on the forming voltage. Low-voltage capacitors have thinner films and, therefore, a higher capacitance/volume ratio than have high-voltage capacitors. Since the working voltage is about 90 per cent of the forming voltage, and the thickest film is formed at about 600 volts, a limit of 500 to 550 volts (at room temperature) is set as the maximum working voltage obtainable. Ripple voltage must be included in this figure if the capacitor is being used for rectifier smoothing. It can also be seen that the surge voltage is limited in this type of capacitor. If the capacitor surge voltage is exceeded, scintillation will occur. This scintillation voltage is the sparking-voltage characteristic of the capacitor and represents partial breakdown of the dielectric, resulting in the formation of gaseous products, the production of local high temperatures and possibly actual carbonization of the separator materials and electrolyte.

The essential parts of an electrolytic capacitor and their functions are as follows:

1. The aluminum foil: positive or anode

2. The oxide film: dielectric

3. The electrolyte (usually an aqueous solution of ammonium borate, boric acid, and glycol): negative or true cathode

4. Spacers (usually kraft paper): necessary to separate the "cathode" and anode film from direct contact

5. A second aluminum foil: a contact electrode to the electrolyte, the "cathode."

A plain-foil dry electrolytic capacitor is made by first forming a coating of aluminum oxide on both sides of an aluminum foil about 0.002 to 0.005 in. thick. Two strips of aluminum foil are used (the formed foil as the anode and the plain foil as the contacting electrode for the electrolyte cathode), separated by two layers of porous paper (2 to 3 mils thick) soaked with electrolyte.

The electrolyte must be brought into intimate contact with the dielectric. In addition to performing the function of the true cathode in the operation of an electrolyte capacitor, the electrolyte provides a healing mechanism for re-forming the dielectric layer if minor break-down of this layer occurs.   This assembly is rolled up and then sealed in an aluminum container, as shown in Fig. 9-2.

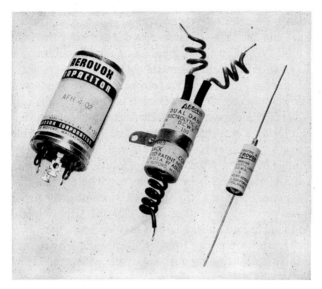

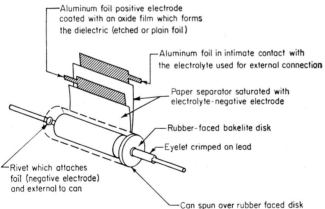

Fig. 9-2. Construction of plain- or etched-foil dry-electrolytic capacitor.   (*Aerovox Corporation.*)

The corrosive effects of heat and moisture are counteracted by making an effective seal for the container and using aluminum for all metal parts.   An effective seal also prevents the electrolyte from drying out with a corresponding shortening of the capacitor life.

During the last few years considerable work has been undertaken to obtain greater surface area on the anodes and develop new anode materials and new electrolytes. It has been known for some time that an increase in the purity of aluminum foil would reduce the leakage current and lengthen the life of aluminum electrolytic capacitors. The two important limitations in the use of aluminum for electrolytic capacitors are the existence of copper and iron impurities in aluminum and the solubility of aluminum oxide in acid solutions. The former probably has the greater effect on the shelf life of the capacitor. The impurities immersed in the electrolyte react like a battery and cause current to flow, which results in corrosion of the electrodes and reduced shelf life. With the appearance of these impurities on the surface of the foil, high leakage currents with local hot spots result when voltage is applied.

For a number of years, aluminum electrolytics have been made with aluminum foil that is 99.87 per cent pure. The availability of high-purity 99.99-per-cent-pure aluminum foil, domestically produced, has resulted in the production of aluminum electrolytics with leakage currents a decade lower and an increase of life expectancy of several years.

Nonpolar electrolytic capacitors are also made by preforming both aluminum foils and bringing out separate contacts. Each film is effective during the half cycle that the other is ineffective. Since this process doubles the thickness of the oxide film (two films), the capacitance of the nonpolar unit for a given voltage rating and foil area is halved. The container of the nonpolar unit must be provided with a vent, since at times the generation of gas with this type of capacitor may be excessive and may cause an unvented container to explode. The vent must be so designed as not to permit contaminants to enter the capacitor nor allow the electrolyte to evaporate.

Electrical Characteristics

The principal characteristics to be considered are:
1. Capacitance and the effect of temperature and frequency
2. Power factor and the effect of temperature and frequency
3. Leakage current and the effect of time, temperature, and voltage

A typical capacitor, Fig. 9-3, shows the variation in capacitance due to temperature and frequency. It can be seen from the upper curve that electrolytic capacitors lose a great deal of their effectiveness at low temperatures. This is due to the freezing of the electrolyte and consequent increase in series resistance.

The lower curve shows the variation of capacitance with frequency. From zero to 10 kc/sec the capacitance decreases slightly; the equivalent series resistance, after falling rapidly up to 500 cps, decreases more slowly up to 10 kc/sec.   The power factor increases from a low value to 50 per cent through the same range.   Above 10 kc/sec the capacitance increases slightly but does not rise more than 10 per cent at 50 kc/sec.

Electrolytic capacitors can be used as smoothing capacitors at these frequencies to ensure a d-c supply, the a-c energy being dissipated.

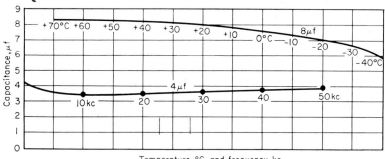

Fig. 9-3. Variation of capacitance with temperature and frequency for dry-electrolytic capacitors.

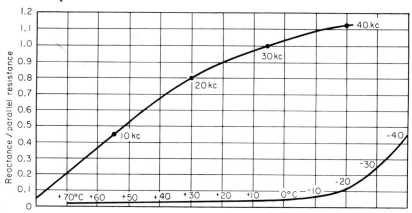

Fig. 9-4. Variation of power-factor (ratio of reactance to) parallel resistance with temperature and frequency for electrolytic capacitors.

At radio frequencies they provide a low resistance path of approximately 1 ohm at room temperature.   They can therefore be used with tuned circuits, provided a loss of this order can be tolerated.

Figure 9-4 shows the effect on power factor of variations in temperature and frequency.   The high power factor of electrolytic capacitors is due to the resistance of the electrolyte, the equivalent series resistance of an electrolytic capacitor being very little greater than the resistance of the electrolyte.   This high power factor is inevitable—

any attempt to reduce the resistance of the electrolyte by using a thinner separator would lead to increased leakage current, lower breakdown voltage, and shortened life.   On the other hand, the power factor must not be made any higher (even if a high power factor can be tolerated at normal temperature) because the corresponding value at low temperatures would be excessive.

At $-30°C$, an increase in value of the power factor of ten times that at $+25°C$ is quite normal.   It is fortunate that the power factor increases toward the lower end of the temperature range, since the worst effect of the high power factor is the heat produced in the capacitor itself, and an important feature is the continued decrease of power factor with increase of temperature, which ensures safe working.   If

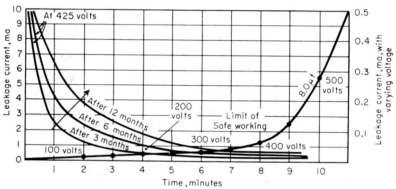

FIG. 9-5. Variation of leakage current with time and applied voltage for electrolytic capacitors.

the power factor were to increase with temperature faster than the rate of cooling, an unstable condition would be reached, and the capacitor would eventually blow up.

Since power factor $= R/Z = R\omega C$, approximately, the decrease of capacitance at low temperature tends to keep the power factor down. The equivalent series resistance R must, therefore, increase more quickly than the power factor at low temperatures.   Thus, if the capacitance is halved and the power factor increases to ten times its value, the equivalent series resistance must have increased to twenty times its value, about 100 ohms for a typical 1 μf condenser at 25°C.

The safe working voltage of the capacitor is determined by the leakage current/voltage characteristics, as shown in Fig. 9-5.   In the example the limit of safe working occurs at about 400 to 450 volts. The leakage current rises rapidly above this voltage region, and breakdown soon sets in.

The leakage current also increases with increase of temperature and becomes very large as breakdown is approached. The leakage-current/temperature curve is similar in shape to the leakage-current/voltage curve.

During shelf life, both curves become shallower in the direction shown by the arrow on the leakage-current/voltage curves, the reverse process taking place in operation. It is primarily this upward drift of the leakage-current/time curve (with the simultaneous effect on the leakage-current/voltage curve) which is responsible for the failure of electrolytic capacitors after a long period of storage.

In general, the disadvantages of electrolytic capacitors may be summarized as the high power factor (about ten times that of an average paper capacitor), the variation in capacitance (capacitance variations from -20 to $+150$ per cent of the nominal value are possible), the small safety factor, and the high leakage current.

The great advantages of electrolytic capacitors are, of course, their very high capacitance/volume ratio and their reasonably low cost. For smoothing, decoupling, and bypass purposes these advantages may outweigh all the disadvantages.

The following general conditions should be satisfied whenever a polar electrolytic capacitor is used.

1. The peak voltage applied should be less than the rated voltage. When an a-c ripple is superimposed on d-c, the peak voltage is equal to the d-c, plus the peak of the a-c. The a-c ripple should not normally exceed 10 per cent of the d-c voltage.

2. The applied voltage should never be reversed. The d-c should always be in the correct polarity, but a small alternating voltage may be applied for a few minutes without any polarizing voltage. It is, in fact, convenient to do this when measuring the impedance.

3. The ripple current should not produce overheating. The maximum ripple current allowed for each size of capacitor is usually given.

ETCHED-FOIL TYPES

The etched-foil capacitor is similar in construction to the plain-foil type except that the anode foil is acid-etched before forming, with a consequent increase in anode surface area. Since the electrolyte is a solution or paste, it is able to make contact with the whole of the thin film that is formed on this undulating surface. It is essential to control the etching process closely so that "thin" spots are not left on the foil and also to ensure that no acid is left which might contaminate the foil. The increase in surface area results in a considerable increase in the capacitance obtainable for a given anode area. An effective increase of 6:1 can be accomplished with a hydrochloric acid etch. The over-all physical dimensions of the etched-foil capacitor can be reduced in accordance with this increase in anode surface area. Although the etched-foil capacitors are much smaller than plain-foil types for a given rating, they are less stable. The power factor is increased by a factor of 2 to 4, as shown in Fig. 9-6. This figure illustrates the variation of power factor with voltage rating at 25°C and 120 cps for plain- and etched-foil solid-electrolytic capacitors.

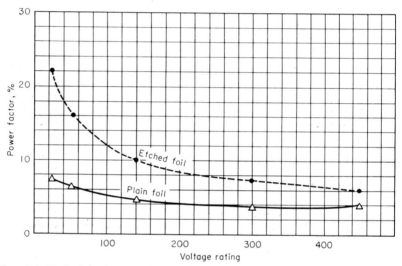

Fig. 9-6. Variation of power factor with voltage for plain- and etched-foil electrolytic capacitors.

At −40°C, the 120 cps impedance is usually from five to seven times the 25°C; the capacitance will vary from 25 to 75 per cent of the 25°C value. Since different electrolytes are used, the amount of variation of the above parameters will depend upon the voltage rating and capacitance value. In general, a higher-resistance electrolyte is used for higher-voltage ratings to prevent voltage breakdown of the electrolyte.

Dual-section capacitors of different voltage ratings are not of optimum design, since both sections are impregnated with the same electrolyte. The electrolyte ordinarily used would be best suited for the higher-voltage section; thus, the low-voltage section will have a higher series resistance and power factor than an equivalent single-section design.

METAL-SPRAYED-GAUZE OR FABRICATED-PLATE TYPES

The sprayed-gauze anode consists of a fine aluminum gauze, on which pure aluminum is sprayed from a metal-spraying pistol. The effective area is still greater than can be achieved by the etched-foil process, and capacitance can be obtained up to ten times that of an

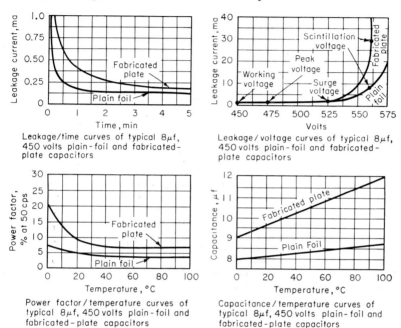

Leakage/time curves of typical 8μf, 450 volts plain-foil and fabricated-plate capacitors

Leakage/voltage curves of typical 8μf, 450 volts plain-foil and fabricated-plate capacitors

Power factor/temperature curves of typical 8μf, 450 volts plain-foil and fabricated-plate capacitors

Capacitance/temperature curves of typical 8μf, 450 volts plain-foil and fabricated-plate capacitors

Fig. 9-7. Characteristics of plain-foil and fabricated-plate 8-μf 450-volt electrolytic capacitors. (*Plessey Company, Ltd.*)

equivalent plain-foil electrode. A comparison between the characteristics of the sprayed-gauze or fabricated-plate type and the plain-foil type is shown in Fig. 9-7.

Because of the higher leakage current, greater variation of capacitance, and impedance at low temperature, this type of construction is not satisfactory for application in military equipment.

TANTALUM ELECTROLYTIC CAPACITORS

At the present time, three basic types of tantalum anodes are being produced and used in tantalum capacitors. They are: sintered slug, plain- and etched-foil, and plain- and etched-wire. The use of these anodes and the application of different impregnants and construction techniques have resulted in capacitors with entirely different characteristics.

Tantalum-pellet Electrolytic Capacitors

The tantalum-pellet capacitor is made by sintering a porous capsule of pressed tantalum powder in a high vacuum at approximately 2,100°C. The pellet is then placed in a forming bath, and an oxide

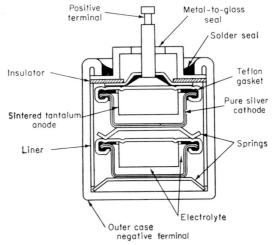

FIG. 9-8. Construction of a two-cell hermetically sealed tantalum-pellet electrolytic capacitor. (*P. R. Mallory Company.*)

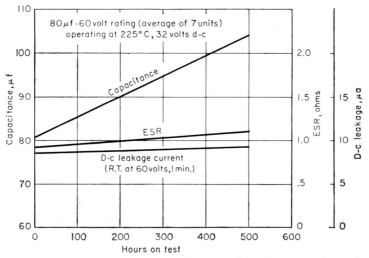

FIG. 9-9. Variation of leakage current, equivalent series resistance, and capacitance with time for the conditions specified. (*P. R. Mallory Company.*)

coating is formed over the surface area. It is then mounted inside a silver cup containing sulfuric acid or lithium chloride as the electrolyte. Thus, these capacitors are essentially "wet" electrolytic capacitors. Since a highly conductive electrolyte must be selected, the use of the

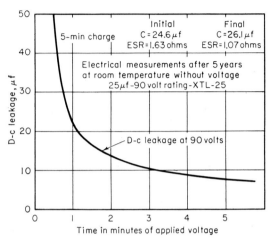

Fɪɢ. 9-10. Variation of leakage current with time for idle storage. (*P. R. Mallory Company.*)

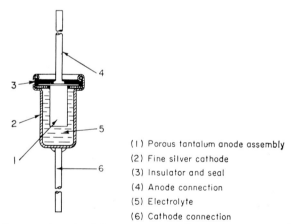

(1) Porous tantalum anode assembly
(2) Fine silver cathode
(3) Insulator and seal
(4) Anode connection
(5) Electrolyte
(6) Cathode connection

Fɪɢ. 9-11. Construction of miniature-type tantalum-pellet electrolytic capacitor. (*Fansteel Metallurgical Corporation.*)

tantalum anode slug with its silver-cup cathode is limited to low voltages. This type of electrolyte is used to lower the internal resistance, since the distance between anode and cathode is greater than in the foil tantalum capacitor.

Two basic types of tantalum capacitor construction are being produced. One is a hermetically sealed unit, which is sealed by pressing together the cup-shaped cathode and the plate-mounted sintered anode over a ring of polytetrafluoroethylene (PTFE), which serves as the seal and insulating washer. The electrolyte used in this "cell" is

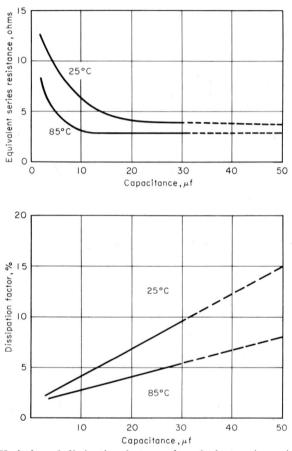

Fig. 9-12. Variation of dissipation factor and equivalent series resistance with capacitance (sintered-slug tantalum capacitors of 6- to 100-volt rating).

sulfuric acid. This cell is then sealed in a steel case as shown in the detailed construction of a two-cell capacitor of this type in Fig. 9-8.

This capacitor is rated at 25 μf at 180 volts. Except for the number of cells, other voltage ratings are constructed similarly. Capacitors with 90-volt and lower ratings are of single-cell construction, while those with higher-voltage ratings have additional cells; the 630-volt unit, e.g., has seven cells.

These capacitors are capable of operating over a temperature range of −55 to +175°C, though the upper limit may be extended to 200°C if a special plating to preserve the solder seal is used as the finish. The capacitance tolerance is −15 to +75 per cent, while the range of capacitance available is from 7 to 240 μf with voltage ratings at 85°C from 630 to 18 volts d-c, respectively. These capacitors are available

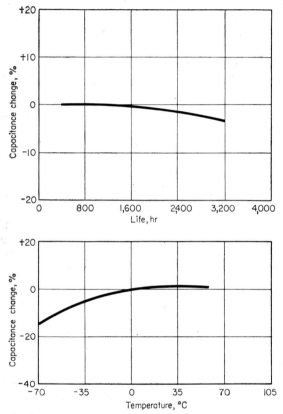

Fig. 9-13. Variation of capacitance with temperature and life (4 μf, 60 volts d-c).

with several different types of leads and methods of mounting. Figure 9-9 gives the variation of d-c leakage current, the equivalent series resistance, and the capacitance with time at 225°C for typical units. The variation of d-c leakage current with time to show the effect of idle storage is given in Fig. 9-10.

For the second type of construction for the sintered tantalum-pellet electrolytic capacitors, a neoprene rubber end seal and a silver case are used. The silver case is rolled over the rubber end seal, which is placed against the plate-mounted sintered slug. The detailed construction of this miniature-type capacitor is shown in Fig. 9-11. The characteristics of this capacitor are listed as follows:

    a. Temperature range: -55 to $+85°C$

    b. Voltage rating at 85°C: 6 to 125 volts d-c

    c. Capacitance range: 1.7 to 60 μf

    d. Capacitance tolerance: -15 to $+30$ per cent

Figure 9-12 shows the variation of dissipation factor and equivalent series resistance with capacitance for typical capacitors of this type. Capacitance change with temperature and life are shown in Fig. 9-13 for a 4-μf 60-volt d-c capacitor.

Recently, a variation in the construction shown in Fig. 9-11 has resulted in a capacitor with a case of the same diameter throughout its entire length. Other characteristics generally remain about the same.

Solid-electrolyte Tantalum Capacitor

A recent development in the tantalum capacitor field is the small low-voltage "solid-electrolyte" capacitor. In this development, a solid semiconductor replaces the aqueous solution as the electrolyte. The solid electrolyte, usually introduced into the pores of the previously anodized sintered slug as a manganous nitrate or sulfate solution, is converted to manganese dioxide by heating. The dielectric film requires re-forming by placing the slugs in a forming bath and anodizing as before to repair the damage to the dielectric film caused by the hot reactive nitrogen oxides during introduction of the MnO_2. Owing to scintillation, the original forming voltage cannot be reached. It is this scintillation which limits the rated voltage to approximately one-third the original forming voltage. The use of this semiconductor in place of the liquid electrolyte changes the characteristics of the capacitor considerably. The absence of the aqueous solution removes the problem of electrolysis and associated problems of varying internal gas pressure. A seal is required with use of the liquid system which must allow gas to escape as the pressure increases in order to prevent an explosion due to excessive pressure. Since this is not a hermetic seal, a certain amount of vapor is lost; the rate of this loss determines the life of the capacitor. Also, the maximum operating temperature of this type of capacitor is limited by the vapor pressure of the liquid system. By eliminating these considerations, the solid electrolyte has potentially longer life expectancy and higher operating-temperature capabilities.

In addition to these improvements, the electrical characteristics are improved considerably. D. A. McLean and F. S. Power (see Bibliography) have shown a flat temperature coefficient of capacitance (0.07 per cent/°C) and dissipation factor for the solid-electrolyte types. The improvement of these characteristics is attributed to the high conductivity of MnO_2 over the temperature range (-80 to $100°C$). The

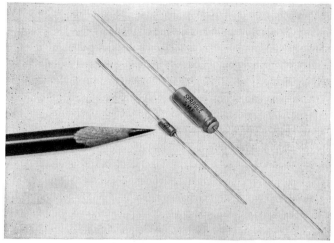

FIG. 9-14. Comparative size of 4.7-μf 10-volt d-c solid-electrolytic tantalum capacitor and miniature aluminum electrolytic capacitor of comparable rating. (*Sprague Electric Company.*)

conductivity of conductive solutions decreases as the viscosity increases and has a sharp peak when the solution freezes. The solid-electrolyte capacitor exhibits superior capacitance vs. frequency characteristics, which may be due to the charge separation across the Ta_2O_5, brought

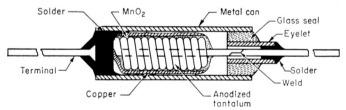

FIG. 9-15. Construction of a solid-electrolyte tantalum capacitor. (*Sprague Electric Company.*)

about by electronic conduction through the semiconductor (see A. V. Fraioli under Bibliography).

In general, the characteristics, other than the capacitance/volume ratio, are more comparable with a paper-dielectric capacitor than with a liquid-electrolyte electrolytic capacitor. For the lower capacitance

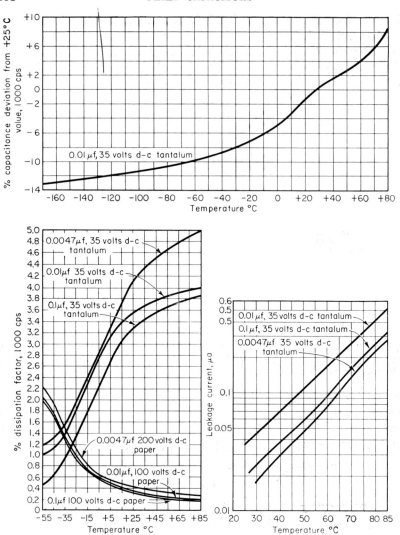

FIG. 9-16. Variation of dissipation factor, capacitance, and leakage current with temperature. (*Sprague Electric Company.*)

values (usually up to approximately 0.1 μf), plain tantalum wire is used as the anode. Etched wire on sintered pellets is used for the higher capacitance values. The comparative sizes of two capacitors, an aluminum electrolytic and a sintered-tantalum pellet with solid electrolyte of similar rating, are shown in Fig. 9-14.

With increased life expectancy, higher operating-temperature capability, and superior electrical characteristics, these capacitors are

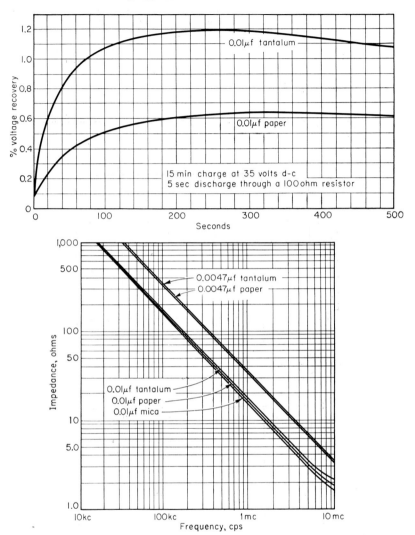

FIG. 9-17. Comparison of dielectric absorption vs. time and impedance vs. frequency between typical tantalum and paper capacitors. (*Sprague Electric Company.*)

finding widespread application in transistor circuitry. At the present time, the maximum working voltage available is 50 volts d-c over the temperature range −55 to 85°C, although considerable development work is in progress to increase the voltage rating and operating-temperature range (see A. V. Fraioli in the Bibliography). The constructional details of a typical capacitor of this type are shown in Fig. 9-15.

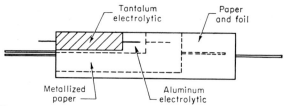

FIG. 9-18. Size (i.e., volume) of tantalum-foil capacitor compared with other tubular types.

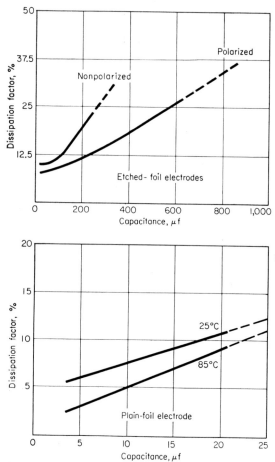

FIG. 9-19. Variation of dissipation factor with capacitance value for plain- and etched-foil types.

The variation of dissipation factor, capacitance, and leakage current with temperature is shown by Fig. 9-16. Figure 9-17 further illustrates the characteristics of dielectric absorption and impedance vs. frequency for typical capacitors.

Tantalum-foil Electrolytic Capacitors

The primary advantage of the tantalum-foil electrolytic capacitor is the high capacitance-to-volume ratio. These capacitors are similar in construction to the aluminum electrolytic except that ½-mil tantalum foil is used for the electrodes. Tantalum is an inert material which resists attack by most acids so that little, if any, galvanic corrosion can

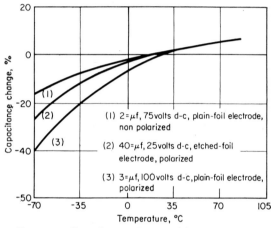

FIG. 9-20. Capacitance change with temperature.

occur when it is used with an electrolyte. The spacing material is usually two ½-mil sheets of a strong, porous paper impregnated with the electrolyte. Different electrolytes are used for different voltage-rating requirements. Lithium chloride, a low-resistance electrolyte, may be used for low-voltage capacitors, while succinic and boric acids, higher-resistance electrolytes, may be used for medium- and high-voltage capacitors. The cases are made of silver-plated brass or copper. At the present time, the film-tantalum capacitors are capable of operating over a temperature range of −55 to +125°C when the double seal (elastomer and polytetrafluoroethylene) is used. Single-cell foil-type capacitors have the following characteristics:

Type of foil	Capacitance range, μf	Voltage range
Etched	1–580	15–150
Plain	1–300	3–150

Foil capacitors can be produced in either polarized or nonpolarized units. Comparison of sizes of a typical tantalum-foil capacitor with capacitors having other dielectrics (for 100 working voltage) is shown in Fig. 9-18.

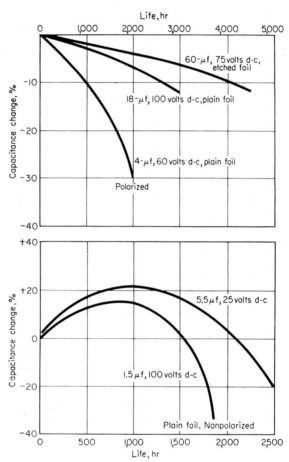

FIG. 9-21. Capacitance change with life for plain- and etched-foil, polarized and nonpolarized types.

Since the tantalum oxide film is very stable, the re-forming required for aluminum electrolytics is unnecessary, and the capacitors possess long storage lives. Typical capacitance values and voltage ratings for the etched-foil polarized type, which can be obtained in a can length of $\frac{3}{4}$ in. and a diameter of $\frac{11}{16}$ in., are 15 μf at 15 volts or 1 μf at 150 volts. Tolerance on capacitance value is -15 to $+75$ per cent.

Variation of dissipation factor with capacitance value for plain- and etched-foil types is shown in Fig. 9-19.

Capacitance change with temperature for typical units is shown in Fig. 9-20. Capacitance change with life for typical units for both plain- and etched-foil, polarized and nonpolarized types is shown in Fig. 9-21.

Tantalum-foil capacitors can be used as coupling or decoupling capacitors. When used as coupling capacitors in timing circuits, the steep front is likely to deteriorate because of phase changes introduced by the series resistance. When used at higher frequencies, losses begin to increase seriously at about 1 to 10 kc/sec.

CHAPTER 10

AIR-, VACUUM-, AND GAS-DIELECTRIC CAPACITORS

AIR-DIELECTRIC TYPES

Air-dielectric fixed capacitors are used mainly as laboratory standards of capacitance, particularly as high-voltage standards. They are either parallel-plate or concentric-cylinder types. In both types, great care is taken in obtaining and preserving dimensional stability. The parallel-plate types are similar in principle to the precision variable capacitors, but designed to function at one fixed capacitance; these plates are circular, square, or triangular in shape.

The insulating material used is fused silica, and the whole capacitor is shielded in a metal case. Fixed-value air-capacitor standards are available from about 50 to 10,000 pf. The accuracy of adjustment to a nominal value varies from 0.01 to 0.05 per cent, according to capacitance value and construction. For capacitors above 200 pf the accuracy to which actual values are reported is between 0.01 and 0.02 per cent. The probable permanence of value throughout a number of years varies between 0.01 per cent for the larger capacitance values and 0.04 per cent for the smaller values.

Miniature types are made, designed to have low residual inductance and conductor resistance, so that they can be used at higher radio frequencies.

Both types are temperature-compensated, and the temperature coefficient of capacitance is usually less than ten parts in 10^6 per degree centigrade.

An example of European manufacture is the range of fixed capacitors made by Philips Ltd., Eindhoven, Holland, and their construction is shown in Fig. 10-1. Two sets of circular brass plates are interlaid horizontally. One set is soldered to two brass rods insulated from the brass base, the other set to two brass rods fixed to the base. The number of plates is determined by the capacitance required.

For calibration, a small, circular brass plate on a screw thread is used, the plate being locked after final adjustment. For this type of fixed capacitor the maximum deviation from the nominal capacitance at 20°C is ±0.15 per cent, and the average temperature coefficient is 25 × 10⁻⁶ parts/°C. The maximum loss angle at 1 Mc/sec (tan δ) is 0.0003, provided the relative humidity of the air is not greater than 75 per cent. Standard capacitors of this type are made in many capacitance values, ranging from 10 to 1,000 pf.

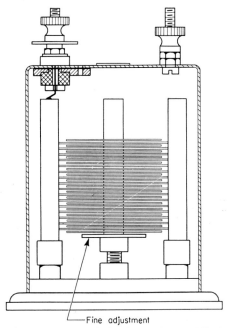

Fine adjustment

Fig. 10-1. Construction of air-dielectric fixed capacitor.   (*Philips Ltd., Eindhoven.*)

The concentric-cylinder type is similar in principle to the vacuum capacitor described in the next section.

VACUUM CAPACITORS

The principal of using vacuum as a dielectric for capacitors is not new. Vacuum capacitors were first developed in the United States although they are now manufactured in other countries, including Great Britain. Their primary use is as blocking or decoupling capacitors either in transmitting equipment (including airborne) or in high-powered industrial applications.

For airborne use the high internal breakdown voltage is achieved by using a hard vacuum. The operating voltage is then theoretically limited by the value of external breakdown voltage, which depends on the ambient-air density and on the spacing and shape of the external terminals. In industrial use, these capacitors are unaffected by extreme variations of temperature, moisture, and humidity, and can be made very strong mechanically with a consequent high order of capacitance stability.

The capacitance-to-volume ratio is low since the dielectric constant is essentially equal to that of air. They are limited in capacitance value to about 5,000 pf, in voltage rating to about 120 kv, and in current rating to about 225 amp. The current rating can usually be doubled by cooling with forced air or water. The power factor is low— on the order of 0.0002—and is dependent on the eddy-current and I^2R losses in the plates and conductors. These capacitors are very reliable, and life continues as long as the vacuum is maintained. The dielectric is self-healing, so that even if the voltage limit is exceeded and internal breakdown and flashover occur, no permanent damage is caused. However, damage can result if the arc is maintained.

The limit of breakdown voltage across a perfect vacuum is determined by the material and shape of the electrodes. In theory, the voltage can be increased to the point where cold emission from the electrodes occurs, but this cannot be reached in practice because of the occluded gas given off by the metal used for the electrodes.

The main difficulty in construction is always experienced in the end seals; in early capacitors, tungsten glass seals were used and outgassing arrangements were similar to those used in tube manufacture. Some vacuum capacitors use electrode cylinders made from high-quality copper; another type uses nickel. The capacitance between two cylindrical concentric electrodes is given by

$$C = \frac{Al_e}{\log r_2/r_1}$$

where C = capacitance, pf
   l_e = length of electrodes, cm
   r_1 = radius of inner electrode, cm
   r_2 = radius of outer electrode, cm
   A = a constant

In the type of construction using nickel electrodes, each set of electrodes is mounted on a plate attached to a Kovar sealing ring which is fused into the glass envelope. The capacitor is assembled in a bell jar in an atmosphere of nitrogen, to avoid oxidation of the nickel electrodes. R-f heating is used to seal the Kovar rings to the glass.

The capacitors are usually subjected to a temperature of approximately 400°C for several hours and then "spot knocked," a process which consists of charging up a relatively large capacitor and discharging it through the vacuum capacitor, which is in series with a suitable current-limiting resistor. The object of this process is to clean up minute projections on the electrode surfaces. This is repeated several times with the charging voltage raised progressively until a pre-determined high value can be applied without further discharge. A barium getter is then fired by passing a current through it, and the capacitor is sealed by squeezing the piecing tube between rollers under high pressure, thus forming a cold weld. Contact caps of silver-plated brass are finally soft-soldered to each end of the capacitor.

The characteristics of the vacuum capacitor are best suited for fairly low capacitance values up to the order of 500 pf. Above this the capacitors become large and are more difficult to manufacture, and the ceramic capacitor then becomes a serious competitor. Two typical fixed capacitors are shown in Fig. 10-2.

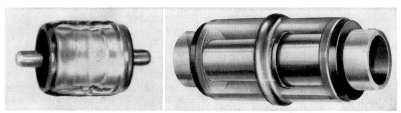

FIG. 10-2. Typical fixed vacuum capacitors. (*Dolinko and Wilkens, Inc.*)

The characteristics of a typical small vacuum capacitor, manu-factured by Dolinko and Wilkens, Inc., are as follows:

Length............................ 2⅝ in.
Diameter.......................... 1¹⁄₁₆ in.
Maximum capacitance............ 50 pf
Maximum voltage rating.......... 15 kv

The characteristics of a typical large vacuum capacitor, using copper electrodes, manufactured by the Jennings Radio Company, are as follows:

Length............................ 9¼ in.
Diameter.......................... 5 in.
Capacitance values............... 75,100 and 125 pf
Maximum voltage rating.......... 60 kv
Maximum current rating.......... 175 amp

GAS-FILLED TYPES

Gas-filled capacitors are used mainly as high-voltage components. The electrode structure is usually simple, consisting of an inner metal tube suitably spaced inside an outer steel tube. Domed heads and stress distributors are used for voltages above 150 kv. The gas is usually compressed, and normal working gas pressures are around 150 psi. The gas may be air or nitrogen, and it must be clean and dry.

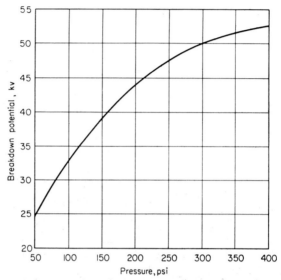

Fɪɢ. 10-3. Increase in breakdown potential of nitrogen with pressure.

A typical 250-kv capacitor of 50 pf would have a loss angle of less than 0.00001 radian. The temperature coefficient is higher than that of the vacuum types, and the pressures are much greater. The increase in breakdown potential of nitrogen with pressure is shown in Fig. 10-3.

CHAPTER 11

EXPERIMENTAL TYPES OF FIXED CAPACITORS

HIGH-TEMPERATURE MICA CAPACITORS (500°C)

By employing 0.001 stainless-steel electrodes welded to strips of stainless steel for terminations in conjunction with sheet mica for a dielectric, the General Electric Company has developed a capacitor capable of operating at 500°C. The capacitor is encased in an Inconel case, whose construction allows for the large expansion characteristic

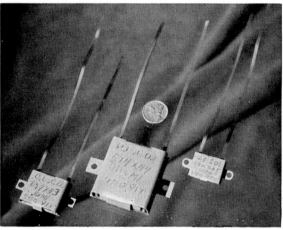

Fig. 11-1. Typical 500°C mica capacitors (rated at 0.01, 0.05, and 0.001 μf at 250 volts d-c). (*General Electric Company.*)

of mica at 500°C with a minimum effect on the electrical characteristics of the capacitor. The dielectric material is phlogopite mica, approximately 0.001 in. thick. One of these capacitors, rated at 0.01 μf at 250 volts d-c has remained operative for 2,000 hr at 500°C. One hundred and two hundred volts each had been applied for 1,000 hr, respectively. Capacitors are capable of operating for 1,000 hr at rated voltage (250 volts d-c) at 500°C. These capacitors cover a capacitance range from 0.001 to 0.05 μf, all rated at 250 volts d-c. Typical units are shown in Fig. 11-1. The insulation resistance for these capacitors is shown in Fig. 11-2.

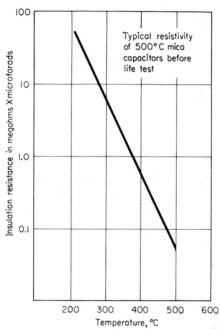

Fig. 11-2. Insulation resistance of 500°C mica capacitor. (*General Electric Company.*)

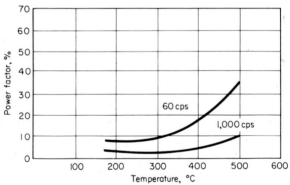

Fig. 11-3. Typical 60- and 1,000-cycle power-factor variation for 500°C mica capacitors. (*General Electric Company.*)

Since the losses of mica rise with temperature, the power factor for these capacitors is rather high. Typical 60- and 1,000-cycle power-factor variations with temperature are shown in Fig. 11-3. Capacitance variation with temperature is shown in Fig. 11-4. The capacitance-to-volume ratio is rather low as the 0.01 μf capacitors have a

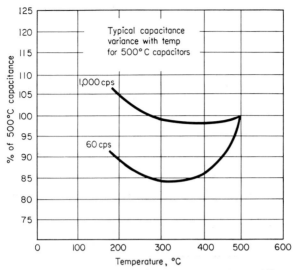

FIG. 11-4. Capacitance variation with temperature for 500°C capacitors.

volume of approximately 0.3 in.³. The capacitors are capable of operating when subjected to radiation.

ROLLED-GLASS CAPACITOR

The Corning Glass Works, using a 0.0015-in.-thick glass ribbon, has developed, under a Signal Corps contract, a rolled-glass capacitor with a rating of 0.1 μf at 600 volts d-c. The glass ribbon and the aluminum foil are wound on a glass mandrel inside a furnace. The temperature of the furnace is high enough to soften the glass to the point where it becomes flexible. The structure of the capacitor is similar to that of a paper capacitor. Life tests at 125°C indicate satisfactory performance. The form factor of this type of construction has the advantage of a greater capacitance-to-volume ratio over the existing "flat stack" type of glass capacitor. To prevent moisture absorption, encapsulating in a protective enclosure is required. Results so far have been promising although much development work remains to be done on type of enclosure and thinner glass ribbon.

SOLID-ELECTROLYTE ALUMINUM-OXIDE CAPACITORS

Some experimental work has been carried out by the U.S. Army Signal Corps Engineering Laboratories in attempting to apply the techniques used in the construction of the tantalum solid electrolyte (manganese dioxide) to a capacitor with an aluminum anode. The capacitors were constructed using high-purity aluminum etched foil (99.99-per-cent-pure aluminum) approximately 0.0042 in. thick. The oxide coating was formed in the conventional manner, although a study in forming electrolytes resulted in an electrolyte enabling better control of the electrical parameters of the finished capacitor. The foil was first formed, then coated with manganese dioxide. The most successful method of deposition for the manganese dioxide was by pyrolitic decomposition of manganous nitrate. A coat of silver paint was brushed on to provide an electric contact with the manganese dioxide.

The coated foil was then hand-wound into the experimental capacitors. For comparison purposes only, approximate values are given in Table 11-1.

TABLE 11-1. CHARACTERISTICS OF HAND-WOUND SOLID-ELECTROLYTE
ALUMINUM CAPACITORS

	Aluminum electrolytic, per MIL-C-62	Solid tantalum	Solid aluminum
Capacitance change:			
from 25°C to −40°C	−70%	−5%	−15%
+85°C	+20%	+3%	+ 7%
Leakage in $\mu a/\mu f$-volts			
at 25°C	.04	0.0005–0.05	.08
Equivalent series resistance times			
capacitance, ohm-μf	600	20	160

This work indicates that construction of capacitors for low-voltage applications (30 volts or lower) is feasible.

As a continuation of this work, the Bell Telephone Laboratories, under Signal Corps sponsorship, has a program to develop a finished capacitor of this type. Investigation of high-purity aluminum 99.99+ wire, etched wire, etched foil, and sintered pellets is in progress.

SUPPORTED- AND STRIP-FILM CAPACITORS

In the United States, both the supported- and strip-film types of capacitor are under development, while in Germany considerable development has gone into the strip-film type, using polystyrene as the dielectric material. A very thin film from 0.06 to 0.40 mil thick is employed in both types of construction. For the supported-film type, the film is deposited on a support, usually paper or Mylar, which has been metalized. After the deposition of the dielectric, the second electrode, usually a metalized film, is applied. Then, either one or two of these entire structures are wound into a capacitor. Some work has been done on the use of one sheet of aluminum foil as the support. First, the dielectric film and then the other electrode (metalized) would be applied to form the structure for winding into a capacitor.

In constructing the strip-film type, the film is first deposited on a support, usually paper, and then the entire surface except for a margin on one side is metalized. The capacitor is then wound out of two of the metalized-plastic sheets, which are stripped off the support during the winding operation.

Various plastic materials, such as polystyrene, cellulose acetate, and Teflon, can be used as the dielectric film. Since the dielectric is very thin, the capacitors have a high capacitance-to-volume ratio.

Thus these low-voltage capacitors are suitable for use with transistors where small size and high capacitance-to-volume ratio are advantageous for such applications as filtering, coupling, integrating, timing, and frequency determination.

SILICON DIOXIDE FILM CAPACITORS

There has been considerable development in using silicon monoxide as a capacitor dielectric. The silicon monoxide is evaporated slowly in a partial pressure of oxygen to form a film about 9 microns thick, predominantly of silicon dioxide. The Courter Products Division of the Model Engineering and Manufacturing Corporation, under Air Force sponsorship, has developed such a capacitor, using the silicon dioxide dielectric formed on a substratum of nickel-iron alloy and capable of 200°C operation. To form the second electrode or plate, an aluminum or nichrome evaporated film is placed upon the dielectric layer. Experimental capacitors, which were made using these techniques, had the following characteristics:

a. Insulation resistance: at 25°C, 1,000 ohm-farads; at 200°C, approximately 1 ohm-farad.

b. Temperature coefficient: below 120°C, less than 100 ppm/°C; above 120°C, increased rapidly to about 300 ppm/°C at 190°C.

c. Life test at 200°C: considerable change in capacitance for first 200 hr. While this change continued for the entire 1,000-hr test, it tended to decrease with time, and insulation resistance increased from 10^2 megohms to 10^5 megohms plus.

Film is susceptible to moisture, which causes large changes in capacitance. Therefore, the packaging, type of seal, etc., are important, and considerable development remains to be done.

MINIATURE METALIZED-PAPER CAPACITORS

Utilizing a silicone-impregnated 0.23-mil metalized paper (0.2-mil kraft paper metalized), the Aerovox Company, under Signal Corps sponsorship, has developed a small low-voltage capacitor for use with transistors. This capacitor has the following characteristics:

    a. Voltage rating: 50 volts

    b. Capacitance value: 0.1 to 4 μf

    c. Insulation resistance: at 25°C, 10,000 ohm-farads; at 85°C, 750 ohm-farads

    d. Capacitance change with temperature over the range -55 to 85°C: ± 2 per cent

    e. Maximum dissipation factor at 1,000 cycles: 0.008

These capacitors are about 50 per cent smaller than any equivalent capacitor now available.

SPUN THIN-FILM CAPACITORS

A process which has been developed experimentally in the United Kingdom for obtaining extremely thin metalized dielectric films to form capacitors is as follows. A glass surface is silver-mirrored (copper or aluminum may also be used) by one of the common metalizing processes, such as chemical reduction in aqueous solutions for silver, or thermal evaporation in vacuo for copper and aluminum. The dielectric is then applied to the metalized surface in the form of a solution by dipping, painting, or spinning. Spinning is preferred, since more uniform layers may be obtained in this way. In spinning techniques the glass plate is revolved in a horizontal plane and a solution of the dielectric poured in the center. Under the correct conditions the solution spreads itself in a uniform layer. The variables in the process are the strength of the solution, the viscosity, the temperature, and the spinning speed. The speed most often used is about 500 rpm. After spinning for a few minutes, during which the solvent evaporates, the layer is dried, by curing when necessary, and the composite layer of metal and dielectric is removed from the plate by floating it in a suitable liquid (usually water or alcohol) until the layer parts from the plate. After further drying the metalized film is ready for cutting and assembly.

The advantages of the process are that thin, uniform films of metalized dielectric can be obtained—for example, films of 0.0002 in. or less. In addition, if pinholes are present in the dielectric, the metalizing does not penetrate as it does when the metal film is applied to the dielectric.   These techniques may be used in the development of subminiature capacitors for use with transistors.

ANODIZED-TITANIUM CAPACITORS

Titanium metal readily forms a chemically inert oxide coating similar to that formed by aluminum, and it is possible that this film

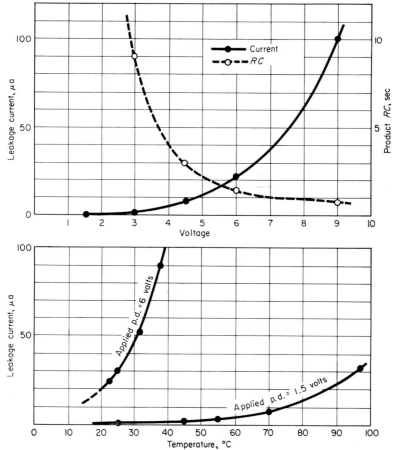

FIG. 11-5. Leakage-current characteristics for experimental anodized-titanium capacitors.

may possess similar insulating properties, modified by the extremely high dielectric constant of titanium dioxide.   Experimental capacitors have been made in the United Kingdom in the following way.   Commercial high-purity titanium is anodized by direct current in various baths of concentrated solution of potassium dichromate, potassium phosphate, or common salt—the last is fully as effective in forming a dielectric layer and is usually used. Oxidation is carried out by raising the voltage step by step from 1.5 to between 6 and 10 volts, each step lasting until the current falls to a stationary value before the next increase is applied.

The capacitance of a circular disk electrode of diameter 1.4 cm and thickness 2 mm is 6 μf, the effective capacitance over both surfaces

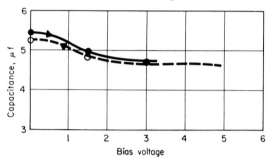

Fig. 11-6. Experimental titanium capacitor—capacitance as a function of bias.

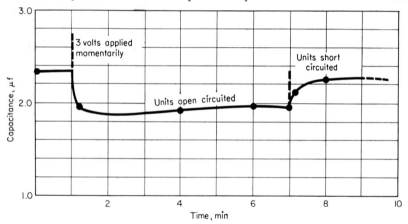

Fig. 11-7. Experimental titanium capacitor—memory effect.

being therefore 1.5 μf/cm². The working voltage is, however, only about 6 volts. The leakage-current characteristics are given in Fig. 11-5.

The effect of d-c bias on the capacitor is shown in Fig. 11-6, measured at 1.6 kc/sec. Since the measured capacitance is affected by a small d-c bias, the presence of charge should be detectable until it has leaked away completely and, in fact, the "memory" may persist for a very long time. Results obtained on a pair of titanium capacitors after initial charge are shown in Fig. 11-7.

CHAPTER 12

FAILURES WHICH MAY OCCUR
IN FIXED CAPACITORS

Fixed capacitors have some inherent deficiencies which in many cases can be related either to the design or poor production control during manufacture. Some of the more common deficiencies are as follows:

a. Seal failure

b. Reduced life due to residual contaminants

c. Reduced life due to silver migration

d. Noise generation

One of the most common deficiencies in the fixed capacitor is seal failure. Deterioration of the insulation resistance caused by the penetration of moisture through an incomplete seal is a well-known problem. For certain fixed molded and wax-dipped capacitors with paper, paper-plastic, and plastic dielectrics, varying humidity and temperature often cause moisture vapor to be sucked in along the connecting leads to the electrodes or through the material by molecular penetration. Since this vapor is trapped, it remains as moisture, which lowers the insulation resistance, increases the loss, and can result in failure of the capacitor.

For liquid-impregnated capacitors, a seal failure will allow the impregnant to leak out, usually resulting in a dielectric failure of the capacitor. When this type of capacitor is temperature-cycled, the seal must retain the impregnant as it expands and contracts. To provide an adequate moisture seal and prevent deterioration under arduous environmental conditions, a metal case with glass-to-metal compression end seals is necessary.

Reduced operating life of fixed paper, paper-plastic, and plastic dielectric capacitors will result from any contamination during production. Such things as contaminated impregnants, improper removal or handling of solder flux, and poor quality or contaminated dielectric(s) must all be avoided.

Molded-silver-mica capacitor failures occur because the conducting material builds up slowly with time across the dielectric or because silver migration over the surface of the mica is slow. Either of these conditions causes low insulation resistance followed by dielectric failure. This migration may be caused by corona effects from excessive alternating voltage, or it may be due to the presence of electrolytic impurities in combination with moisture inside the case.

Silvered-ceramic capacitors may suffer from similar growths or migrations of silver with time away from the silvered-electrode areas, and in some cases actual breakdown has followed the path of one of these growths through a flaw in the ceramic.

In electrolytic capacitors, difficulties due to corrosion caused by leakage of electrolyte through the case are now rare; they were due mainly to faulty assembly, and this problem has been overcome. High leakage currents are often caused by depolarization during storage, and old capacitors should be re-formed before use.

The electrolyte is usually the main cause of failure in aluminum-oxide electrolytic capacitors. At high temperatures, drying out of the electrolyte eventually produces a high power factor and loss of capacitance. At low temperatures the electrolyte freezes and causes a high power factor and low capacitance. Any corrosion effects are generally attributable to the electrolyte. Surges over the working voltage in this type of capacitor should be avoided in the design of equipment, by using, where necessary, indirectly heated rectifier tubes, delay switches, etc.; otherwise, "scintillation" will occur with consequent breakdown of the capacitor.

Leaks and the unwanted production of pulses have caused difficulties with high-voltage capacitors. Mechanical leaks can be avoided by proper sealing of the can, but the spontaneous pulsing and noise generation by capacitors is a fundamental problem which is discussed below.

RANDOM PULSE AND NOISE GENERATION IN CAPACITORS

"Pulsing" and random noise generated in capacitor units may have varied origins, and only a little is known about these, especially infrequent noise pulses which would not be noticed in the ordinary tests that capacitors have been subjected to in the past. Certain sources of noise have been well established during such tests, and it is possible that they may persist under other conditions in causing random pulses, and thus be important sources of error in counting circuits, although for normal purposes the component is completely satisfactory.

Five possible sources of noise or random pulses are considered here.

1. Internal Discharge. The best known of these normal sources is the incipient internal discharge which precedes normal breakdown.

This phenomenon is due to local ionization under high stress when there are any air occlusions or voids.   Under a-c excitation, this leads to a new discharge twice per voltage cycle: its onset is an indication that the component has been stressed beyond the safety limit.   Under direct current, a pulse of current may be followed by a quiescent period during which stress is built up again by leakage or by general relaxation of the dielectric until there is another flash.

It is quite feasible that such local pulses might be built up under d-c stresses considerably lower than those at which the noise becomes appreciable in normal tests, owing to the indefinite time available for such stresses to accumulate.   Noise caused in this way, however, may be expected to fall off as the stress is reduced, by connecting elements in series for a given voltage.

In badly designed or faultily assembled components, the existence of incomplete leakage paths, or of exposed points and edges at which corona and sparking can form, will obviously be bad sources of noise; these can be regarded as extreme, and removable, causes of incipient noise.

2. Scintillation, or Flutter.   This is a possible source of random noise in r-f components of silvered-mica or silvered-ceramic type.   This consists of random jumps in capacitance, and therefore of charge stored. It is attributed to incomplete adhesion of the silver to the material of the dielectric so that, when there is thermal expansion or mechanical shock, complete areas are jolted in or out of circuit.   This source of noise is not to be expected in large paper-dielectric capacitors, where foil electrodes are usual, except in capacitors having inserted tab contacts.   These often make poor contact when carrying small currents, and should not be used if freedom from noise is important.   It can, however, occur in mica and ceramic elements, although rarely in modern types.   Correct metalizing and, in some cases, electroplating, overcomes the fault.   From its nature, however, it cannot be assumed that a component will not become liable to the fault as a result of rough usage—probably any such tendency would be brought out by subjecting a sufficient number of specimens to stringent high- and low-temperature cycling.

3. Dielectric After-working.   At very low rates of occurrence, it is possible that the effects of dielectric after-working may produce noise pulses, and unfortunately this is most marked with good dielectrics, such as polystyrene and quartz.   The stressing of the whole material is not released at once, but regions are left in a stressed condition, which is relaxed by processes of a viscous nature but is taken up in the structure, thus restoring some of the original polarization.   A similar process may be expected to occur during charging, and the temporary release of such stresses may be represented by impulses of voltage. Liquid dielectrics might be used to reduce this effect.

4. Polymerization. It is known that in such plastic materials as polyethylene, polymerization is incomplete and will continue with time, so that eventually stresses may be built up which may possibly be released either as a slow variation, or as an incipient pulse.

5. Radiation. The action of light, or of radioactive particles and X rays, on all the "good" dielectrics—polyethylene, quartz, mica—produces ionization, and is therefore a potential source of noise, especially in components of small capacitance. It is of interest that a single crystal of anthracine, a pure hydrocarbon, is a standard form of β-ray counter—the scintillations being photoelectrically magnified. Hence, if components of these materials are exposed to radiations, some noise may be expected as a result, and there can be no protection from such noise except by adequate shielding and disposition of the apparatus.

In ferroelectrics there is the analogue of the Barkhausen effect. This is well established and produces large voltage pulses.

The above list of sources of noise may not be exhaustive, and mechanical movements of electrodes, etc., due to thermal expansion overcoming friction, may cause pulses to be generated, either by change of capacitance or contact resistance or by tribo-electric effects, but it is a summary of the principal causes of trouble which, from present limited knowledge, may be expected to cause noise. The list shows especially the causes of noise at low frequencies which would not have been detected in ordinary capacitor tests.

CHAPTER 13

FUTURE DEVELOPMENTS IN FIXED
CAPACITOR DESIGN

In general, the five primary aims of future development in capacitor design are:

1. Improvement in reliability
2. Reduction in size
3. Increasing the operating-temperature range
4. Development of capacitors suitable for operation in nuclear environments
5. Improving stability (with temperature, age, frequency, etc.)

These aims are necessitated by the ever-increasing complexity of electronic equipments, such as the introduction of the transistor, and the increasing as well as changing severity of operating conditions for military electronic equipment. Future developments are discussed under the headings of the various dielectrics (given in the same order as that of the previous chapters).

PAPER DIELECTRICS

Future development of paper-dielectric capacitors will be concerned largely with increased reliability, greater capacitance for a given volume, and improved stability, particularly at low temperatures. Considerable effort has gone into producing more reliable paper capacitors. Great care must be exercised during production to assure that all operations are reproduced uniformly and no contaminates are introduced. A line of highly reliable paper capacitors, covered by specification MIL-C-14157, for use in missiles and aircraft is now being produced. These capacitors, for the most part, incorporate one sheet of polyethylene terephthalate with two or more sheets of paper.

During the last few years, the impregnants used in paper capacitors have changed considerably. The higher insulation resistance requirements, as well as the higher operating temperatures for paper capacitors (K characteristic of specification MIL-C-25), have resulted in greater

191

and greater usage of the silicone fluids and the polyisobutenes as impregnants. All these impregnants exhibit the undesirable characteristics of increasing power factor and capacitance variation (usually due to change of dielectric constant) at $-55°C$. An ideal impregnant should have in combination as many of the following individual characteristics of existing impregnants as possible:

1. The high capacitance-to-volume ratio of castor oil
2. The nonflammability and long life afforded by the chemical stability of pentachlorodiphenyl (with stabilizer)
3. The high insulation resistance of polyisobutylene
4. The thermal stability of the silicon fluids
5. The linearity in the relationship of dielectric constant to temperature of certain mineral oils

The Naval Research Laboratory (see Bibliography) working toward the development of such an impregnant has developed the ester bis (ψ'—heptyl) 3—methylglutarate. A sample capacitor impregnated with this material had the characteristics shown in Table 13-1.

TABLE 13-1. CHARACTERISTICS OF BIS (ψ'—HEPTYL) 3—METHYLGLUTARATE
IMPREGNATED CAPACITOR

Capacitance, mfd			Power factor, %			Insulation resistance, ohm-farads		
$-55°C$	25°C	85°C	$-55°C$	25°C	85°C	$-55°C$	25°C	85°C
3.12	3.04	2.99	1.8	0.36	0.40	76×10^5	4,200	180

This ester-impregnated capacitor stored slightly more energy at 25°C than an equivalent capacitor impregnated with pentachlorodiphenyl. Both of these capacitors would store from 45 to 50 per cent more energy than an equivalent capacitor impregnated with mineral oil. However, at $-55°C$, the bis (ψ'—heptyl) 3—methylglutarate-impregnated capacitor will store 45 to 50 per cent more energy than either of the other two types. Figure 13-1 shows a comparison of power factor and capacitance of similar capacitors impregnated with pentachlorodiphenyl and bis (ψ'—heptyl) 3—methylglutarate.

Life tests for 250 hr at 130 per cent of rated voltage and 85°C show a capacitance change of 1.6 to 5.6 per cent, with no decrease in insulation resistance (ohm-farads). The impregnant is flame-resistant, thermally stable, of low viscosity, nonirritating to the skin, and it will not cause rubber or plastics to swell or become tacky. Study and development is continuing to produce paper-dielectric capacitors to operate under higher temperatures and higher voltages.

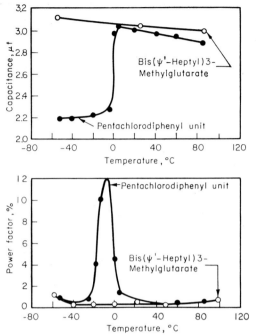

Fig. 13-1. Comparison of capacitance and power factor at a frequency of 60 cps for similar capacitors impregnated with bis (ψ—heptyl) 3—methylglutarate and pentachlorodiphenyl.

METALIZED-PAPER DIELECTRICS

Design changes have brought considerable improvement in the electrical parameters of metalized-paper capacitors. The use of one sheet of polyethylene terephthalate and lacquered tissue has greatly improved insulation resistance and life characteristics. Some of the latest types available now have a performance approaching that of the foil types.

Future development will be aimed toward improving characteristics of the existing types, as well as further development and improvement of the small low-voltage units for application in transistor circuitry.

Increased use of the metalized types is to be expected, and they may supplant the foil types in many applications.

MICA DIELECTRICS

New developments may be regarded under two headings:

a. Mica itself
b. Capacitor construction

Mica is a natural product, its structure is complex, and its properties are, therefore, somewhat fortuitous. Its characteristics are largely controlled by such factors as impurities and air inclusions, and it is necessary to select mica extremely carefully for use as a dielectric.

Present methods of selection produce mica which usually has a satisfactory power factor and dielectric strength, but needs improvement of temperature coefficient. Measurements on a batch of silvered-mica plates show that the temperature coefficients may vary considerably, although the plates appear essentially identical in other respects. To measure the temperature coefficient of each plate, before incorporating it in a capacitor, would normally involve a prohibitive amount of labor. It will be useful if the temperature coefficient could be related to some more simply measurable factor; or a rapid method of testing might be developed for comparing temperature coefficients.

Although mica has been known and used as a dielectric for many years, there still remains scope for considerable research into its properties. For example, at high temperatures (above 200°C), the power factor of a silvered-mica plate increases considerably and the insulation resistance falls. On cooling, the insulation resistance rapidly increases, but the power factor takes several hours to return to a low value. The reason is not known and, as high temperatures are reached during silvering and molding, the effect has caused manufacturing difficulties.

A further problem is the serious increase in power factor, at high frequencies, of some silvered-mica capacitors. This effect is being studied; it may be due to the nature of the silvering.

The greatest need for development, however, lies in the engineering involved in converting the dielectric into a usable capacitor. The materials and methods of construction are chosen primarily to produce a mechanically strong and hermetically sealed unit. Unfortunately the processes involved often react adversely on the properties of the capacitor, and the excellent properties of mica as a dielectric may be largely lost. If the volume of protecting material is compared to the volume of dielectric being protected, the existing standard types of mica capacitors appear to be very inefficient units. By suitable design, appreciable reduction of over-all size should be possible without affecting performance.

The reevaluation of the mica dielectric, as well as the development of an improved molding material and method of termination, has resulted in development and production of two lines of high-temperature capacitors. The Cornell-Dubilier Company is producing two axial-lead lines for operation at rated voltage at temperatures of 130 and 160°C, respectively.

These capacitors are available in the same case sizes and temperature coefficients as those specified in specification MIL-C-5 for the axial-lead types. The mica stack is not wax-impregnated.

The General Electric Company has developed a mica capacitor capable of operating at 500°C, with a life in excess of 1000 hr. For additional information on this capacitor see Chap. 11.

Development work is in progress on the use of mica papers for high-temperature capacitors. Capacitors have already been fabricated for operation in the 300 to 350°C temperature range with an insulation-resistance product in excess of 4 ohm-farads. Development work on the further application of mica and mica papers to high-temperature applications will continue.

CERAMIC DIELECTRICS

Development in the field of ceramic dielectrics has been considerable. The developments can be subdivided as follows:

a. Investigation and development of new materials

b. Development of new configurations and improvement of fabrication techniques

Considerable effort is being devoted to increasing the stability of high-dielectric-constant materials with temperature, frequency, voltage, and time. Development work on magnesium oxide, aluminum oxide, and boron nitride is in progress and will continue. These materials show promise of having RC products in excess of 5 ohm-farads at 500°C. Studies of several methods of fabrication indicate that the RC product is influenced by the pressure applied to the dielectric and to the interface of the dielectric and electrode.

Preliminary studies indicate that aluminum oxide, when under an intense radiation field, suffers no permanent damage although there is considerable increase in leakage current. Additional studies on these and other materials will continue.

A recently developed perovskite-type ceramic has a dielectric constant in excess of 1,000 over the temperature range of −60 to 250°C. At 25°C, the 1 kc/sec dissipation factor is 3 per cent, while at 250°C, it is 0.2 per cent. The resistivity at 250°C is approximately 7×10^{11} ohm-cm.

Additional work on this and similar material is in progress with the aim of developing a ceramic capacitor with electrical characteristics equivalent to a paper capacitor—a higher operating-temperature range and a capacitance-to-volume ratio of 2 to 100 $\mu f/in.^3$ for capacitance values from 5 to 100 μf.

The small low-voltage multiribbon electrode ceramic capacitor is in the early stages of development. A paper ribbon is continuously coated with a ceramic slurry to produce a continuous strand composed of thin ceramic layers, separated by paper with a surrounding ceramic jacket to provide the necessary strength. Burnout of the paper during firing leaves slots into which the electrode material can be introduced. The slots are alternately offset by appropriate positioning of the ribbon during the coating operation in order to permit lead attachment to alternate electrodes. Considerable development is required to make this a practical means for capacitor construction.

Future research is expected to provide (a) temperature-compensating capacitor materials with wider operating-temperature ranges and closer tolerances on the temperature coefficient envelope, (b) ceramic materials capable of operating with a dielectric stress in excess of 500 volts/mil (with less than 10 per cent variation of dielectric constant) for energy-storage capacitors.

GLASS DIELECTRICS

Future developments will deal primarily with improving the design of existing glass capacitors. Glass capacitors can be made very small, and they are of sound engineering construction, since the same material is used for the sealing (case) as for the dielectric. Another advantage is that glass, being a synthetic product, can be produced with a considerable degree of consistency, and the resulting capacitor has a high degree of stability and cyclicity. Glass postage-stamp capacitors being produced at the present time have higher temperature coefficients than those obtainable for equivalent mica capacitors. Development of other glasses may reduce this.

The vitreous-enamel capacitor which is now being produced has electrical characteristics similar to those of the glass-film type. The Corning Glass Works has developed a rolled-film glass capacitor. For additional information see Chap. 11.

In the field of glass for capacitors much effort is yet required on:

a. The development and use of thinner glass ribbon

b. The development of glasses capable of higher operating temperatures

c. The development of a glass with lower-temperature coefficient

PLASTIC DIELECTRICS

Considerable progress has taken place in this field in the last few years. At the present time polystyrene, polytetrafluoroethylene, cellulose acetate, and polyethylene terephthalate capacitors are in production. Development work is in progress on metalized polytetrafluoroethylene capacitors. Polystyrene, as well as other plastic films of a micron or less in thickness, has been developed by a new process in an endeavor to produce a small low-voltage high capacitance-to-volume ratio capacitor. The objective of this development is to develop a capacitor with the following characteristics:

a. Power factor: For capacitance values below 0.1 μf, it shall not exceed 0.0015 at 100 kc/sec; for capacitance values of 0.1 μf and above, it shall not exceed 0.005 at 1 kc/sec.

b. Insulation resistance at 25°C: For capacitance values below 0.1 μf, it shall be greater than 1×10^5; for capacitance values of 0.1 μf and above, it shall be greater than 1×10^4 ohm-farads.

c. Insulation resistance at 85°C: For capacitance values below 0.1 μf, it shall be greater than 1×10^4 megohms; for capacitance values of 0.1 μf and above, it shall be greater than 1×10^3 ohm-farads.

d. Capacitance to volume ratio: Minimum ratio of 15 μf/in.^{3} for cased units with capacitance values below 0.1 μf, and 50 μf/in.^{3} for capacitance values of 0.1 μf and above.

e. Length-to-width and length-to-thickness ratio: Shall not exceed a factor of three.

f. Capacitance value: Range of values from 0.015 μf to 4 μf.

g. Voltage rating: 50 volts d-c.

Further investigations will be directed toward:

a. Improvement of the existing films, $\frac{1}{4}$ mil and thicker

b. Improvement of the metalizing techniques for such films

c. Development and production of thin films, 0.1 to 2 microns

d. Development of the necessary techniques to satisfactorily apply such films (c, above) to a wound capacitor structure

e. Development of entirely new materials (films)

f. Development of improved impregnants

ELECTROLYTIC TYPES

There are two main lines of development:

a. To improve the aluminum-foil type

b. To make use of alternative materials

Research is confirming that the performance and reliability of the aluminum-foil type is determined primarily by the degree of purity of its various constituents. The future will be largely a matter of economics. Manufacture of extremely reliable aluminum-foil capacitors necessitates very close production control, and extreme care and cleanliness throughout.

The study of alternate materials in the past has led to the development of the tantalum capacitor. This type has a greater operating-temperature range, although at the present time it is restricted to a lower operating voltage per cell. Investigation of other materials for electrolytic application will continue. Niobium, for example, looks promising. This material would have a higher capacitance per unit square than tantalum. Future investigations will be directed toward:

a. Development of a low-voltage aluminum-foil capacitor with solid electrolyte (similar to the tantalum types)

b. Increasing the voltage rating of the solid-electrolyte tantalum capacitor

c. Increasing the voltage rating of the wet-electrolyte tantalum capacitor

d. Development of other electrolytes (both wet and solid)

e. Study of alternate electrode materials; for example, niobium, silicon carbide, etc.

PART 3

VARIABLE CAPACITORS

CHAPTER 14

GENERAL INFORMATION ON VARIABLE CAPACITORS

For general information on capacitance, dielectric constant, losses in dielectric materials, dielectric strength, effect of frequency on dielectric materials and capacitor assemblies, insulation resistance, leakage current, and impedance of variable capacitors, reference should be made to Chap. 2, since this information applies to both fixed and variable capacitors.

SPECIFICATIONS

For variable capacitors as for fixed capacitors, there are two main sets of specifications in use in the United States today: those prepared by the Department of Defense (the military series) for military electronic parts, and those prepared by the Electronic Industries Association (EIA) for commercial electronic parts.

Department of Defense Specifications

Specifications for variable capacitors published by the Department of Defense are as follows:

MIL-C-81: Capacitors, variable, ceramic-dielectric
MIL-C-92: Capacitors, variable, air-dielectric (trimmer capacitor)
MIL-C-14409: Capacitors, variable (piston-type, tubular trimmer)
MIL-C-26235(USAF): Capacitors, variable, air-dielectric tuning

Except the Air Force specifications, these Defense Department specifications are obtainable from the Armed Services Electro Standards Agency (ASESA), at Fort Monmouth, N.J. Air Force specifications are obtained from the Commanding Officer, Wright Patterson Air Force Base, Ohio.

EIA Specifications

Specifications published for the use of the electronics industry by the Electronic Industries Association are as follows:

REC-101: Capacitors, variable, air-dielectric Class B
REC-106A: Capacitors, variable, air-dielectric Class A

These specifications are obtainable from the Electronic Industries Association, Engineering Office, Room 650, 11 West 42d Street, New York 36, N.Y.

BRITISH SPECIFICATIONS

British specifications on variable capacitors may be of interest and are given below. The United Kingdom has two main sets of specifications in general use today: those prepared by the Radio Components Standardization Committee (RCSC) for use by the military (equivalent to the U.S. military (MIL) specifications) and those prepared by the Radio Industrial Council (RIC) for use by the commercial electronic industries (equivalent to our EIA specifications).

RCSC Specifications

RCL 141: List of standard capacitors, variable air-dielectric
RCS 141: Specification for capacitors, variable, precision air-dielectric
DEF 5143: Capacitors, variable, precision air-dielectric
These specifications are obtainable from the Radio Components Standardization Committee, 77/91 New Oxford Street, London, W.C.I. England.

RIC Specifications

RIC 141: Capacitors, variable, air-dielectric tuning
RIC 142: Capacitors, variable, preset, air-dielectric
RIC 143: Capacitors, variable, preset, mica-dielectric

These specifications are obtainable from the Radio Industrial Council, 59 Russell Square, London, W.C.I. England.

VARIABLE-CAPACITOR SYMBOLS

Symbols which are in general commercial and military use, listed in Standard MIL-STD-15A, Electrical and Electronic Symbols, are given in Fig. 14-1.

Adjustable or variable capacitor.

If it is desired especially to distinguish trimmer capacitors, the letter "T" should appear adjacent to the symbol.

Split-stator capacitor.

Capacitances of both parts increase simultaneously.

Phase shifter capacitor.

Variable capacitors with mechanical linkage of units.

Variable differential capacitor.

Capacitance of one part increases as the capacitance of the other part decreases.

Note: When it is necessary to identify the capacitor electrodes, the curved element shall represent the moving element in variable and adjustable capacitors.

FIG. 14-1. Variable-capacitor symbols.

MARKING

Variable capacitors in accordance with specifications MIL-C-81, MIL-C-92, and MIL-C-14409 require the part to be marked with the complete type designation and the manufacturer's name or symbol.

LAWS (FUNCTION) OF CAPACITANCE WITH SHAFT ROTATION

The change of capacitance with angular rotation of the driving shaft is determined by the shape of the fixed and moving vanes or plates.   There are four common relationships:

1. Linear capacitance (or SLC = straight-line capacitance)

2. Linear frequency or inverse square-law capacitance (SLF = straight-line frequency)

3. Linear wavelength or square-law capacitance (SLW = straight-line wavelength)

4. Logarithmic or exponential law of capacitance (Exp)

Other relationships are possible by special design, such as straight-line percentage frequency or straight-line percentage wavelength, which are used in receivers and measuring equipment.   W. H. F. Griffiths in 1926 worked out the design equations for several capacitance/shaft-angle laws as follows:

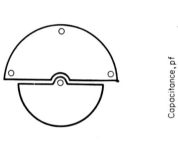
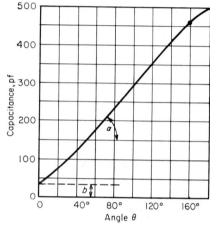

FIG. 14-2. Capacitance-rotation law for semicircular plate shape.

$$C_1 = a\theta + b$$

a = constant determining the slope $dC/d\theta$ (or tan α)
b = constant determining the position of intersection of the curve with C

Linear Capacitance

If semicircular plates are used, the change of capacitance with shaft rotation follows the straight-line law:

$$C = a\theta + b$$

where C = capacitance
θ = angular rotation, degrees
a = constant determining slope of line
b = constant determining starting position of line

Because of field distortions at the edges of the plate assemblies, the straight-line law holds good only over the center portion of the line, a few degrees at each end being nonlinear, as shown in Fig. 14-2.

Corrected Square Law

In order that the curve plotted between wavelength and degree scale-reading shall be a straight line, the capacitance value at any point on the scale must be proportional to the square of the scale-reading. A true "square-law" plate shape would, however, be of little use in practice because the residual capacitance of the capacitor would be neglected, and a corrected law must be obtained. This has been calculated by Griffiths, as shown in Fig. 14-3. This opens out the rate of increase of capacitance over the first quarter of the scale and closes up the scale over the last quarter.

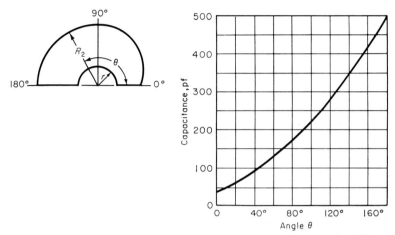

FIG. 14-3. Corrected square-law plate shape (straight-line wavelength).

$$C_2 = (a_2\theta + b_2)^2$$

$$\text{Plate area} = k\{(a_2\theta + b_2)^2 - \text{resid. cap.}\} + K\theta$$

$$R_2 = [114.6\{2ka_2(a_2\theta + b_2) + K\}]^{1/2}$$

$$a_2 = \frac{\sqrt{(\text{max cap.})} - \sqrt{(\text{resid. cap.})}}{180} \qquad b_2 = \sqrt{(\text{resid. cap.})}$$

$$k = \frac{\text{total plate area} - 180K}{\text{max cap.} - \text{resid. cap.}} \qquad K = \frac{r^2}{114.6}$$

Straight-line Frequency

In superheterodyne receivers, the beat note is governed by frequency difference. The tuning-capacitance scale should therefore be evenly divided in frequency, i.e., it should have a straight-line law of frequency variation with degree scale-reading. The plate shape for this is given in Fig. 14-4.

Logarithmic Law

A further useful law for capacitance variation is the exponential law. When using a variable capacitor having plates shaped to follow this law in an oscillatory circuit, the same *percentage* detuning is obtained for all equal-degree scale movements at all parts of the scale. The plate law and shape for constant percentage change of wavelength or frequency is shown in Fig. 14-5.

If any of these specially shaped plate capacitors are connected in series or in parallel with another capacitor, the law will, of course, be altered. Griffiths has given equations for all laws for any series capacitance. Examples of the effect of a 500-pf series capacitance when using capacitors of the following constants have been worked out from these equations—maximum capacity of variable capacitor is 500 pf,

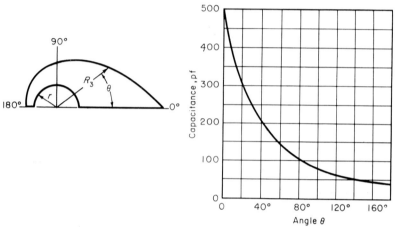

FIG. 14-4. Inverse square-law shape (straight-line frequency law).

$$C_3 = \frac{1}{(a_3\theta + b_3)^2}$$

$$\text{Plate area} = k\left\{\frac{1}{(a_3\theta + b_3)^2} - \text{resid. cap.}\right\} + K(180 - \theta)$$

$$R_3 = \left[114.6\left\{\frac{2ka_3}{(a_3\theta + b_3)^3} + K\right\}\right]^{\frac{1}{2}}$$

$$a_3 = \frac{1}{180}\left\{\frac{1}{\sqrt{(\text{resid. cap.})}} - b_3\right\} \qquad b_3 = \frac{1}{\sqrt{(\text{max cap.})}}$$

$$k = \frac{\text{total plate area} - 180K}{\text{max cap.} - \text{resid. cap.}} \qquad K = \frac{r^2}{114.6}$$

minimum capacitance of variable capacitor is 36 pf, total plate area is 20 cm², radius of inactive semicircular area of moving plate (r) is 1.2 cm. Table 14-1, by Griffiths, shows the new radii with degrees rotation compared with the old.

TABLE 14-1. EFFECT OF ADDING SERIES FIXED CAPACITANCE OF C pf

θ, degrees	Radius, cm							
	Linear law		Square law		Inverse square law		Exponential law	
	$C = \infty$	$C = 500$	$C = \infty$	$C = 500$	$C = \infty$	$C = 500$	$C = \infty$	$C = 500$
0	3.46	2.74	2.49	2.16	8.25	9.25	1.93	1.82
10		2.80			6.70	6.95		
20			2.76	2.35	5.62	5.57	2.13	1.96
30		2.92			4.80	4.65		
40			3.05	2.56			2.36	2.15
50		3.06						
60			3.24	2.78	3.32	3.15	2.64	2.38
70		3.22						
80								
90	3.46	3.40			2.56	2.42	3.16	2.85
100			3.66	3.37				
110		3.66						
120					2.10	2.02	3.85	3.57
130		3.88						
140			4.03	4.25				
150		4.18			1.83	1.78	4.71	4.74
160			4.20	4.85				
170		4.52						
180	3.46	4.73	4.38	5.66	1.65	1.62	5.80	7.16

In every case it is seen that the series capacitance C has the effect of reducing the plate radius at minimum capacitance and increasing it at maximum capacitance, i.e., a series capacitance always accentuates the shape—the smaller the series capacitance, the greater the accentuation.

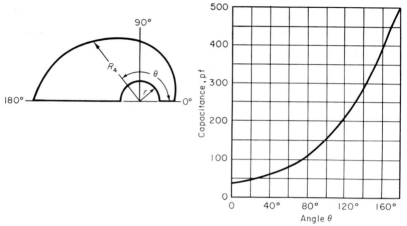

FIG. 14-5. Exponential-law plate shape (straight-line percentage wavelength or frequency).

$$C_4 = a_4 e^{b_4 \theta}$$
$$\text{Plate area} = k\{a_4 e^{b_4 \theta} - \text{resid. cap.}\} + K\theta$$
$$R_4 = [114.6\{ka_4 b_4 e^{b_4 \theta} + K\}]^{\frac{1}{2}}$$

$a_4 = \text{resid. cap.}$ $b_4 = \dfrac{\log (\text{max cap.}) - \log (\text{resid. cap.})}{78.174}$

$k = \dfrac{\text{total plate area} - 180K}{\text{max cap.} - \text{resid. cap.}}$ $K = \dfrac{r^2}{114.6}$

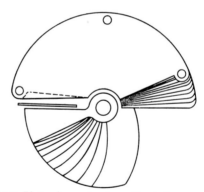

FIG. 14-6. Plate shapes for logarithmic-law capacitor.

Griffiths, in 1934, designed a capacitor in which the capacitance is varied by continually varying the shape, as well as the number of the fixed and moving vanes which are interleaved. This results in a more compact capacitor, with much greater stability in consequence, and the plate shapes for a capacitor with a logarithmic law are shown in Fig. 14-6.

CHAPTER 15

GENERAL-PURPOSE VARIABLE CAPACITORS

DESIGN AND CONSTRUCTION OF
MULTIGANG AIR-SPACED TYPES

The shape of the vane for the type of law desired is discussed in Chap. 14. Where ganged units are used, as in the oscillator and tuning sections of a superheterodyne receiver, it is necessary to "trim" the capacitances of the units so that they will vary in step. Any slight mismatches are balanced out by adjustment of the end vanes, which are radially slotted for this purpose. Typical end-vane shapes are shown in Fig. 15-1.

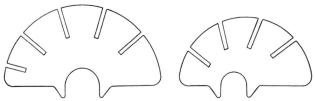

FIG. 15-1. Typical end-vane shapes in superheterodyne receivers.

Curves of capacitance change and values of $C^{-\frac{1}{2}}$ (inverse square-law capacitance) are usually plotted against spindle rotation θ. If the total minimum circuit capacitance is assumed to be 60 pf (including the capacitor minimum capacitance), a typical set of curves would be of the form shown in Fig. 15-2.

Two of the main requirements in a broadcast receiver type of variable capacitor are: (1) There must be frequency stability so that the tuning positions of the station names on the dial do not change. (2) The vanes must be rigidly fixed to prevent microphonics. The latter is particularly important for very high frequency and for f-m tuning. To achieve frequency stability, there must be no short-term or long-term change in vane spacing or in the dimensions of the frame. This is obtained by relieving the vanes of all internal stresses before assembly and by rigid mechanical construction of the frame. Sometimes, too, the oscillator section of a multiple capacitor is double-

209

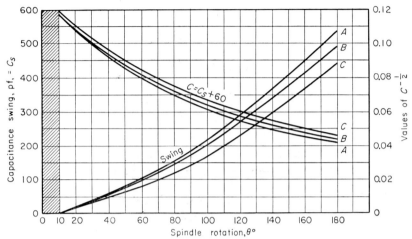

Fig. 15-2. Curves of capacitance swing vs. spindle rotation. (*Plessey Company, Ltd.*)

spaced. To prevent microphonics, there must be no mechanical resonance over the audio range of frequencies. For frequency modulation and very high frequency, the vanes are either thicker than for the normal broadcast frequencies or spaced more widely, and a greater emphasis is placed on the rigidity of frame and mountings.

The Construction of the Frame

There are four possible methods of frame construction for this type of capacitor:

1. The built-up type
2. The bent-frame type
3. The bent-frame type with tie bars
4. The die-cast type

1. The Built-up Type. This method of construction has the advantage of being flexible in that any number of sections may be added and it is also possible to accommodate alternative capacities, special sections for band spread, etc. Figure 15-3 gives an illustration of this type of capacitor.

The front and back plates are held together by rigid tie bars, which may be turned circular rods or flat pressings, or a combination of both. In some cases, the tie bars are of ceramic to provide insulation for the stators. The inherent rigidity of this construction provides reasonable frequency stability and freedom from microphonics. It does, however, require more space and is more costly to produce than the bent-frame type.

2. The Bent-frame Type. The bent-frame variable capacitor is designed primarily as a low-cost component. The frame is a one-piece pressing, in which the two end plates are integral with the base

Fig. 15-3. Built-up type of variable capacitor. (*Radio Condenser Company.*)

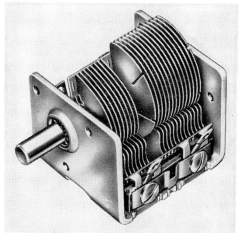

Fig. 15-4. Bent-frame type of variable capacitor. (*Radio Condenser Company.*)

plate which carries the stators. Figure 15-4 gives an illustration of this type.

Heat treatment is usually necessary to relieve stress in the bent-up portion of the frame, but even then the frame is inherently less stable than the built-up type, in which any stress imposed by the loading of the bearings is absorbed by the springiness of the frame.

3. The Bent-up Frame with Tie Bars. A one-piece pressed bent frame can be fitted with tie bars, but even then considerable internal stress may be induced in the frame. This type has been little used, and for the larger types it is probably more economical to produce the built-up frame type, which can be more flexible. Where a miniature capacitor of rigid construction is required, however, this type is now finding more favor.

4. The Die-cast Type. It is possible to produce the frame by any of the well-known die-casting methods, but while at first sight the die-cast type seems to offer many advantages, e.g., in rigidity, there are four main disadvantages of this form of construction:

a. Die-casting metals are not generally suitable for a bearing track for the spindle.

b. To obtain sufficient strength, the sections have to be thicker than those of a pressed-steel frame, with a consequent increase in bulk and weight.

c. It is essential to provide access to the vanes for inspection and adjustment, which prevents a simple box-casting being used. Access windows would be required in all faces, necessitating a complicated molding die.

d. A separate mold is necessary for each frame size.

In view of these disadvantages most manufacturers adopt the built-up tie-bar construction or the pressed-frame construction.

The Construction of Rotor and Stator

Vanes for capacitors of the broadcast type are generally punched from aluminum strip. The strip is rolled to a very close tolerance to achieve the required capacitance tolerance when assembled. After punching, heat treatment of the vanes is desirable in order that they shall be completely flat. The stator vanes are normally assembled into slots in the stator mounting brackets. A jig is used to maintain the position of the vanes accurately when their ends are swaged where they project through the brackets. Rotor vanes are produced similarly and are assembled in spindles grooved to fit them. The vanes may be a close fit in the grooves, subsequently secured by swaging, or they may be a forced fit in the grooves. In that case no further operation is required to secure them. At one edge of the vanes a slotted tip spacer is fitted to maintain the accurate spacing and to serve as a rotational stop. It is essential that the flatness and thickness of the vane material be as perfect as possible after the processing stages. The accuracy of the grooves and slots in the spindle, brackets, and tip spacer is also of extreme importance in order to achieve a high and repeatable standard of performance.

The Construction of the Spindle and Bearing

The spindle is generally made from brass which is grooved to accept the vanes. At the forward end it carries an annular track for the location of the balls, which run in a track embossed in the front plate of the capacitor frame. The embossing of the track causes work-hardening of the material, which provides satisfactory hard-wearing properties. At the rear end of the spindle a single ball is often used, located in a recess in the end of the spindle and rotating in a similar recess in the rear bearing bushing. This bushing must be adjustable either by a screw with a lock nut or by pressure-adjusting forced-fit bushing, so that the required operating torque may be obtained. If lower torques are required, the single ball may be replaced by a thrust bearing, using four or more balls in a pyramid construction. It is also possible, without increasing the size of the capacitor, to use the front ball race as an epicyclic reduction drive by fitting a smaller-diameter spindle, grooved to engage the inner face of the balls. Reduction ratios from 4 to 1 up to 7 to 1 can be achieved in this way.

The scale pointer is usually operated by a cord drive from a drum fitted to the spindle. A reduction drive on the capacitor permits a smaller cord drum to be used. As the slip inherent in epicyclic drives of the type just described would effect scale calibration, a gear reduction drive is used in this case, the gears being spring-loaded to avoid backlash.

Methods of Assembly

The method of assembly which is almost universal is based on fitting the spindle, to which the rotor vanes have already been assembled, into the frame and adjusting the bearings to give the required operating torque. The stators are then inserted and positioned accurately in relation to the rotor sections by the use of feeler gauges and other suitable jigs. The stator assembly, to which the ceramic insulators and separate caps have already been fitted, are then secured in position by soldering the caps to the frame. The stator is not therefore fixed in a predetermined position, since it is secured to achieve the correct alignment with the previously assembled stator. Contact forks are also fitted at this stage; they usually consist of simple pressings of brass or other spring material, which engage with surfaces provided by grooving the spindle.

In capacitors for very high frequency (e.g., f-m band), contact forks of improved performance are needed. The capacitor shown in Fig. 15-3 employs contact wipers of spring brass formed in a V shape and mounted on and soldered to the shield and end plates.

It will be seen from this description that great care is taken in the design and assembly of the broadcast type of variable capacitor, and, for its cost, the performance of a modern capacitor reaches a very high standard of accuracy and stability.

Mounting Methods

It is possible to mount a variable capacitor in two ways, fixed or floating. In the former method, the capacitor is rigidly bolted to the chassis and in the latter, rubber grommets or mounts are used to assist in damping out microphonics. Three-point mounting is often used. It is essential that no distortion or warping of the frame be caused by fixing, and resilient rubber mounts are again useful in preventing mounting distortion. For vhf tuning, however, the inductance of the ground return circuit must be minimized, and rigid mounting to the chassis is preferable in this case.

BAND-SPREAD VARIABLE CAPACITORS

With normal 500-pf tuning capacitors, short-wave signals are difficult to tune unless some method of slowing down the rate of change of capacitance is used. This is known as band spreading and may be effected either mechanically or electrically. Mechanical band-spreading systems often consist of a two-speed drive to the rotor. One speed operates the capacitor directly, and the other operates it through a reduction gearing, which may be of the order of 100 to 1. There is a practical limit to most mechanical arrangements due to backlash, and electrical methods are often used.

There are a number of ways in which electrical band spreading may be effected, but all work on the principle of connecting an additional tuning capacitor of small capacitance across the larger tuning capacitor. Some of the possible systems are shown in Fig. 15-5.

In Fig. 15-5a, the main capacitor may be of the order of 500 pf, while the band-spread capacitor may be 10 or 60 pf, depending on the receiver circuit. In Fig. 15-5b, two small band-spread capacitors are used, connected in series across the main tuning capacitor. One band-spread capacitor is mechanically ganged to the main capacitor as shown in the diagram. In this way the relative amount of band-spread tuning of the other band-spread capacitor can be made the same over the complete range of the main capacitor. This overcomes the disadvantage of Fig. 15-5a, where the band which can be covered by the band-spread capacitor at the high capacitance values of the main capacitor is only a fraction of the width at the lower values. Figure 15-5c shows a method of band spreading by connecting the band-spread capacitor across a small portion of the tuned circuit. This has the advantage that the tapping point on the coil can be adjusted for each coil so that constant band spread can be achieved for each range, but it has the disadvantage that image interference may be produced in a super-heterodyne circuit unless additional tuned circuits are used. Figure 15-5d illustrates a further method of equalizing the band spread over a wide range of frequencies. The two band-spread capacitors may be

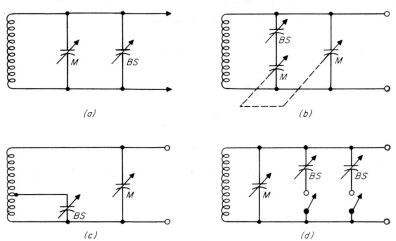

FIG. 15-5. Possible systems of electrical band spreading: M = main-tuning capacitor; BS = band-spread capacitor.

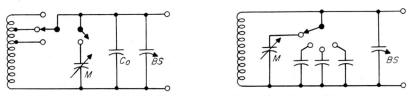

FIG. 15-6. Switched capacitor method of band spreading.

50 or 60 pf and 10 or 15 pf, respectively. The larger capacitor is switched in for the lower-frequency short-wave bands, and the smaller one for the higher frequencies. Care is needed in the layout of the switching arrangements to take care of stray capacitances, etc.

A commonly used circuit (Fig. 15-6) disconnects the main tuning capacitor on band-spread ranges, using only band-spread section, with switched fixed capacitors (a) or inductances (b) to select individual ranges. C_0 may also be varied by switching to adjust band spread as desired on various ranges.

The same result is achieved, with more accuracy, by the circuit of Fig. 15-7. In this the effective capacitance change of the band-spread capacitor is varied from 2 to 70 pf in steps of 2:1 by the six-position switch, with the particular values shown.

In some broadcast receivers, it is possible to provide compromise bands which can cover more than one short-wave channel. For

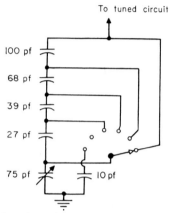

FIG. 15-7. Circuit giving six variations of effective band-spread capacitance.

FIG. 15-8. A typical two-gang a-m/f-m tuning capacitor. (*Radio Condenser Company.*)

instance, the 13- and 16-meter, 11- and 13-meter, or 41- and 49-meter channels may be used only occasionally, and a substantial improvement over normal tuning is effected by covering two channels in one tuning band with a 60-pf band-spread capacitor. To provide band spread on the 60-, 90-, and 120-meter channels the larger capacitance swing of 60 pf will also be necessary. In Fig. 15-8 a new design is shown of a ganged capacitor for receivers for the a-m/f-m band.

CHAPTER 16

PRECISION VARIABLE CAPACITORS

1. SINGLE UNITS

In 1936, H. A. Thomas set out in the order of relative importance the design requirements for a variable precision capacitor as follows:

Metal portions of condenser (stator, rotor, and frame)	a. Absence of mechanical constraint in the assembly of each part in the method of support
	b. Uniform temperature over whole of each portion
	c. Absence of residual stress
Insulating portions of condenser	d. Small value of the temperature coefficient of dielectric constant, and reduction of capacitance of solid dielectric to a minimum value
	e. High degree of mechanical stability
	f. Accuracy of location of the insulator supporting the stator assembly
	g. Small dielectric loss and high electrical strength (for transmitting condensers)
General thermal requirements applying to all component parts	h. Value of mass $\times$ specific heat/area to be same for each part
	i. Value of emissivity coefficient to be identical for each part

In later capacitors the desirability of low inductance for precision capacitors to raise the upper frequency range became apparent.

Modern capacitors fulfill these requirements as far as it is possible to fulfill them by careful design and the use of correct materials.

Typical performance figures for such a variable linear-capacitance-law silica capacitor, manufactured by H. W. Sullivan in the United Kingdom, are shown in Table 16-1.

The capacitors are aged before calibration and use fused silica as the vane-supporting material to ensure permanence of calibration. The power losses in such capacitors are almost negligible at all usable frequencies. In practice the losses of a capacitor are added to those of the inductance with which it is used in a tuned circuit. The losses in an inductance are usually given as effective resistance (at any given frequency). W. H. F. Griffiths has given an expression of the effective

217

TABLE 16-1. PERFORMANCE FIGURES FOR PRECISION VARIABLE CAPACITOR

Capacitance change, pf	Approximate capacitance range, pf	Capacitance permanence over a period of years, pf		Scale accuracy, pf
		At min cap.	At max cap.	
100	35–155	0.01	0.05	±0.005
1,500	90–1,600	0.03	0.1	±0.05

resistance of an air capacitor as

$$R = R_s + \frac{a}{\omega C^2} + \frac{1}{\beta \omega^2 C^2}$$

where the first term is the conductor resistance of the plate systems, the second term is the resistance equivalent to the inherent power loss of the fused silica (a being a constant proportional to the power loss factor of that material), and the third term is the series resistance

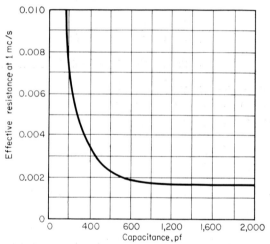

FIG. 16-1. Effective resistance of precision silica—insulated variable capacitor. (*H. W. Sullivan, Ltd., and W. H. F. Griffiths.*)

equivalent to the loss in the parallel resistance—the insulation resistance β. This loss is not necessarily the insulation resistance of the silica itself (which is not easily defined for a-c and not easily separated from the normal power loss of the material) but rather that of surface contamination and of the air between the plates of the capacitor.

The effective resistance of a modern silica-insulated variable air capacitor is given in Fig. 16-1. Curves showing the relationship between power factor and frequency for four typical values of capacitance are given in Fig. 16-2.

The minimum power factor occurs between 1,000 cps and 1,000 kc/sec, since the power factor of a silica capacitor is mainly a function of series resistance at high frequencies and a function of parallel resistance at low frequencies.

The scale reading of this type of capacitor can be better than one part in 20,000 by the use of a simple vernier, and the linearity of the law is so perfect that the interpolation inaccuracy is less than that due

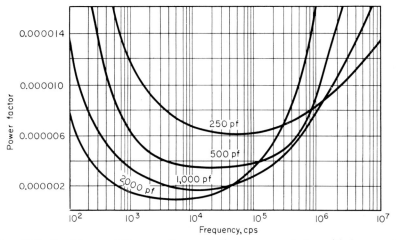

FIG. 16-2. Precision variable capacitor: variation of power factor with frequency. (*H. W. Sullivan, Ltd., and W. H. F. Griffiths.*)

to scale reading. The temperature coefficient can be guaranteed if necessary to be less than ten parts in 10^6 per 1°C, showing that this type of capacitor has reached an extraordinarily high performance.

The effect of humidity on precision variable capacitors has been investigated in the United Kingdom by L. H. Ford, and tests on the National Physics Laboratory substandard variable capacitor have shown that readings taken at 30 to 80 per cent rh nearly all fall within the estimated limits of error of ± 3 parts in 100,000 from the mean line through the points. The changes in capacitance of a well-designed variable capacitor in high humidity are therefore remarkably small. The construction of precision variable capacitors, made by the General Radio Company, is shown in Fig. 16-3.

Either low-loss steatite or quartz bars are used to insulate the stator assemblies from the cast-aluminum frame. The frame, spacers, stator rods, rotor shaft, and plates are all constructed of the same aluminum alloy, so that all parts will have the same temperature coefficient of linear expansion. To obtain a very accurate setting, a worm device gear is used. To avoid any eccentricity that could occur when a worm gear is fitted to a shaft, the gear and shaft are machined out of one piece of metal. The dial end of the worm gear is supported by a self-aligning ball bearing, while the other end is supported by an adjustable spring mounting. The rotor shaft is supported on each end by a

Fig. 16-3. Construction of the precision air-dielectric variable capacitor. (*General Radio Company.*)

sealed self-lubricating lightly stressed ball bearing. Electric connection to the rotor is made by means of a silver-alloy brush, making contact with a silver overlay drum to assure positive electric contact. Backlash does not exceed 0.01 per cent of full-scale value, but maximum accuracy is achieved by consistently approaching a setting from one direction. Capacitance ranges available are shown in Table 16-2.

Special models, including three-terminal designs, are available. These capacitors have a linear capacitance characteristic resulting from the semicircular rotor plate shape.

The maximum voltage rating on all types is 1,000 volts, peak. The dielectric losses are very low, since the figure of merit D_0C_0 (dissipation

TABLE 16-2. CAPACITANCE RANGES FOR PRECISION AIR-DIELECTRIC
VARIABLE CAPACITOR

Capacitance range, pf	Direct-reading* accuracy	Approximate capacity at zero scale setting, pf
100–1,150	±1 pf or ±0.1%	—
25–115	±0.2 pf or ±0.1%	—
0–1,050*	±1 pf or ±0.1%	1,140
0–105*	±0.2 pf or ±0.1%	135
0–10.5*	±0.05 pf or ±0.1%	35

* Direct reading is in capacitance removed from the capacitor and intended for
use in capacitance measurement by the direct-substitution method.

(*General Radio Company*)

factor times capacitance) when measured at 1 kc/sec is approximately
0.03×10^{-12} for quartz. Insulation resistance under standard conditions (25°C and 50 per cent rh) is greater than 10^{12} ohms. The
temperature coefficient of capacitance is approximately +0.002 per
cent/°C for small temperature changes. The backlash is less than

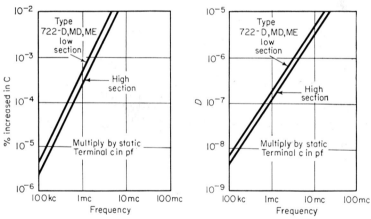

FIG. 16-4. Variation of effective capacitance and dissipation factor for precision
variable capacitor. (*General Radio Company.*)

one-half division corresponding to 0.01 per cent of full-scale value. If
the desired setting is always approached in the direction of increasing
scale reading, no error from this cause will result. Effective series
inductance is approximately 0.06 μh for all high-capacitance sections
and 0.10 μh for low-capacitance sections. Effective series resistance
at 1 Mc is approximately 0.02 ohm for high-capacitance sections and
0.03 ohm for low-capacitance sections. The series resistance varies

as the square root of the frequency and is negligible below 100 kc. Variation of capacitance with frequency is shown by Fig. 16-4.

2. MULTIGANG UNITS

Modern communications receivers for the military require ganged precision capacitors which are stable over long periods. They must be made in large quantities and must be small enough to be fitted into portable communications receivers.

In the United Kingdom, Mullard, Ltd., has developed for use in military applications a very stable precision capacitor capable of being ganged. This capacitor is rather small, being 2.672 in. in length and 3.0 in. in diameter.

Fig. 16-5. Precision variable capacitor construction for ganging. (*Mullard, Ltd.*)

For its construction a tubular framework is used to provide rigidity between the bearings and to ensure accurate bearing alignment. The spindle is supported on two high-precision ball bearings, built into the end plates, to reduce side and end play to a minimum. This design ensures that the capacitor may be reset accurately and that the necessary resistance to capacity change, due to side and end thrust on the spindle, is provided.

To reduce strain effects and shifts in capacity due to temperature changes, the capacitor is constructed throughout of carefully annealed brass, except that the ceramic insulating shaft and steel parts are cemented precisely together in jigs, using an epoxy cement. Jigs are used throughout each stage in assembly to ensure uniformity between units. Low h-f inductance is obtained by the use of a rhodium-flashed wiper contact, operating centrally on the rotor shaft and by

coaxial lead-out connections.   The temperature coefficient is controlled
by means of a bimetallic vane at one end of the rotor stack.   Mounting
the capacitor without strain on the chassis is essential, and the capacitor is mounted on a rigid die-cast frame by means of concentric spigots
on the end plates.   The construction of a typical capacitor is shown in
Fig. 16-5.   Four types are made, all having a nominally straight-line
frequency law:

Type F0: An extra-high-precision double-spaced single unit, with a
capacitance swing from 20 to 340 pf.   This capacitor may be reset to
within ±0.01 per cent.

Type F2: A high-precision two-gang capacitor having a capacitance
swing of 20 to 340 pf per section (resetting accuracy ±0.1 per cent).

Type G: A high-precision single unit with a common rotor and a
split stator, having the following capacitance swings:

Section A: 11 to 112 pf
Section B: 16 to 226 pf

and a resetting accuracy of ±0.01 per cent.

Type H0: As Type F0, but with a greater free shaft length.

These capacitors are normally matched in value to the following
accuracy:

Type F0: ±0.03 per cent in capacitance over 15° to 165°
Type F2: ±0.25 per cent in capacitance over 15° to 165°
Type G: ±0.1 per cent in capacitance over 15° to 165°

The last two can be made with each section matched to ±0.1 per
cent and ±0.03 per cent, respectively.   The shape of the vane in Type
F0 and F2 units is designed to give an SLF law when the minimum
capacitance is brought up to 86 pf by means of parallel capacitance.
Normally this parallel capacitance will consist of tube, coil, and circuit
stray capacitances, together with a small trimmer, which may be used
to equalize capacitances near minimum.   A temperature-compensating
vane to bring the over-all temperature coefficient to −15 ppm/°C
at minimum capacitance can be included if required.   For use in
ovened circuits without the temperature-compensating vane, the temperature coefficient is +20 ppm/°C.   Figure 16-6 shows the temperature coefficient with and without the compensating vane.

Type F0 capacitor conforms to a straight-line frequency law to
within ±0.1 per cent in capacitance for a rotation of 26 to 176°, provided the total minimum capacitance (including trimmer, strays, and
minimum capacitance of the variable) is brought up to 86 pf.

Type F2 capacitor gives an SLF law to within ±0.25 per cent (in frequency) when the minimum capacitance is similarly brought up to 86 pf. Table 16-3 gives the incremental capacitances for Type H0 and Type F0 capacitors.

The table gives the approximate capacitance law of the instruments as experimentally determined. These figures apply with the cover in

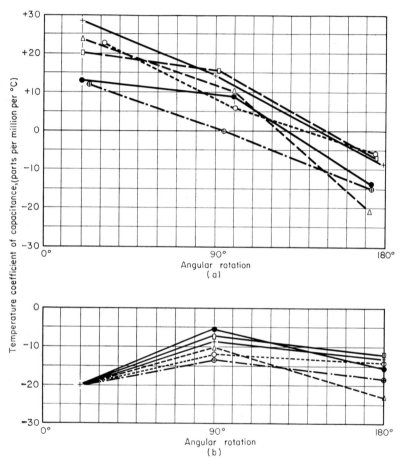

Fig. 16-6. Temperature coefficient of six Type F0 capacitors: (a) without compensating vanes; (b) with compensating vanes.

position. The capacitors are matched so as to yield 2:1 frequency-coverage with SLF law between 26 and 176°. The capacitance at 0° = 19.00 ± 1.00 pf.

Type G capacitor is not normally intended to be ganged with the F0 and F2 types. The vane shape being similar, however, it is pos-

TABLE 16-3. INCREMENTAL CAPACITANCES FOR TYPES F0 AND
HO CAPACITORS WITH MODIFIED LAW

Angle, °	Capacitance, pf	Angle, °	Capacitance, pf
0	0	80	59.09
5	0.36	90	71.61
10	2.45	100	85.92
15	5.09	110	102.25
20	7.94	120	121.02
25	10.98	130	142.72
26	11.61	140	168.00
30	14.26	150	197.63
40	21.41	160	232.76
50	29.31	170	275.01
60	38.11	175	299.35
70	47.98	176	304.44

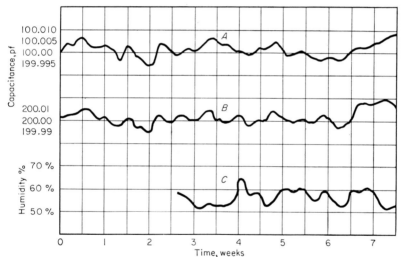

FIG. 16-7. Long-term stability of Type F0 capacitor: (A) capacitance measured at
100-pf setting; (B) capacitance measured at 200-pf setting; (C) humidity measured
between 20 and 21°C.

sible to provide an SLF law close to that attainable with Type F0
capacitor by the use of parallel capacitance.

The long-term stability of the F0 capacitor is shown in Fig. 16-7.
The variation in capacitance appears to be related to changes in the
relative humidity, and therefore if the highest possible constancy is

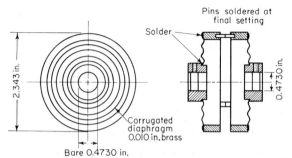

FIG. 16-8. Flexible coupler for ganged precision variable capacitor.   (*Mullard, Ltd.*)

required, the equipment must be humidity-controlled.   It is also necessary for the rotor to be at the same r-f potential as the case, and the F0 capacitor is normally supplied with a metal shaft so that the rotor is not insulated from the case.

When ganging these capacitors, a flexible coupler is necessary.   A special coupler has been designed to avoid mechanical "creep"; it is shown in Fig. 16-8.

CHAPTER 17

TRANSMITTER VARIABLE CAPACITORS

While this field is somewhat specialized because transmitter capacitors are usually designed for specific transmitters, particularly where high powers are involved, there are some general design points which are of interest. The basic operation of a transmitter capacitor is similar to that of the small receiver types, but transmitter capacitors are designed to operate at high voltages, high powers, and high frequencies. In a transmitter, the voltage applied across the capacitor may vary from direct current through the low-frequency range to steady continuous wave (CW) or modulated CW. There may also be d-c with super-imposed CW or modulated CW. The frequency may vary from a few tens of cycles per second up to about 100 Mc/sec or more, when special construction of the capacitor is necessary. Powers may vary from those of the smallest amateur transmitter to those of the largest broadcasting transmitter of several hundreds of kilowatts.

The main problems are those of spark-over, necessitating adequate spacing of the vanes, consistent with reasonable size, and losses at high frequencies due to the insulation used between rotor and stator. It is possible for appreciable heating of insulation to occur at radio frequencies owing to dielectric losses in the capacitor insulating material.

There are four main types of transmitter capacitor:

Air-spaced types
Oil-filled types
Pressurized and gas-filled types
Vacuum variable types

AIR-SPACED TYPES

For voltages up to about 3,000 volts at normal temperatures and pressures, it is possible to obtain standard transmitter capacitors from most variable-capacitor manufacturers. They are usually of similar general construction to those common in radio receivers, using aluminum or bronze vanes which are here, however, more widely spaced and have rounded polished edges. Ceramic insulation is used between fixed and moving vanes. Square-law capacitors up to 500 pf and straight-line capacitors up to 1,000 pf are available. The construction of a typical transmitter capacitor is shown in Fig. 17-1.

Fig. 17-1. Construction of typical transmitter variable capacitor. (*Hammarlund Manufacturing Company, Inc.*)

The design of the shapes of vane for a particular law have been previously given, p. 203.

The characteristics which may be expected from well-constructed air-spaced transmitter capacitors are approximately as follows:

Capacitor tolerance................. .... +10 per cent
Accuracy of adjustment.................... 0.1 per cent
Temperature coefficient of capacitance........ 0 0001 per pf per °C
Contact resistance......................... 5 to 15 milliohms
Insulation resistance...................... minimum 1,000 megohms between
                                             rotor and stator

Figure 17-2 shows the plate spacing for typical capacitors at frequencies up to 20 Mc/sec.

The breakdown of air as a dielectric, at high frequencies and high voltages, has been the subject of much study which has contributed to the design of large transmitter capacitors. Most of the work has been done using sphere gaps, or needlepoint electrodes. Breakdown actually commences at the first sign of corona before actual spark-over takes place. Corona may occur at a considerably lower voltage than spark-over, and this is the result of local ionization of the air, which becomes a conductor at a given critical voltage gradient. In all high-voltage capacitors it is necessary to avoid the presence of dust and fiber particles as these particles are drawn between the plates by electrostatic attraction and form partial conducting bridges which can cause premature breakdown. Breakdown voltage of a capacitor is inversely proportional to frequency, and at any given spacing the voltage to cause spark-over decreases as the frequency increases.

Figure 17-3 shows a typical curve of electrode spacing (using spherical gaps), against breakdown voltage, at different frequencies.

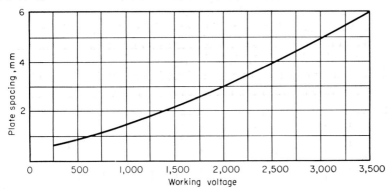

Working voltage

FIG. 17-2. Approximate relationship between plate spacing and voltage at frequencies up to 20 Mc/sec.

In 1932, F. Miseré showed that the reduction in breakdown voltage across insulated spheres 995 kc/sec was about 15 per cent of the corresponding voltage at 50 cps. In 1939, E. W. Seward showed a reduction of 6 to 7 per cent at 700 kc/sec from the 50 cps breakdown voltage, using both 0.5 and 1.4-cm spheres with one sphere grounded.

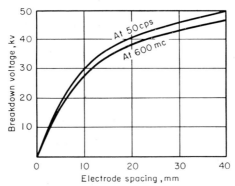

Electrode spacing, mm

FIG. 17-3. Breakdown with 14-mm spherical electrodes.   (*After Seward.*)

In 1940, P. A. Ekstrand, using ultraviolet irradiation to obtain consistent results, found that at radio frequencies up to 1.8 Mc/sec the spark-over voltage was 17 to 20 per cent below the 60 cps voltage. By plotting curves of spark-over with various-shaped electrodes he found that, with small spacings, the curves flattened out when the spacing was about twice the diameter of the electrode, which indicated that r-f capacitors should be built with thick plates. With well-rounded plates the thickness should be from one-half to one-third of the capacitor air-gap spacing. He also made measurements on the spark-over voltage of various capacitors at frequencies between 60 and 1,500 kc/sec. Here he found that capacitors with thick plates and small spacings held the voltage quite well, while a capacitor rated at 20 kv with thin plates and large spacings sparked over at 25 kv at 60 cps, 14.28 kv at 700 cps, and 11.7 kv at 1.57 Mc/sec.

Transmitter capacitors used in aircraft communication equipment must take into account the reduced breakdown voltages which occur

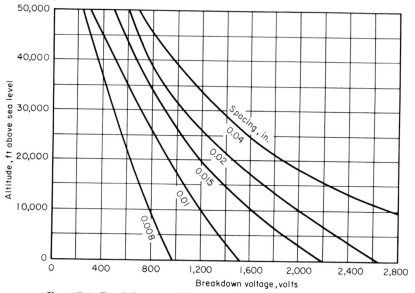

FIG. 17-4. Breakdown at different altitudes and plate spacings.

at high altitudes, and the plate spacings must therefore be still further increased. Vacuum variable capacitors may be used where available.

The approximate breakdown voltage at different altitudes for various capacitor spacings is shown in Fig. 17-4.

In the United Kingdom, measurements have been carried out at the Royal Aircraft Establishment by Fougere at 227 and 378 Mc/sec using transmission-line methods, and results at 226.8 Mc/sec for gap widths from 0.025 up to 0.15 in. are given in Fig. 17-5.

It has been shown by A. A. Varela and others that the breakdown strength of air appears to increase when a small d-c stress is added to the ultra-high frequency. Measurements by Fougere have shown that

for frequencies of 227 and 378 Mc/sec a superimposed d-c voltage of
125 volts d-c increases the strength by a factor of two for a gap width
of 0.08 in.   Some typical breakdown curves by RAE showing the

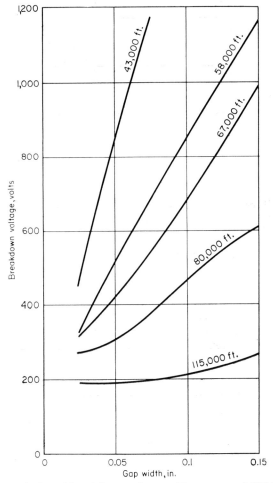

FIG. 17-5. Variation of breakdown voltage with pressure at 226.8 Mc/sec.

effect of d-c bias on breakdown voltage at 378.5 Mc/sec are given in
Fig. 17-6.

OIL-FILLED TYPES

The dielectric constant of liquids ranges from about 1.5 to 100, and
with nonpolar liquids whose dielectric constant is substantially independent of frequency it ranges from about 2 to 5.   It is possible,

therefore, to obtain an increased dielectric constant, and therefore increased capacitance, by filling the transmitter capacitor with a non-polar liquid, such as mineral oil.   The dielectric constant of this oil is 2.2.   Purified castor oil, which has a dielectric constant of 4.7, can be

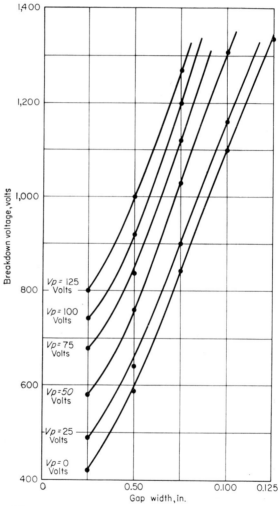

Fig. 17-6. Breakdown curves at 378.5 Mc/sec and 80-mm Hg pressure (equivalent altitude 52,000 ft).

used for capacitors with a corresponding gain in capacitance.   The breakdown of mineral oil is about 30,000 to 40,000 volts rms in a standard 0.1-in. gap between 1-in.-diameter disks.   Chlorinated hydro-carbon oils with a dielectric constant of 4.5 can also be used.   It is essential to ensure that oils used for this purpose are carefully purified, "clean," and free from moisture, and many filtering methods have been devised for dehumidifying and purifying oils.

The thermal conductivity of mineral oil is 0.0003 cal/sec/cm/°C, so that good heat conduction to the walls of the capacitor case is obtained.

The sealing of variable capacitors sometimes presents some difficulty, but oil-sealed glands and rubber ring seals in series are used for the rotary vane drive. The capacitor assembly is fitted in a soldered can, leads being taken through soldered ceramic or alumina seals. Where the volume is large, the expansion coefficients must be watched, as the expansion of oil with heat is comparatively large. The coefficient of thermal expansion of mineral oil is 0.0063/°C, and bellows expansion reservoirs must, therefore, be used where necessary.

Silicone oils have a wider range of operational temperature and a much higher flash point, but also a large expansion rate. The dielectric constant of an oil such as D.C.200 is 2.83, power factor is 0.002 at 1 Mc/sec, and the dielectric strength is 250 to 350 volts/mil.

PRESSURIZED AND GAS-FILLED TYPES

The size of high-power variable capacitors can be reduced by using compressed gas such as nitrogen for the dielectric. Compressed air,

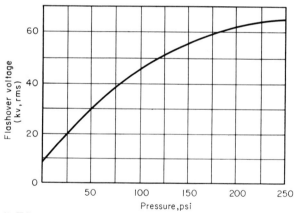

FIG. 17-7. Effect of pressure on breakdown of a typical 2,000-kva capacitor.

although not now used because the extra oxygen readily supports combustion, increases the voltage which the capacitor will withstand without changing the capacitance. The effect of increased pressure on the flashover gives the curve in Fig. 17-7.

Compressed nitrogen capacitors have the advantages of safety, low loss, and permanent characteristics. They are manufactured in capacitances up to 20,000 pf and with flashovers up to 60 kv rms. Pressures used for nitrogen are up to 2,000 psi.

Sulfur hexafluoride, a stable and inert gas, is also used as a dielectric. It has an electrical strength at 30 psi equal to that of nitrogen at 200 psi. Where low inductance is required, it is usual to design coaxial electrodes similar in pattern to the multiple-plate concentric trimmer described on page 240, although, of course, larger. The interleaving circular metal vanes are usually fitted into a vitrified ceramic cylinder, with end caps of Invar and pressurized to about 35 psi. The inductance of this type of variable capacitor is sufficiently low to enable it to be used as a harmonic bypass element in the harmonic rejector circuits of a transmitter.

VACUUM VARIABLE TYPES

Vacuum variable capacitors are basically similar in construction to the vacuum fixed capacitors, but contain a bellows system to allow

FIG. 17-8. Typical vacuum variable capacitor. (*Jennings Radio Manufacturing Corporation.*)

movement of one set of electrodes. They are made in capacitance ranges such as 12 to 1,000 pf and, by using series and parallel combinations, the capacitances, working voltages, and currents can be appropriately doubled or quadrupled. A typical vacuum variable capacitor is shown in Fig. 17-8.

CHAPTER 18

TRIMMER CAPACITORS

AIR-DIELECTRIC ROTARY TYPES

There are two uses to which trimmer capacitors can be put: for trimming, in which the capacitor is set to a given value and left; and for tuning, in which continuous adjustment is necessary.

Air-dielectric trimmer capacitors are of two main types—the moving-vane and the concentric-cylinder capacitor. Moving-vane capacitors are also constructed in differential and split-stator types.

All air-spaced rotary capacitors are basically similar and follow the general design shown in Fig. 18-1. They are often fitted with a locking

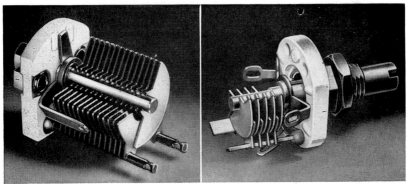

FIG. 18-1. Typical air-dielectric trimmer capacitors. (*Hammarlund Manufacturing Company, Inc.*)

device on the shaft, such as a tapered split bearing with a suitable nut for locking. Some shafts are slotted for preset use, while others are plain, for use with a knob. The common method for mounting is tapped brass studs fitted to a silicone-treated steatite base. An alternate method is for the bearing to be threaded for panel mounting. The law of capacitance with rotation of an air-dielectric trimmer is usually straight-line capacitance. The spacing between vanes is of the order of 0.01 in. for use at low voltages and up to 0.05 in. for use at high voltages. Silver-plated brass vanes are usual for r-f use. The

235

vanes should be soldered, not staked to the rotor shaft, with stator supports to assure good electrical contacts when used at high frequency. The capacitance swings vary from about 2 to 3 pf for low capacitance values to about 150 pf for high values. The over-all tolerance in capacitance is about ±10 per cent. Typical capacitance ranges available vary from 3.5 to 10 pf as one of the smallest, and from 9 to 143 pf as one of the largest. Characteristics are: operating torques from 5 to 15 in.-lb at 25°C; Qs of 250 minimum at a minimum capacitance setting for capacitors with ceramic bases; operating voltages of 500 to 600 volts for the 0.01-to-0.02-in.-spaced vanes and 1,000 to 1,500 volts for the 0.03-to-0.05-in.-spaced vanes. The insulation resistance at 25°C on the ceramic-base type varies from about 10,000 to over 100,000 megohms, depending upon the construction and the materials used. These capacitors are covered by military specification MIL-C-92.

Miniature Air-spaced Trimmer Capacitor

Recently a very small capacitor was developed for use by either tab-mounting on dip-soldered printed wiring boards or screw-mounting on a conventional chassis. This capacitor is illustrated in Fig. 18-2.

Fig. 18-2. Miniature air-spaced trimmer capacitor. (*Radio Condenser Company.*)

The rotor and stator plates are silver-plated brass, soldered to the rotor shaft and stator supports. The rotor contact is silver-plated beryllium copper, and the torque varies from 1.5 to 6 in.-oz. Other characteristics are shown in Table 18-1.

The rotor-to-stator insulation resistance is 100,000 megohms when measured at a potential of 500 volts d-c at 25°C. These capacitors have been designed to meet the environmental factors of vibra-

TABLE 18-1. CHARACTERISTICS OF MINIATURE AIR-SPACED
TRIMMER CAPACITOR

Nominal min cap., pf	Effective max cap., pf	Nominal air gap	Number of plates	Dielectric strength*	Temperature coefficient, ppm/°C†
1.2	5	0.014	9	400	50
1.2	10	0.008	11	300	50
1.5	15	0.008	15	300	50

* Volts 60 cps rms.
† For 50°C rise.

tion, shock, humidity, thermal shock, and salt spray for military applications.

Split-stator Air-spaced Types

Split-stator trimmers are used where accurate adjustment of push-pull or symmetrically built tuned r-f circuits have to be made with

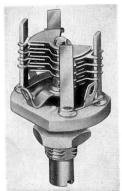

FIG. 18-3. Split stator (butterfly type) trimmer capacitor. (*Hammarlund Manufacturing Company, Inc.*)

very small changes in capacitance. They are constructed so that, as the rotor is turned, the capacitance of each set of vanes increases or decreases to the same degree. Two methods of construction are used: one in which two separate sets of stator vanes are engaged by two sets of rotor vanes on the same shaft, and the other in which butterfly-shaped vanes are used, meshing into separate sets of stator vanes. Owing to the compactness of construction, the latter type is more widely used. This is shown in Fig. 18-3.

Differential Air-dielectric Trimmer Capacitors

These capacitors can be used for r-f variable capacitative voltage, dividing where accurate adjustments have to be made with very small changes in capacitance. As the rotor is turned, the capacitance of one

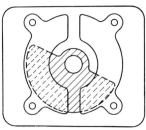

FIG. 18-4. Construction of typical differential trimmer capacitor.

set of vanes increases as that of the other decreases.   The construction of a typical capacitor is shown in Fig. 18-4.

Temperature-compensating Air-dielectric Trimmer Capacitors

While ceramic temperature-compensating capacitors have been made for some years in Europe (e.g., Hescho in Germany) operating on the principle of the rotating vane varying the relative amounts of two kinds of dielectric in the circuit, an air-dielectric compensating trimmer has been designed in the United Kingdom by Oxley Developments

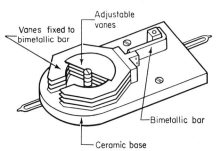

FIG. 18-5. Construction of air-dielectric temperature-compensating capacitor. (*Oxley Developments Company, Ltd.*)

Company, Ltd.   This capacitor is intended to be connected across an oscillatory circuit to stabilize the frequency between the time the equipment is switched on until the maximum operating temperature is reached.   The construction is similar to that of a standard air-dielectric trimmer capacitor having five half-circular vanes which can be rotated in a set of four horseshoe vanes, as shown in Fig. 18-5.

The four horseshoe vanes are mounted on a bimetallic bar, which moves them laterally as the temperature changes, causing a capacitance change whose magnitude depends on the initial setting of the half-circular vanes.   The normal capacitance is approximately 6.5 pf, and it remains substantially constant at a given mean temperature as the rotor vanes are rotated.   The temperature coefficient can be set from $-2{,}000$ to $+2{,}000$ ppm/°C, depending on the position of the rotor vanes, so that there can be a capacitance change as large as 2.5 pf from the nominal, at a normal temperature, over a temperature range of -40 to $+100$°C.   The variation of capacitance with temperature over this range is shown in Fig. 18-6.

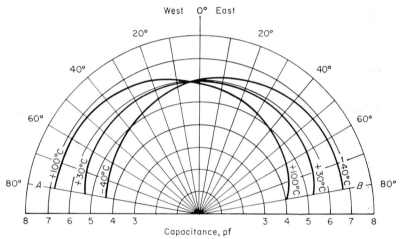

FIG. 18-6. Temperature-compensating trimmer (6-pf unit) variation of capacitance with temperature at: (A) 2,600 parts in 10^6 per °C, $\Delta C = 2.1$ pf in 140°C; (B) 3,500 parts in 10^6 per °C, $\Delta C = 2.8$ pf in 140°C.   (*Oxley Developments Company, Ltd.*)

It will be seen that at $+100$°C the capacitance is greater than at $+30$°C by approximately 1.3 pf at one end of the vane's travel and smaller by approximately 1.2 pf at the other.   There is no change in capacity between -40 and $+100$°C at a setting of the vanes of 4°W.

Where many measurements have to be made it becomes inconvenient to express the results as absolute capacitance change and Oxley Developments Company, Ltd. uses an expression of "pf per 10°C" instead of the more usual "parts per million per degree centigrade," which lines up readily with other circuit data.   A nomogram by the makers showing the relationship between capacitance, temperature coefficient, and change of capacitance in a capacitor having a temperature change of 140°C is given in Fig. 18-7.

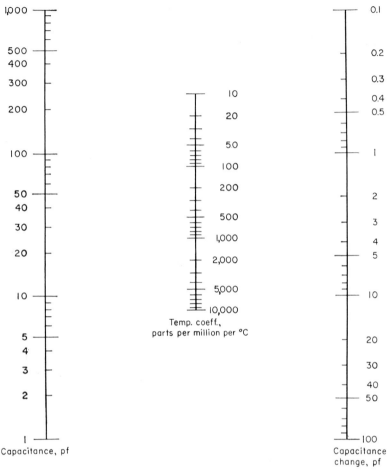

FIG. 18-7. Nomograph showing relationship between capacitance, temperature coefficient, and change of capacitance over 140°C. (*Oxley Developments Company, Ltd.*)

Concentric Types

This type of trimmer capacitor is manufactured in the United Kingdom. These trimmers consist of concentric cylinders made of extruded metal with the rotor moving on a ceramic pillar. They are low loss and are designed for use in high-Q circuits. Their lightness and small size make them suitable for use within a coil can or for suspension in the wiring. Two types have been designed, one with a range from 2.0 to 8.0 pf, the other from 3.0 to 30.0 pf. The power factor is 0.007 at 1 Mc/sec, measured with the capacitor set at maximum capacitance. The working voltage is 75 volts, and the component is remarkably free from the effects of vibration. It can be locked with a suitable wax. A diagram of the capacitor is given in Fig. 18-8.

The main advantage of this type of trimmer is that, being a screw-thread device, it is capable of very fine resolution. Concentric designs, in addition to resisting the effects of vibration, have the advantage that mechanical shocks have little effect on the adjustment, provided eccentricity can be limited.

A modification of this design has been made for military use, in which a polytetrafluoroethylene friction bushing is introduced. The

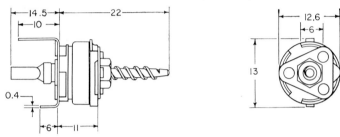

FIG. 18-8. Concentric type of trimmer capacitor—dimensions in millimeters. (*Mullard, Ltd.*)

friction created by this material is sufficient to hold the setting under severe shock and yet provides an extremely smooth adjustment.

MICA COMPRESSION TYPES

These capacitors are used primarily for coil trimming, and while widely used for commercial applications, such as radio and television, are not recommended for military applications. Shock, vibration, and moisture all influence the characteristics of this type. The simple design consists of a single mica plate or series of mica plates interleaved with spring brass or phosphor-bronze (tin-plated), which are compressed by screw adjustment to vary the capacitance. There are two common types:

	Capacitance, pf	
Type	Minimum	Maximum
1. Small two-plate types.........	7.5–50	80–240
2. Twin multiplate types.........	15–1,400	130–3,065

1. The small double-plate or postage-stamp types are used in coil packs for waveband trimming. The pitch of the screw adjustment is usually very fine, of the order of 60 turns per inch, and most trimmers of

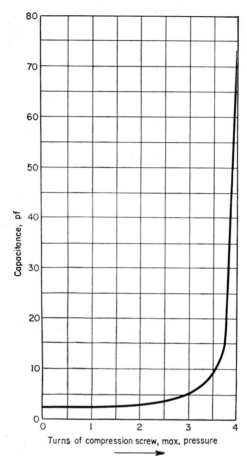

FIG. 18-9. Capacitance-turns relationship for single-plate postage-stamp-type mica-dielectric trimmer capacitor.

this type will withstand 500 volts d-c across the plates. The variation of capacitance with rotation of the screw adjustment is markedly nonlinear; a typical curve for a single-plate mica compression capacitor is shown in Fig. 18-9.

FIG. 18-10. Postage-stamp- or single-unit-type mica compression trimmer capacitor. (*S. S. Bird and Sons, Ltd.*)

The size of the single-plate types is approximately $1 \times \frac{1}{2} \times \frac{1}{2}$ in. overall. It is possible to manufacture these units in banks up to six for coil packs or fixed station tuning; a typical construction of a single unit is shown in Fig. 18-10,

2. The i-f trimmer capacitors are usually constructed as twin capacitors on a ceramic base and are used to trim primary and secondary coils of an i-f transformer. Typical capacitance ranges are from about 7.5 to 80 pf for the smallest, to about 1,400 to 3,065 pf for the largest.

CERAMIC-DIELECTRIC TRIMMER CAPACITORS

There are two main forms of construction, the rotary and the concentric types, which are described below.

Rotary Types

Ceramic-dielectric capacitors can be designed either to increase the capacitance ratio over air-spaced trimmers with negligible or zero temperature coefficient or, by using high-dielectric-constant ceramic with a

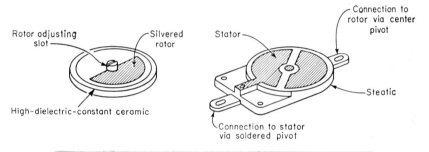

Rotor adjusting slot — Silvered rotor — Stator — Connection to rotor via center pivot

High-dielectric-constant ceramic

Steatic

Connection to stator via soldered pivot

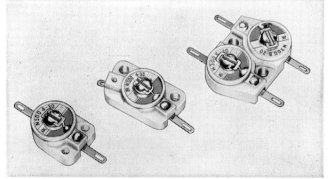

FIG. 18-11. Construction of rotary-type ceramic trimmer capacitors (single and double units). (*Erie Resistor Company.*)

suitably chosen negative temperature coefficient material, to allow compensation for a positive temperature coefficient coil in a tuned circuit. The basic construction of both temperature coefficient types is similar and is shown in Fig. 18-11.

The base of the capacitor is usually made of low-loss low-dielectric-constant steatite. The silver stator plate and balancing plate (to ensure smooth friction between rotor and stator) are fired on the ceramic by reducing from silver paste at about 500 to 600°C; the top rotatable plate is made of high-dielectric-constant material with a suitably chosen temperature coefficient, and a half-circular area silvered and soldered to the center pivot. The base of the pivot is riveted over a springy metal disk to form contact to the rotor and to allow rotation. The top surface of the base ceramic and the undersurface of the high-dielectric-constant ceramic are lapped flat to provide as intimate a contact as possible and to exclude air between the plates. On a good capacitor the grinding should be such that the plates will stick together like magnets when the retaining screws are removed. Even with this degree of grinding, there is still a layer of air mixed with lubricant, which has a much lower dielectric constant than the ceramic. This may cause slight instability over wide temperature changes by variation in the effective distance between the solid dielectric and the electrode. As capacitance is adjusted by varying the amount of overlap between the rotor and stator plates, the capacitance change per degree of rotation is constant, giving an SLC law. Capacitance ranges vary from 1.5 to 7 pf for the smallest to about 7 to 45 pf for the largest. These capacitors are covered by military specification MIL-C-81.

Piston or Cylindrical Types

Other types of ceramic-dielectric trimmers (including glass-dielectric) are the cylindrical or piston types with rotary-screw adjustment. The capacitance of a cylindrical capacitor is ideally given by:

$$C \text{ (pf)} = \frac{\kappa l}{4.14 \log_{10} (d_1/d_2)}$$

where κ = dielectric constant of dielectric
l = length of tubular element
d_1 = inside diameter of outer element
d_2 = outside diameter of inner element

This formula, however, neglects the air gap which is due to unavoidable manufacturing tolerances in the bore of the glass or ceramic tube and the diameter of the inner electrode (piston). This reduces the capacitance considerably and introduces an uncontrollable variation.

Small piston capacitors are used to balance out stray capacitance in such applications as tuners and i-f strips. The trimmer capacitor is essentially either a long metal screw or a piston attached to such a screw which forms one plate.   This plate moves up and down inside a ceramic or glass tube, which is silvered on the outside along half its length.   The cylindrical capacitor is reasonably linear.   Capacitance values available range from 1.5 to 3 pf for the smallest to 1 to 30 pf for the largest.   The small glass-piston trimmer capacitor is covered by military specification MIL-C-14409.   A typical capacitor is shown in Fig. 18-12.

In the United Kingdom a small sealed ceramic trimmer capacitor has been designed for military applications, which has a capacitance range of 1.5 to 12 pf.

The capacitor consists of an outer casing of ceramic, approximately $7/16$ in. diameter and $1/2$ in. long, fitted with a mounting bushing which

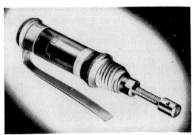

FIG. 18-12. Glass piston-type trimmer capacitor.   (*Corning Glass Works.*)

forms one electrode.   The ceramic dielectric is a small tube soldered to the end of the adjusting threaded rod.   The small metal tube, into which the inner rod and ceramic dielectric move, forms the outer electrode, which is soldered to the outer ceramic casing.   A flying lead of tinned copper makes connection to this electrode.   The inner assembly and spindle is impregnated with silicone grease.   The performance of this capacitor under adverse military conditions is satisfactory.

PLASTIC-DIELECTRIC TRIMMER CAPACITORS

Plastic-dielectric trimmers are usually of the tubular concentric type, consisting of a metal rod controlled by a screw thread which slides inside a metal tube.   The plastic dielectric is in the form of a tube between the inner rod and outer metal tube.

Plastics which have been used primarily are polytetrafluoroethylene and polyethylene.   The chief use of these capacitors is for neutralizing in i-f amplifiers; for this requirement the capacitance must be quite small, of the order of a few picofarads, with a very low minimum capacitance.

For a miniature trimmer at the low values of, say, 0.5 to 3.5 pf the tubular design has much to recommend it over either a vane or disk type, since the over-all diameter can be made small and a fine degree of adjustment is possible. The vane type permits only 180° adjustment, whereas the tubular pattern with a fine screw thread permits many complete revolutions of 360°. With the screwed disk type, the initial change in capacitance is too large.

For a plastic material, such as polytetrafluoroethylene or polyethylene, the tube wall must be very thin as these materials have a comparatively low dielectric constant. One advantage of the low-dielectric-constant material is that any air gaps between the movable element and the tube have not so much effect on the total capacitance.

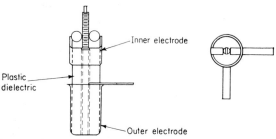

Fig. 18-13. Construction of plastic-dielectric trimmer capacitor for dip soldering.

The variation of capacitance is obtained by sliding the outer tubular element over the fixed inner one along the screw thread. The active thickness of the polyethylene may be 0.01 in. and the inner element can be bored out to take the supporting screw of the outer sleeve so as to ensure adequate rigidity of the component despite the thin wall of polyethylene. The calculated maximum capacitance (taking $\kappa = 2.5$) is

$$C = \frac{0.28 \times 2.54 \times 2.5}{4.14 \log_{10} (0.14/0.12)} = 6.3 \text{ pf}$$

As there is bound to be a small air gap between the sleeve and the polyethylene, the actual capacitance will be somewhat less than this. Measured at 45 Mc/sec the minimum capacitance is 0.41 pf with the outer element removed, and 4.0 pf with the outer element fully screwed in. The power factor of this type of capacitor is about 0.0015. A miniature concentric trimmer of simpler design is shown in Fig. 18-13.

This type of construction is primarily for small capacitors used on printed circuit boards. The variation in capacitance occurs as a result of the relative position of the screw (one plate) to the other plate.

CHAPTER 19

SPECIAL TYPES OF VARIABLE CAPACITOR

PHASE-SHIFTING CAPACITORS

These capacitors are used in conjunction with the accurate measurement of time intervals in radar systems. They are also useful where phase shifting is required for three- or four-phase alternating current. The construction of a typical capacitor is shown in Fig. 19-1. A three-phase capacitor is similar in construction, but has three segments in the bottom plate instead of four.

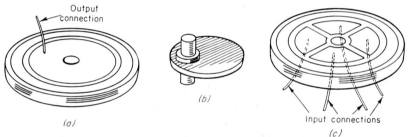

FIG. 19-1. Construction of typical phase-shifting capacitor: (a) top plate; (b) dielectric rotor; (c) bottom plate.

In radar systems, the timing of the pulse oscillations can be controlled by a sine wave whose phase is altered to compare the time delay between the transmitted and the received pulse. The basic sine wave is split into four separate phases 90 degrees apart by resistance–capacitance networks and then recombined in the right proportions in a capacitance mixer to produce a resultant of any required phase. Referring to Fig. 19-1, the variation of capacitance is produced by the rotation of the eccentric Mycalex[1] plate between the top single plate and the bottom four-segment plate. The Mycalex rotor must be accurately surface-ground on both sides to ensure flatness, and the whole assembly must be made as accurately as possible. With a well-constructed capacitor, the accuracy of phase shift of output volt-

[1] Registered trademark of Mycalex Corporation.

247

ages is within 1 per cent of the position of the rotor.   Typical capacitors are about 2 in. in diameter and approximately 1 in. deep.

SWEEP-SCANNING CAPACITORS

Exactly as a potentiometer ganged to the scanner rotation in a radar system is used to generate time-base voltages, so a linear-sweep capacitor voltage divider can be similarly used; it is useful with high-speed

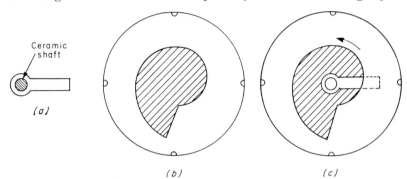

Fig. 19-2. Vane shapes for sweep-scanning variable capacitors: (a) rotor-vane shape; (b) fixed-vane shape; (c) assembly.

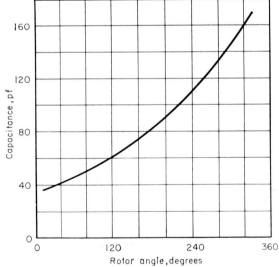

Fig. 19-3. Sweep-scanning capacitor: relation between capacitance and rotor angle.

scanner systems.   The shape of the stator vanes is unusual in that they are circular plates with "hollowed-out" conventional rotor vane shapes.   The rotor itself is an oblong metal vane rotating on its long axis, as shown in Fig. 19-2. As capacitances of 150 pf or so are required, there are usually 15 to 20 fixed and rotating vanes. Typical shapes of fixed and rotating vanes are shown in Fig. 19-2.

Useful detailed information on both phase-shifting and sweep-scanning capacitors is given in Chap. 9, Vol. 17 in the "Components Handbook" of the M.I.T. Radiation Laboratory Series.

Extreme accuracy is again essential in the construction of these capacitors. The type of curve relating capacitance with rotor angle for a typical capacitor is shown in Fig. 19-3.

THE SINE CAPACITOR

The sine capacitor consists of a variable capacitor which has two semicircular stator plates and a specially shaped rotor plate for developing the sine, cosine, or other functions of the rotor shaft angle.

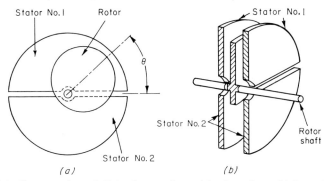

FIG. 19-4. Construction of "sine" capacitor: (a) plan view; (b) isometric cross section showing opposed stator plates. (*General Physical Laboratories.*)

When balanced input voltages are applied to the stator plates, the rotor-plate output voltage will be proportional to the product of the input voltage and the function of the capacitor setting. The capacitor can therefore be used for the solution of problems involving two independent variables, such as the solution of a right-angle triangle, given the hypotenuse and one angle. The construction of a precision sine capacitor, developed by General Physical Laboratories, is shown in Fig. 19-4.

The rotor is carried on insulated bearings and can be rotated through 360°. The two stator plates are insulated from each other and from the rotor, and are made appreciably larger than the rotor to minimize edge effects. The difference between the capacitance formed between the rotor and the upper stators and that between the rotor and the lower stators is proportional to the sine of the displacement angle.

In order to obtain the maximum accuracy of which the capacitor is capable (i.e., about 0.1 per cent, or 3 to 4 min of arc), the rotor is constructed of stainless steel $\frac{3}{32}$ in. thick, flat ground with thickness uniform to ± 0.00003 in. The stators are of $\frac{1}{4}$-in. plate glass suitably metalized to enable the necessary high stability to be obtained.

SEMIBUTTERFLY AND BUTTERFLY CAPACITORS

Because of residual inductance in the capacitor and self-capacitance of the inductor, there is an upper limit to the frequency at which a conventional coil and capacitor resonant-tuned circuit may be realized. The generally accepted figure for this upper limit is 100 to 200 Mc/sec. Perhaps the greatest difficulty with the conventional coil and capacitor circuit is in locating the terminals of the system.

Alternatives to transmission line circuits with their bulk and associated contact difficulties at frequencies higher than 200 Mc/sec are butterfly and semibutterfly circuits, which are arrangements of inductances and capacitances as integral parts of resonant circuits. The terminals are points subtending impedance maxima at resonance.

The Semibutterfly Circuit

A semibutterfly circuit is shown in Fig. 19-5. The stator plates of the capacitor are supported by a semicircular band which forms the

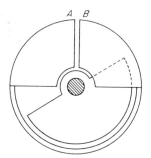

FIG. 19-5. Semibutterfly capacitor.

inductor. The rotor forms not only a series-gap capacitor with the stator plates, but acts as an eddy current shield which blocks off part of the space available to the magnetic field of the inductor. When the rotor is fully meshed the capacitance is a maximum and the inductance is substantially that of the semicircular band. When the rotor is completely out of mesh the capacitance is a minimum, and the inductance is reduced by the shielding effect of the rotor. Movement of the rotor thus varies both inductance and capacitance.

The rotor requires no electric connection. The rotor shaft can be made of insulating material, and flow of r-f currents through the shaft bearings is easily avoided, which is desirable in the tuned circuit of an oscillator used for some applications. The circuit is a two-terminal impedance, the terminals of A and B being the adjacent sides of the stator plates. No point on the circuit maintains its position relative to these terminals—e.g., it is impossible to center-tap the inductance.

The Butterfly Circuit

A diagram of a butterfly circuit is shown in Fig. 19-6. It may be considered to consist of two of the previous circuits in parallel. The rotor in this circuit is always symmetrically placed between the terminals A and B, and variation of its capacitance to earth does not affect

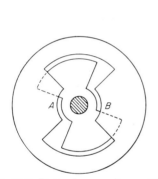

FIG. 19-6. Butterfly capacitor. (*Hammarlund Manufacturing Company, Inc.*)

the balance of the circuit. The elimination of the gap in the outer contour of the circuit which appears in the semibutterfly makes this circuit more stable mechanically and less susceptible to temperature variation.

ELECTRICALLY VARIABLE GAS-DIELECTRIC CAPACITORS

If a neon diode is fitted between two semicircular plates of an air-dielectric capacitor, the dielectric constant will be varied in proportion to the diode current, thus giving a variation in capacitance between the plates. Although this variation is small, possible applications are frequency control of self-excited oscillators, frequency modulation, etc.

SPECIALIZED VARIABLE CAPACITORS FOR
TRANSMITTER RECEIVERS

The current trend toward wider use of very high frequency and ultra-high frequency for communications at short and medium ranges has resulted in complex gang capacitor units whose design and specification are closely integrated with the equipment design. The use of gang capacitors is dictated by the need, in military equipments, for the provision of multichannel equipment which can be set quickly to

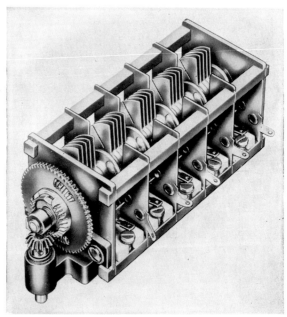

FIG. 19-7. High-frequency five-gang capacitor. (*Radio Condenser Company.*)

any one of a large number of operational channels within the range covered by the equipment. Certain types of equipment for civil applications (e.g., for civil aviation communication and navigation) also have this requirement. As a result, transmitter receivers permitting manual adjustment without instruments or other external equipment to one of several hundred channels are now in use, and in some cases provision is made for automatic selection of a number of preset channels.

In the case of equipment for use on high frequency, the variable capacitors are built to specifications carrying stringent requirements for capacitance law, matching between sections, and temperature coefficient. A five-gang unit of this type is seen in Fig. 19-7.

Units for early types of vhf equipment were constructed along similar lines, sometimes being built up from separate three- and four-gang units mounted on a common base plate with a precision gear coupling. Recent designs have been more compact. The usual capacitance swing of these types is on the order of 50 pf, although sections with dissimilar swings are used, particularly in transmitters employing multiplying stages. Matching between sections to 0.5 pf or better is achieved throughout the tuning range. A high order of accuracy is required because of the large number of channels covered and the high performance expected from the r-f circuits in the equipment.

For some applications in the range of 100 to 150 Mc/sec, capacitors employing butterfly rotor vanes and split-stator construction can be used. Use of this design eliminates the wiper connection to the rotor, enabling the reduction of rotational torque to a minimum. This type of construction is particularly suitable for motor-driven automatic channel selection. A split-stator capacitor can be used only where a limited capacitance range relative to the over-all size is acceptable.

For compact design, required to have capacitance swings on the order of 50 pf, the semicircular vane is usually used. In some cases a ceramic shaft or spindle is utilized to enable the ground returns of individual sections to be isolated for return to the appropriate position in the circuit. A further reason for the use of the ceramic shaft is to minimize the temperature coefficient. With the use of ceramic tie bars, fore and aft expansion is controlled solely by the characteristic of the ceramic material, which can be chosen to have a very low and consistent thermal expansion. Thus, the relative movement of the rotor and stator vanes is prevented and the change of capacitance value with temperature eliminated. A typical four-gang gear-driven tuning capacitor is shown in Fig. 19-8.

Multiple-tuned circuits for the uhf band (e.g., around 300 Mc/sec and higher) have their own special problems and, while tuned lines offer good performance, a multiple unit providing ganged tuning of several sections takes considerable space and is mechanically complex. Conventional capacitance-tuning becomes impracticable because the series inductance of the vanes becomes appreciable and prevents the achievement of the intended tuning range and circuit performance. A satisfactory solution to the problem of providing a wide tuning range at frequencies in the region of 300 Mc/sec can be seen in Fig. 19-9. This three-gang unit is constructed on a rigid base plate, onto which are subsequently assembled the r-f, mixer, and oscillator tubes and associated components. Tuning is achieved by vanes, part of whose travel is used to reduce the inductance of the looped portions of the stator

FIG. 19-8. Dual four-gang semicircular-vane tuning capacitor.   (*Radio Condenser Company.*)

FIG. 19-9. Three-gang semibutterfly uhf capacitor.   (*Plessey Company, Ltd.*)

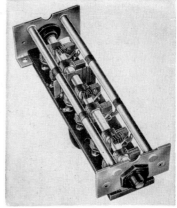

(*Hammarlund Manufacturing Company, Inc.*)   (*Radio Condenser Company*)

(*Radio Condenser Company*)

FIG. 19-10. High-frequency air-dielectric capacitors designed for special applications.

vanes, while the remainder of the travel introduces an increasing capacitance in parallel with the loops. By this means a tuning range of approximately two-to-one in frequency is obtained with reasonably constant gain and bandwidth characteristics.

The few examples given exemplify the techniques now being employed for compact transmitter receivers. The wide variation of physical design reflects the need to match not only electrical characteristics but mechanical detail with the circuit layout of equipment. In spite of this, standardized forms of construction, using common piece-parts built up into gangs with varying numbers of sections and differing capacitance swings, can be envisaged for future vhf equipments. The functional requirements can be summarized as follows:

Small size
Minimum series inductance
Precise matching of capacitance law between sections
Isolation of ground return circuits for each section
Low noise and long life from rotor contacts
Robust shockproof construction
Low torque (in types for automatic tuning)
Wide operational temperature range

It will be realized that this is a formidable list, but capacitors meeting these requirements are already in operational military equipment in large numbers in new types of vhf communications equipment. Figure 19-10 shows several types of the many designs of high-frequency variable air-dielectric capacitors now being produced for special applications.

CHAPTER 20

FAULTS WHICH MAY OCCUR IN
VARIABLE CAPACITORS

In general, variable capacitors have fewer faults than most components. Precision types are designed and assembled with great care, using selected materials. They are generally operated under conditions which preclude the development of any faults that would occur with components subjected to vibration, extremes of temperature, and humidity conditions. They are costly and are maintained and treated as precision instruments. Faults with this type of component are, therefore, rare.

In the general-purpose or broadcast-receiver type of capacitor, faults which occur are mainly due to foreign matter becoming trapped in the vanes, causing "crackle" and noise. Noise may also develop with time from deterioration of the spring contacts to the moving vanes assemblies, but the contacts are usually readily cleaned. Noise in some cases may not be due to residual resistance variations, but to residual inductance variations. Under normal conditions, corrosion of the materials is rare, but when operated under military conditions, corrosion of the ball bearings, etc., may occur, particularly if the component is exposed to long periods of high humidity.

Faults in general-purpose capacitors include microphonics, which is due to inaccurate centering of the rotor and stator vanes. This is avoided by precautions in manufacture of the vanes to ensure flatness and by accurate assembly. Microphonics can develop in a capacitor which was originally satisfactory if the stators move out of position or if bearing wear causes lateral displacement of the rotor. The former fault is eliminated by stable frame construction and use of ceramic stator supports; the latter by using ball bearings of adequate size and by correct adjustment of the torque.

Transmitter types are similar to the precision types in that the conditions of design and use usually avoid the development of faults. Trimmer types, however, are subjected to more severe conditions, par-

257

ticularly in military communication receivers, etc., although even under these conditions faults are comparatively rare.   Corrosion of the materials used under extremes of temperature and humidity is probably the most serious cause of faults, although another fault can be caused by moisture trapped under the movable plate of ceramic or mica types when used in the tropics.

CHAPTER 21

FUTURE DEVELOPMENTS IN VARIABLE
CAPACITOR DESIGN

In the design of the broadcast or general-purpose types, cost is a major factor, consistent with good performance, and future development will be directed to improved methods of assembly, permitting a reduction in cost and an accurately maintained law with less adjustment of the split end vanes. Smaller units, including a variable silicon capacitor (a variation of the diode), are being developed for use with transistors.

For military applications future developments will be directed toward a capacitor which is not affected by vibration and shock. This will require new structures and possibly a dampening agent, such as oil or grease.

Trimmer capacitors for commercial fields will be developed for improved stability and reduced size and cost, and much emphasis will be put on rapid assembly into the equipment chassis with automation in mind. For the normal broadcast receiver, the performance is adequate and production techniques have reached a high state of efficiency.

For air-spaced transmitter types of variable capacitor, it is again difficult to foresee major design improvements; it is probably in the liquid-dielectric-filled types that improvements may be expected with the introduction of new dielectrics. The vacuum variable type has great possibilities for the smaller capacitance values; increases in the capacitance ranges are desirable for the future, along with retention of the many design advantages of this type.

In the design of trimmer variable capacitors, little variation can be expected in the air-spaced types; in the mica-, ceramic-, and plastic-dielectric types improvements will probably be mainly in construction. For sealed trimmers designed for military equipments, a great deal of experimental work is being done which may produce new and improved designs. Many dielectrics in the field of gases, liquids, plastics, and enameled and oxidized metals are being tried. It is possible that,

259

arising from this experimental effort, entirely new trimmer types may be evolved.

BIBLIOGRAPHY ON CAPACITORS

At the present time there are no general bibliographies available on electronic parts. However, the following references on fixed and variable capacitors have been collected in order to form a nucleus for such a bibliography. Very little data are published on the design of electronic parts, such design data usually being retained by the manufacturer on a proprietary basis to protect his commercial interests. There is, however, considerable literature on the operation of electronic parts in circuits, and such references that concern the operation of capacitors are included in this bibliography. Some general electronic-part reviews are also given.

The bibliography has been arranged in an approximate subject sequence (comparable with the order of the material in the book) and under these headings in chronological order. The abbreviations for the names of the periodicals (where they are available and used) are in accordance with the list published by the American Chemical Society.

While at this stage the bibliography is, of necessity, incomplete, it is felt that the references given will be of some value.

General Reviews on Electronic Parts (Components)

Ross, I. M.: Component Development for War-time Service Applications, *J. Inst. Elec. Engrs. (London)*, vol. 94, pt. IIIA, no. 11, p. 231, March–April, 1947.

Reynolds, G. D.: Tests for the Selection of Components for Broadcast Receivers, *J. Inst. Elec. Engrs. (London)*, vol. 95, pt. III, no. 34, p. 54, March, 1948.

Black, D. H., and N. F. S. Hecht: Electronic Components—Government and Industrial Relations and Co-operation, Commercial, Professional and Service Standards, *Proc. Inst. Elec. Engrs. (London)*, vol. 97, pt. III, no. 48, p. 261, July, 1950.

Hall, R. E., and E. Coop: Components for Instruments, *Proc. Inst. Elec. Engrs. (London)*, vol. 98, pt. II, no. 66, p. 738, December, 1951.

———: How Component Specifications Can Help the Design Engineer, *Proc. Inst. Elec. Engrs. (London)*, vol. 99, pt. III, p. 279, July, 1952.

Darnell, P. S.: Miniaturized Component Design, *Radio and Television News* (Radio Electronic Engineering), vol. 48, pp. 10–11 and 30, September, 1952.

Dummer, G. W. A.: Components for Transistors, *Wireless World*, vol. 69, no. 5, p. 196, May, 1953.

Halsey, R. J., and F. C. Wright: Submerged Telephone Repeaters for Shallow Water (Life of Components), *Proc. Inst. Elec. Engrs. (London)*, vol. 101, pt. I, no. 130, p. 173, July, 1954.

———: "Techniques for Application of Electronic Component Parts in Military Equipment," McGraw-Hill Book Company, Inc., New York, 1957.

Capacitor Selection and Application

Halsey, R. J., and F. C. Wright: Coupling Condenser in Audio Amplifiers, *Aerovox Research Worker*, January, 1928.

Smith, B. E.: Proper Condenser Rating Important for Trouble-Free Operation, *Aerovox Research Worker*, April, 1928.

Clark, R. V.: Use of Electrolytic Condensers in B Power Supply Devices, *Radio*, vol. N7, p. 176, August, 1929.

————: Factors Which Must Be Considered in Using Filter Condensers, *Aerovox Research Worker*, January, 1931.

Maddison, R. E. W.: Absorption in Electrical Condensers, *J. Franklin Inst.*, vol. 214, p. 327, September, 1932.

Barclay, W. A.: Decoupling Efficiency, *Experimental Wireless and Wireless Engineering*, vol. 10, p. 307, June, 1933.

————: Uses of Concentrically-wound Electrolytic Condensers, *Aerovox Research Worker*, March, 1934.

————: Influence of Power Factor and Capacity on Filtering Efficiency, *Aerovox Research Worker*, October–November, 1934.

————: Condenser Leakage and Its Effects, *Aerovox Research Worker*, March, 1935.

————: The Use of Condensers in Radio Receivers, *Aerovox Research Worker*, April–May, 1935.

————: Types of Condensers and Their Applications, *Aerovox Research Worker*, April, 1936.

Thomas, H. A.: Electrical Stability of Condensers, *J. Am. Inst. Elec. Engrs.* (*JAIEE*), vol. 79, p. 297, September, 1936.

————: Use of Mica Condensers in Transmitters, *Aerovox Research Worker*, October, 1936.

————: Use of Oil Condensers in Amateur Transmitters, *Aerovox Research Worker*, March, 1937.

————: Fixed Condensers in Radio Transmitters, *Aerovox Research Worker*, March, 1941.

————: Capacitors in Control Circuits, *Aerovox Research Worker*, August, 1942.

Williams, E.: Calculating Charging Time in R. C. Circuits, *Electronic Ind.*, vol. 1, p. 58, December, 1942.

Schick, W.: Temperature Coefficient of Capacitance, *Wireless Eng.*, vol. 21, pp. 65–71, February, 1944.

Rehfisch, T. J.: Temperature Coefficient of Capacitance, *Wireless Eng.*, vol. 21, pp. 175–176, April, 1944.

————: Capacitor Quality Factor, *Aerovox Research Worker*, July, 1944.

Light, G. S.: Condensers in Series-Heater Circuits, *Electronic Eng.* (*London*), vol. 17, pp. 454–455, April, 1945.

Cook, H. A.: Temperature-Capacity Coefficient, *Bendix Radio Eng.*, vol. 2, no. 2, October, 1945.

Price, J. F.: Effectiveness of By-Pass Capacitors at U.H.F., *Communications*, vol. 28, pp. 18–19, February, 1948.

————: New Use for Blocking Condensers, *Radio Ekko*, vol. 11, p. 96, May, 1948.

Gough, K. A.: Choosing Capacitors, *Wireless World*, vol. 55, pp. 55–58, June, 1948.

Bailey, J. T.: Coupling Capacitors Can Be Trouble Makers, *Radio-Electronics*, vol. 20, p. 43, May, 1949.

Gough, K. A.: Choosing Capacitors and Uses of Various Types, *Radio Times*, vol. 4, pp. 10–12, July, 1949.

Skanavi, G. I., and M. D. Neuman: Voltage Stabilization by Means of Barium Titanate Capacitors, *Engineering Digest*, vol. 10, pp. 427–429, December, 1949.

Bennett, A. E., and K. A. Gough: The Influence of Operating Conditions on the Construction of Electrical Capacitors, *Proc. Inst. Elec. Engrs. (London)*, vol. 97, pt. III, no. 48, p. 231, July, 1950.

Ritchey, N. B.: U.H.F. By-Pass Capacitor Nomographs, *Radio-Electronic Engineering*, vol. 24, pp. 14, 36–37, March, 1955.

Tucker, R. W., and S. D. Breskend: Effective Leakage Resistance of Several Types of Capacitors, *IRE Trans. on Component Parts*, PGCP-3, April, 1955.

Killen, C. G.: Factors Influencing Capacitor Reliability, *Proceedings of Fifth Annual Conference on Electronic Components*, Los Angeles, May, 1955.

Franklin, W. S.: Paper Capacitor, First Failures and Their Distribution, *Proceedings of the Fifth Annual Conference on Electronic Components*, Los Angeles, May, 1955.

Warner, D. F.: Application of Tantalum Electrolytic Capacitors, *IRE Trans. Component Parts*, PGCP-4, pp. 7–43, November, 1955.

Wyhs, A.: The Complicated Simple Capacitor, Military Electronics, pp. 10–12, January, 1959.

Measurement of Capacitance and Dielectric Properties

Gunn, R.: On the Measurement of Very Small Changes of Capacitance, *Phil. Mag.*, vol. 48, pp. 224–226, July, 1924.

Griffiths, W. H. F.: Measurement of Small Variable Capacitors at Radio Frequencies, *Experimental Wireless and Wireless Engineering*, vol. 5, p. 452, August, 1928.

Graham, V. M.: Gang Capacitor Testing Device, *Proc. IRE*, vol. 16, p. 1401, October, 1928.

————: How to Test Condenser Capacities, *Aerovox Research Worker*, February–March, 1929.

Braden, R. A., and H. C. Forbes: Condenser Bridge for Factory Inspection of Variable Condensers, *Proc. IRE*, vol. 18, p. 123, January, 1930.

Rayner, E. H.: Low Power-Factor Measurements at High Voltages, *J. Inst. Elec. Engrs. (London)*, vol. 68, p. 1132, September, 1930.

Wyman, P.: Measurement of the Dielectric Constants of Conducting Media, *Phys. Rev.*, vol. 35, p. 623, March, 1930.

Rohde, L.: Power Factor of Condensers at High Frequencies, *Elektrotech. Z.*, vol. 54, p. 580, June, 1930.

Moullin, E. B.: "Theory and Practice of Radio Frequency Measurements," Griffin and Company, London, 1931.

Vassillière, J. L. F.: Dielectric Loss Measurements, *Société Française des Électriciens*, vol. 1, no. 10, pp. 1105–1111, October, 1931.

Boella, M.: H. F. Measurement of Dielectric Loss, *Elettrotecnica*, vol. 19, p. 99, February, 1932.

Angelini, A. M.: Angle of Dielectric Loss in Insulators, *Elettrotecnica*, vol. 19, p. 261, April, 1932.

Bousman, H. W.: Bridge for Capacitance and Low Power Factor Measurements, *Gen. Elec. Rev.*, vol. 35, p. 295, May, 1932.

————: Dielectric Constant Measurement, *Electronics*, vol. 4, p. 264, August, 1932.

Chaffee, J. G.: The Determination of Dielectric Properties at Very High Frequencies, *Proc. IRE*, vol. 22, p. 1020, August, 1934.

Muller, E.: Power Factor at High Frequencies, *Hochfrequenztechnik und Elektroakustik*, vol. 43, p. 45, May, 1934.

Rohde, L.: Dielectric Loss Measurements at Ten Cycles, *Hochfrequenztechnik und Elektroakustik*, vol. 43, p. 156, May, 1934.

Hill, C. F.: Dielectric Breakdown, *Elec. J.*, vol. 31, p. 277, July, 1934.

Griffiths, W. H. F.: The Calibration of Small Variable Condensers at Radio Frequencies, *Wireless Engr.*, vol. 5, no. 59, p. 452, August, 1934.

Kessler, H.: H. F. Dielectric Measurements, *Hochfrequenztechnik und Elektroakustik*, vol. 45, p. 91, March, 1935.

Rohde, L.: Determination of Losses in Insulating Materials, *ASTM Standard of Electrical Insulation*, vol. 4, p. 59, May, 1935.

Deeley, P. M.: Electrolytic Capacitor Testing in Production, *Electronics*, vol. 8, p. 216, July, 1935.

Hummel, F.: Resonance Method of Determining Dielectric Constants, *Z. Tech. Phys.*, vol. 16, p. 264, 1935.

Rohde, L.: Dielectric Measurements at 60 cm, *Z. Tech. Phys.*, vol. 16, p. 637, 1935.

Hartshorn, L., and W. H. Ward: Effect of Electrodes in Measurement of Permittivity and Power Factor, *J. Inst. Elec. Engrs. (London)*, vol. 75, p. 730, 1935.

Curtis, H. L.: "Electrical Measurements," McGraw-Hill Book Company, Inc., New York, 1935.

Campbell, A., and E. C. Childs: "The Measurement of Inductance, Capacitance and Frequency," Macmillan & Co., Ltd., London, 1935.

Hartshorn, L., and W. H. Ward: The Measurement of Permittivity and Power Factor at Frequencies from 10^4 to 10^8 Cycles per Second, *J. Inst. Elec. Engrs. (London)*, vol. 79, p. 597, 1936.

Field, R. F., and D. B. Sinclair: A Method for Determining the Residual Inductance and Resistance of a Variable Air Condenser at Radio Frequencies, *Proc. IRE*, vol. 24, p. 225, February, 1936.

Bull, R.: Theory and Application of Dielectric Constant Determination, *Z. ges. Kälte-Ind.*, vol. 45, p. 110, May–June, 1936.

Buckingham, W. B.: Measurement of Condenser Characteristics, *Electronics*, vol. 10, p. 13, June, 1937.

Boella, M.: Direct Method of Measuring Loss Conductance of Condensers at H. F., *Proc. IRE*, vol. 26, p. 421, April, 1938.

Leonard, S. C.: Measurement of Minute Changes of Capacitance and Inductance, *Electronics*, vol. 11, pp. 18–21, March, 1938.

————: Practical Methods of Testing Condensers, *Aerovox Research Worker*, February, March, April, and June, 1938.

Ford, L. H., and N. F. Astbury: A Note on the Calibration of Decade Condensers, *J. Sci. Instr.*, vol. 15, p. 122, 1938.

Meacham, L. A.: A Bridge Stabilized Oscillator, *Proc. IRE*, vol. 26, p. 1278, 1938.

Neargoard, B. S.: A Survey of Ultra-High Frequency Measurements, *R.C.A. Rev.*, vol. 3, p. 156, October, 1938.

Astbury, N. F., and L. H. Ford: The Precision Measurement of Capacitance, *Proc. Phys. Soc. (London)*, vol. 51, p. 37, 1939.

Chipman, R. A.: A Resonance Curve Method for the Absolute Measurement of Impedance at Frequencies of the Order of 300 Mc/s, *J. Appl. Phys.*, vol. 10, p. 27, January, 1939.

Miller, J. M., and B. Salzberg: Measurements of Admittance at Ultra High Frequencies, *R.C.A. Rev.*, vol. 3, p. 480, April, 1939.

Kaufmann, H.: Impedance Measurement in Decimetre-Wave Circuits, *Hochfrequenztechnik und Elektroakustik*, vol. 53, p. 61, February, 1939.

Jones, T. I.: Mercury Electrodes for Measurements on Solid Dielectrics, *J. Inst. Elec. Engrs. (London)*, vol. 74, p. 179, 1939.

Barrow, W. L., and W. W. Mieher: Natural Oscillations of Electrical Cavity Resonators, *Proc. IRE*, vol. 28, p. 184, 1940.

Hartshorn, L.: "R. F. Measurements by Bridge and Resonance Methods," Chapman & Hall, Ltd., London, 1940.

Sherwood, E. T.: Testing Ceramic Capacitors, *Electronics*, vol. 13, pp. 26–29, September, 1940.

Silva, H.: Measurements on Principle of Superposition in Solid Dielectrics, *Phys. Rev.*, vol. 60, p. 684, November, 1941.

Hague, B.: "Alternating Current Bridge Methods," Pitman, London, 1943.

Kusters, W.: On Measurements of Dielectric Properties of Ceramic Insulating Materials at Centimeter Wavelengths, *Wireless Eng.*, vol. 21, p. 13, January, 1944.

Amphlett, P. H.: The Measurement of Dielectric Constant, *J. Soc. Chem. Ind. (London)*, p. 31, January, 1944.

Englund, C. R.: Dielectric Constants and Power Factors at Centimeter Wavelengths, *Bell System Tech. J.*, vol. 23, p. 114, January, 1944.

————: Cagacitor Impedance and Resistance Measurement, *Aerovox Research Worker*, vol. 16, p. 1, January, 1944.

Schlick, W.: Temperature Coefficient of Capacitance: Its Measurement in Small Radio Condensers, *Wireless Eng.*, vol. 21, p. 65, February, 1944.

————: Production Tester for Mica Capacitors, *Electronics*, vol. 17, p. 156, August, 1944.

Hanopol, L. Y.: Production Tester for Small Values of Capacitance, *Electronics*, vol. 18, p. 160, September, 1945.

Turner, R. R.: Electrolytic Capacitor Checker, *Radio*, vol. N34, p. 38, October, 1945.

Horner, F., T. Taylor, R. Dunsmuir, J. Lamb, and W. Jackson: Resonance Methods of Dielectric Measurement at Centimeter Wavelengths, *J. Inst. Elec. Engrs. (London)*, vol. 93, pt. III, p. 53, 1946.

Garton, C. G.: The Characteristics and Errors of Capacitors Used for Measurement Purposes, *J. Inst. Elec. Engrs. (London)*, vol. 93, pt. II, p. 398, October, 1946.

Roberts, S., and A. Von Hippel: A New Method for Measuring Dielectric Constant and Loss in the Range of Centimeter Waves, *J. Appl. Phys.*, vol. 17, p. 610, July, 1946.

Field, R. F.: Connection Errors in Capacitance Measurements, *General Radio Experimenter*, vol. 21, pp. 1–4, May, 1947.

Shortcut, A.: Rapid Checker for Capacity-Continuity, *Radio Craft*, vol. 18, p. 37, July, 1947.

Works, C. N.: Resonant Cavities for Dielectric Measurements, *J. Appl. Phys.*, vol. 18, p. 605, 1947.

Reynolds, S. I.: Improved Re-entrant Cavity, *Gen. Elec. Rev.*, vol. 50, p. 34, 1947.

Rayner, G. H., and L. H. Ford: The Calibration of Capacitors at the N. P. L. 1947, *J. Inst. Elec. Engrs. (London)*, vol. 95, pt. II, p. 312, 1948.

Montgomery, C. G.: "Technique of Microwave Measurements," Rad. Lab. Series, vol. II, McGraw-Hill Book Company, Inc., New York, 1947.

Dakin, T. W., and C. N. Works: Microwave Dielectric Measurement, *J. Appl. Phys.*, vol. 8, p. 789, 1947.

Daniel, V., A. C. Devonshire, and D. F. Rushman: Summary of Conference on Substances of High Permittivity (London, 1948), *J. Sci. Instr.*, vol. 26, p. 134, 1949.

Surber, W. H.: Universal Curves for Dielectric-Filled Waveguide and Microwave Dielectric Measurement Methods for Liquids and Solids, *J. Appl. Phys.*, vol. 19, p. 514, 1948.

Moreno, T.: "Microwave Transmission Design Data," McGraw-Hill Book Company, Inc., New York, 1948.

————: "Equipment to Measure the Temperature Coefficient of Capacity," Department of Commerce (Office of Technical Services), Pamphlet No. 97203, January, 1949.

Parmeter, R. L.: Two Capacitor Testers, *Radio-Electronics*, vol. 20, pp. 44–45, February, 1949.

Zeluff, V.: Infrared Checks Capacitor Leakage, *Electronics*, vol. 22, p. 159, April, 1949.

Bowdler, C. W.: A Three-Terminal Air Capacitor, *J. Sci. Instr.*, vol. 26, p. 117, April, 1949.

Melton, B. S.: Method of Measurement of the Internal Series Resistance of a Capacitor under Surge Conditions, *Proc. IRE*, vol. 37, pp. 690–693, June, 1949.

Schmitz: Simple Measuring Instrument for Electrolytic Capacitors (Ein Einfachs Gerset zur Messung der Kapozitaet von Elektrodytkodenstoren), *Funk und Ton*, vol. 3, pp. 311–314, June, 1949.

Purper, C.: Production Test for Ceramic Capacitors, *Elec. Mfg.*, vol. 49, pp. 136–141, 310, 312, June, 1949.

Clay, J.: Accurate Determination of the Absolute Capacity of Condensers, *Physica*, vol. 15, pp. 484–488, July, 1949.

Sauer, H. A., and D. A. McLean: Direct Voltage Performance Test for Capacitor Paper, *Proc. IRE*, vol. 37, pp. 927–931, August, 1949.

Willman, W. R.: Capacitance Bridge, *Radio Service Dealer*, vol. 10, pp. 13–15, August, 1949.

————: Capacitance Measurement Bridge with Mechanical Rectifier and Mirror Galvanometer. Elimination of Harmonic Errors (kapacitaet Gleichrichter und Spiegel Galvanometer. Ausschaltung der Fehler durch Oberwellen), *Frequenz*, vol. 3, pp. 259–264, September, 1949.

Soudels, I.: Capacitance Measurement with an A. C. Voltmeter, *Electronic Eng.* (*London*), vol. 21, p. 416, November, 1949.

Gutmann, F.: A Direct Reading Instrument for the Measurement of the Series Resistance of Capacitors, *J. Sci. Instr.*, vol. 27, p. 169, June, 1950.

Tombs, D. M., and J. F. Ward: Measuring Small Changes in Capacitance by Frequency Modulation, *Proc. Inst. Elec. Engrs.* (*London*), vol. 97, pt. II, p. 645, October, 1950.

Mendousse, J. S., P. D. Goodman, and W. G. Cady: Capacitance Bridge (1–50 Mc/s), *Rev. Sci. Instr.*, vol. 21, p. 1002, December, 1950.

Barlow, H. M., and A. L. Cullen: "Principles of Guided Waves and Impedance Measurements" (Chapter on Dielectric Measurements), Constable & Co., Ltd., London, 1950.

Connor, J. A.: A Small Incremental Capacitor, *Electronics*, vol. 24, p. 250, October, 1951.

Parry, J. V. L.: The Measurement of Permittivity and Power Factor of Dielectrics at Frequencies from 300 to 600 Mc/s, *Proc. Inst. Elec. Engrs. (London)*, vol. 98, pt. III, no. 54, p. 303, July, 1951.

Webb, J. K., and H. B. Wood: The Precise Measurement of Capacitance, *Inst. Elec. Engrs. (London)*, Monograph No. 100M, May, 1951.

Schreck, C.: Apparatus for the Measurement of the Temperature Coefficients of Inductors, Capacitors and Tuned Circuits, *Fernmeldetech. Z.*, vol. 4, p. 30, January, 1951.

Loverick, E.: Dielectric Measurements Using Pulsed Voltages, *J. Brit. Inst. Radio Engrs.*, vol. 11, p. 81, March, 1951.

Baker, E. B.: Automatic Measurement, Computation and Recording of Dielectric Constant and Loss Factor against Temperature, *Rev. Sci. Instr.*, vol. 22, p. 376, June, 1951.

Voight, H.: A Measuring Bridge for 0.1 to 1,000 Mc/s, *Arch. Elektrotech.*, vol. 6, p. 414, 1952.

Terman, F. E., and J. M. Pettit: "Electronic Measurements," 2d ed., McGraw-Hill Book Company, Inc., New York, 1952.

Ruehlman, H. E.: Techniques for Measuring Capacitor Dielectric Absorption, *Tele-Tech and Electronic Industries*, vol. 14, pp. 72–74 plus, February, 1955.

————: A Convenient Test Fixture for Small Capacitors, *General Radio Experimenter*, October, 1955.

Peysson, J., and J. Ladefroux: De la Mesure Industrielle du Coefficient de Temperature des Condensateurs a Dietecerique Ceramique, *Annales de Radioelectricite*, vol. 10, pp. 355–371, October, 1955.

Boer, J.: Bridge Tests Capacitor on Production Line, *Electronics*, vol. 29, pp. 146–147, August, 1956.

————: A 120 Cycle Source for Electrolytic Capacitor Testing with Capacitance Test Bridge, *General Radio Experimenter*, August, 1956.

General Reviews on Fixed Capacitors

Coursey, P. R.: "Electrical Condensers," Pitman, London, 1927.

Lewis, D.: Midget Condensers, *Radio*, vol. 12, p. 899, April, 1931.

Bouch, Z.: Oscillator Condenser Design for Single Control Superheterodynes, *Radio*, vol. 13, p. 132, August, 1931.

Houch, W. H.: Life Test for Condensers, *Electronics*, vol. 2, p. 114, September, 1931.

Sowerby, A. L. M.: Non-Inductive Condensers, *Wireless World*, vol. 31, p. 33, July, 1932.

————: Important Features in Design of High Voltage Transmitting Filter Condensers, *Aerovox Research Worker*, August, 1934.

Haskins, R. L.: Resonance Chart, Capacitor and Leads, *Electronics*, vol. 12, p. 35, August, 1939.

Hall, E. L.: V. H. F. Behavior of Capacitors, *Electronics*, vol. 17, p. 114, March, 1944.

————: Glass Sealed Capacitors: *Electronic Eng. (London)*, vol. 17, p. 78, 1945.

Brotherton, M.: "Capacitors—Their Use in Electronic Circuits," D. Van Nostrand Company, Inc., Princeton, N.J., 1946.

————: "Electronic Engineering Patent Index" (F. A. Petraglia, Editor), Electronics Research Publishing Company, 1946.

Hopkins, R. J.: Overvoltage Testing of Capacitors, *Electronics*, vol. 20, pp. 105–107, June, 1947.

Stacy, J. D.: Significance of Watt-Second Rating of Ratings of D-C Capacitors, *Communications*, vol. 27, pp. 24–25 and 41, August, 1947.

Wouch, V.: Energy Wasted Charging a Condenser, *Communications*, vol. 24, p. 48, April, 1948.

————: Standards of Very Small Capacitance, *Radio News*, vol. 3, p. 9, June, 1948.

Zingerman, A. S.: Statistical Method for Determining the Breakdown Voltage of a Dielectric, *J. Tech. Phys. (U.S.S.R.)*, vol. 18, pp. 1029–1043, August, 1948 (in Russian).

Borgars, S. J.: German Radio Condensers, *Electronic Eng. (London)*, vol. 20, pp. 355–357, November, 1948.

Dubilier, W.: Development, Design and Construction of Electrical Condensers, *J. Franklin Inst.*, vol. 248, pp. 193–204, September, 1949.

Coursey, P. R.: Hermetic Sealing of Capacitors, *Proc. Inst. Elec. Engrs. (London)*, vol. 97, pt. III, p. 56, January, 1950.

Jonker, J. L. H., and P. W. Haaijam: Wire Capacitor and Other Composite Drawn Products, *Philips Tech. Rev.*, vol. 13, pp. 145–151, December, 1951.

Davidson, R.: R. F. Characteristics of Capacitors, *Wireless World*, vol. 68, p. 301, August, 1952.

————: Bibliography on Power Capacitors (1925–1950), American Institute of Electrical Engineers, New York, 1952.

Podolsky, L., and J. K. Sprague: Some Characteristics and Limitations of Capacitor and Resistor Components, *IRE Trans. of Professional Group on Components Parts*, vol. PGCP–1, pp. 33–46, March, 1954.

Rockett, F.: Component Design Trends—Fixed Capacitors Undergo Miniaturization, *Electronics*, vol. 27, no. 7, p. 120, July, 1954.

Geiser, D. T.: An Investigation of Lowest Resonant Frequency in Commercially Available By-Pass Capacitors, *Convention Record of the IRE*, pt. 3, p. 43, 1954.

Baumann, N. P., and G. C. Wiseman: Electrical Noise Pulses from Polarized Dielectrics, *J. Appl. Phys.*, vol. 25, no. 11, p. 1391, November, 1954.

Lee, D. B.: Evaluation of Capacitors, *Elec. Mfg.*, vol. 56, pp. 117–121, September, 1955.

Paper Capacitors, Dielectric Properties of Impregnants, Etc.

Gerrant, A.: Dielectric Strength of Paper at High Pressure, *Arch. Elektrotech.*, vol. 25, p. 181, March, 1931.

Whitehead, J. B.: Dielectric Losses in Impregnated Paper, *Trans. AIEE*, vol. 52, p. 667, June, 1933.

Hartshorn, L., and W. H. Ward: Dielectric Properties of Paper, *J. Inst. Elec. Engrs. (London)*, vol. 77, p. 723, November, 1935.

Linder, V. L., and J. Schneidermann: Behavior of Paper Condensers at High Frequencies, *Fernmeldetechnik Z.*, vol. 18, p. 73, May, 1937 (in German).

Katzman, J.: Life of Impregnated Paper Capacitors, *Electronics*, vol. 11, p. 54, June, 1938.

Pelmore, D. R.: Dielectric Loss in Paraffin-Work Solutions, *Proc. Roy. Soc. (London)*, vol. 172, p. 515, 1939.

Frolich, H.: Dielectric Losses in Paraffin-Work Solutions, *Proc. Phys. Soc.*, vol. 54, p. 422, 1942.

McLean, D. A.: Deterioration of Paper Condensers under High D.C. Voltage and High Temperature, *Bell Labs Record*, vol. 21, no. 6, p. 136, 1943.

Brinkmann, S.: Self Discharge and Time Constant of the High Voltage Oiled-Paper Condenser, *Wireless Eng.*, vol. 20, p. 449, September, 1943.

————: Paper Capacitor as Mica Capacitor Substitute, *Aerovox Research Worker*, vol. 14, p. 11, November, 1943.

Brotherton, M.: Paper Capacitors under Direct Voltages, *Proc. IRE*, vol. 32, pp. 139–143, March, 1944.

Luterer, L.: Current and Potential Distribution in Shorted-Edge, Roll-Type Condensers (of Special Importance in Interference Suppression), *Wireless Eng.*, vol. 21, p. 89, February, 1944.

McLean, D. A., and L. Egerton: Paper Capacitors Containing Chlorinated Impregnation; Stabilization by Anthraquinone, *Ind. Eng. Chem.*, vol. 37, p. 73, January, 1945.

Whitehead, J. B., and J. M. Kopper: Dielectric Strength and Life of Impregnated Paper Insulation, *Trans. AIEE*, vol. 64, April, 1945.

Berberich, L. J., and others: Characteristics of Chlorinated Impregnants in Direct-Current Paper Capacitors, *Proc. IRE*, vol. 33, p. 389, June, 1945.

Schweitzer, W. P.: Manufacture of Condenser Paper, *F. M.—Television*, vol. 6, pp. 37–39, February, 1946.

Weeks, J. R.: Capacitor Life Testing, *Bell Labs Record*, vol. 24, p. 296. August, 1946.

McLean, D. A., and L. Egerton: Paper Capacitors Containing Chlorinated Impregnants: Mechanism of Stabilization, *Bell System Tech. J.*, vol. 25, pp. 652–653, October, 1946.

Sauer, H. A.: High Speed Life Test for Capacitor Paper, *Bell Labs Record*, vol. 25, pp. 17–19, January, 1947.

Cornell, J. I.: Metallized Paper Capacitors, *Communications*, vol. 27, p. 22, January, 1947.

Morozov, I. I.: Hermetic Low-Voltage Paper Capacitors, *Radiotekhnika*, vol. 2, pp. 51–62, February, 1947 (in Russian).

Cornell, J.: Metallized Capacitor Data, *Electronics*, vol. 20, p. 174, March, 1947.

Godley, P., and J. C. Balabaugh: Metallized Capacitor Tests, *Electronics*, vol. 20, p. 112, April, 1947.

McLean, D. A., and others: Paper Capacitors Containing Chlorinated Impregnants: Effects of Sulphur, *Bell System Tech. J.*, vol. 26, p. 392, April, 1947.

McLean, D. A.: Paper Capacitors Containing Chlorinated Impregnants: Benefits of Controlled Oxidation of Paper, *Ind. Eng. Chem.*, vol. 39, pp. 1457–1461, November, 1947.

Brooks, H.: Probable Breakdown Voltage of Paper Dielectric Capacitors, *Trans. AIEE*, vol. 66, pp. 1137–1144, 1947.

Miller, H. F., and R. J. Hopkins: New Kraft Paper Capacitor, *Gen. Elec. Rev.*, vol. 50, pp. 20–24, December, 1947.

Cornell, J. I.: Metallized Capacitor Dielectrics, *Tele-Tech*, vol. 6, p. 98, January, 1948.

Dempter, B.: Characteristics of Some Oil-Impregnated Capacitors, *Electronics*, vol. 21, p. 168, May, 1948.

Farley, C. C.: Paper Capacitors Using Chlorinated Liquid Impregnants, *Proc. IRE (Australia)*, vol. 9, p. 13, July, 1948.

Wehe, H. G.: Metallizing Paper for Capacitors, *Bell Labs Record*, vol. 17, pp. 317–321, September, 1949.

————: Metallized Paper Capacitors, *Wireless World*, vol. 55, pp. 510–512, December, 1949.

Renne, V. T.: Application of Semi-Conducting Liquids in Impregnating Paper Capacitors, *J. Tech. Phys. (U.S.S.R.)*, vol. 19, p. 218, 1949 (in Russian).

————: Calculation of Dielectric Strength of Non-Impregnated Capacitor Paper— New Theory of Breakdown Related to Paper Structure, *Elektrichestvo*, no. 5, pp. 16–18, May, 1950.

Straeb, H.: The Metallized Paper Capacitor, *Elektrotech. Z.*, vol. 70, no. 9, p. 287, August, 1950.

McLean, D. A.: Metallized Paper for Capacitors, *Proc. IRE*, vol. 38, p. 1010, 1950.

Weeks, J. R.: Metallized Paper Capacitors, *Proc. IRE*, vol. 38, p. 1015, 1950.

Fisher, J. H.: Metallized Paper Capacitors, *Electronics*, vol. 23, p. 122, October, 1950.

————: Metallized Paper Capacitor, *Aerovox Research Worker*, June, July, August, 1951.

Church, H. F.: The Life of Impregnated Paper Capacitors with Special Reference to the Influence of Contaminants, *Proc. Inst. Elec. Engrs. (London)*, vol. 98, pt. III, p. 56, 1951.

Eveson, R. K.: Low Voltage Self Healing Capacitors, *Bell Labs Record*, vol. 29, p. 56, 1951.

McLean, D. A., and H. A. Sauer: Stabilized Mineral Oil Capacitors, Annual Report of the 1951 Conference on Electrical Insulation, National Research Council, Washington, D.C.

Sauer, H. A., D. A. McLean, and L. Egerton: Stabilization of Dielectrics Operating under Direct Current, *Ind. Eng. Chem.*, vol. 44, pp. 135–140, January, 1952.

————: High Temperature Metallized Paper Capacitors, *Aerovox Research Worker*, January–February, 1952.

Souder, W., and S. B. Newmann: Measurement of the Thickness of Capacitor Paper, *NBS Circular*, no. 532, 1952.

Church, H. F.: Stabilization of Impregnated Paper Capacitors, Pilot Scale Tests with Azobenzene, *Electrical Research Association (London)*, Report L/T 268, 1952.

Elsner, H.: Metallized Paper Capacitors, *Bull. Schweiz. Elektrotech. Ver.*, vol. 43E, p. 721, September, 1952.

Burnham, J.: Breakdown and Leakage Resistance Investigation of Metallized Paper Capacitors, *IRE Trans. of Prof. Group on Components Parts*, VPGCP–1, pp. 3–17, March, 1954.

Drvostep, J. J.: Impregnated Paper Capacitors, *Radio and Television News (Radio-Electronic Engineering)*, vol. 24, pp. 17–19, May, 1955.

Lee, D. B.: Evaluation of Capacitors (Paper "K" Characteristic), *Elec. Mfg.*, vol. 56, pp. 117–121, September, 1955.

Anderson, H. A.: Standards for Capacitor Paper, *Proc. Electronic Components Symposium*, May, 1956.

Callinan, T. D., and J. B. Romans: Fluorinated Liquid Dielectrics for Fixed Paper Capacitors, *Elec. Mfg.*, p. 146, May, 1957.

Mica Capacitors, Dielectric Properties of Mica, Etc.

Dye, D. W., and L. Hartshorn: The Dielectric Properties of Mica, *Proc. Phys. Soc. (London)*, vol. 37, p. 42, 1924.

Jackson, W. W., and J. West: The Crystal Structure of Muscovite, *Z. Krist*, vol. 76, p. 211, 1930.

Brown, W. W.: Properties and Application of Mycalex to Radio Apparatus, *Proc. IRE*, vol. 18, pp. 1307–1315, August, 1930.

Donnatt, C., and S. E. Goodall: Permittivity and Power Factors of Micas, *J. Inst. Elec. Engrs. (London)*, vol. 69, p. 490, April, 1931.

Lewis, A. B., E. L. Hall, and F. R. Caldwell: Some Electrical Properties of Foreign and Domestic Micas and the Effect of Elevated Temperatures on Micas, *J. Research Nat. Bur. Standards*, vol. 7, p. 409, August, 1931.

Maloff, I. G.: Mica Condensers in High-Frequency Circuits, *Proc. IRE*, vol. 20, p. 647, April, 1932.

Curtis, H. L., and others: Capacitance and Power Factor of a Mica Capacitor as Measured at the Bureau of Standards and the National Physics Laboratory, *J. Research Nat. Bur. Standards*, vol. 8, p. 507, April, 1932.

Jackson, W. W., and J. West: The Crystal Structure of Muscovite, *Z. Krist.*, vol. 85, p. 160, 1933.

Theissen, R. E.: Recent Developments in Mica Condensers, *General Radio Experimenter*, vol. 7, p. 1, January, 1933.

Schrveder, R.: Mica and Mica Products, *Elektrotech. Z.*, vol. 54, p. 541, June, 1933.

Brown, W. W.: Properties of Mycalex, *Proc. IRE*, vol. 21, p. 1939, September, 1933.

Sklar, L. B.: Padding Condenser, *Electronics*, vol. 10, p. 40, May, 1937.

Tatarinov, P. M.: "Micas of the U.S.S.R.," Moscow, Leningrad, 1937.

Rushton, E., and L. Hartshorn: Power Losses in Mica, *Electrical Research Association (London)*, Report L/T 60, 1939.

Nicholls, F. B.: Alsifilm—a Mica Substitute, *Chem. Eng. Mining Rev.*, vol. 32, p. 438, 1940.

Hackett, W., and P. M. Thomas: Electric Strength of Mica and Its Variation with Temperature, *J. Inst. Elec. Engrs. (London)*, vol. 88, pt. I, p. 295, August, 1941.

———: Power Factor in Indian Mica, *Electronic Ind.*, vol. 3, p. 121, March, 1944.

Green, A. P., and C. T. McComb: Resonance in Mica By-Pass Capacitors, *Electronics*, vol. 17, p. 219, March, 1944.

Thomas, A. M.: Defects in Mica Plates and Capacitors and the Use of Emergency Substitute Grades, *Electrical Research Association (London)*, Report D/T 30, 1944.

———: Absorption Measurements on Mica and Other Capacitors, *Electrical Research Association (London)*, Report D/T 31, 1944.

Austen, A. E. W.: The Dielectric Properties of Mica at High Electric Stress, *J. Inst. Elec. Engrs. (London)*, vol. 92, pt. I, p. 373, 1945.

Coutlee, K. G.: Judging Mica Quality Electrically, *Trans. AIEE*, vol. 64, pp. 735–741, November, 1945.

Chapman, A. T.: Manufacture of Silvered Mica Capacitors: New Production Techniques Conserve Mica Stocks and Improve Quality of Finished Units, *Electronics*, vol. 18, pp. 146–149, November, 1945.

Garton, C. G.: The Characteristics and Errors of Capacitors Used for Measurement Purposes, *J. Inst. Elec. Engrs. (London)*, vol. 93, pt. II, p. 398, October, 1946.

———: Synthetic Mica Developed in Germany, *Chem. Eng. News*, vol. N24, p. 3396, December, 1946.

Thomas, A. M.: The Elimination of Defective Mica Plates for Capacitors by Visual Inspection, *Electrical Research Association (London)*, Report D/T 34, 1946.

Christopher, A. J., and J. A. Rater: Mica Capacitors for Carrier Telephone Systems, *Bell System Tech. J.*, vol. 26, p. 213, January, 1947.

Schick, W.: Capacitance Stability of Ruby Muscovite Mica, *J. Inst. Elec. Engrs. (London)*, vol. 94, pt. I, pp. 371–376, August, 1947.

Church, H. F.: Spontaneous Capacitance Fluctuations in Silvered Ceramic and Silvered Mica Capacitors, *Electrical Research Association (London)*, Report L/T 181, 1947.

Mahanti, P. C., and S. S. Mandal: Electrical Properties of Indian Mica: Effect of Pre-heating, *Indian J. Phys.*, vol. 22, pp. 7–13, January, 1948.

Middel, V. J.: Synthetic Mica—Report on the Process Developed in Germany by the Siemens Concern, *Electrical Research Association (London)*, Report D/T 40, 1948.

Green, A. P., and C. T. McComb: Resonance in Mica Capacitors, *Electronics*, vol. 17, p. 119, March, 1949.

Roberts W. G.: Silvered Mica and Ceramic Capacitors, *Radio Times*, pt. 1, vol. 4, p. 11, June, 1949; pt. 2, vol. 4, p. 9, July, 1949; pt. 3, vol. 4, p. 9, August, 1949.

Tyler, P. B.: Synthetic Mica Research, U.S. Dept. of Commerce, 32545.

Griffeth, R. L., and E. R. Younglove: Manufacture and Processing of Mica Paper, Annual Report of the 1951 Conference on Electrical Insulation, National Research Council, Washington, D.C., 1951.

Rayner, G. H., and L. H. Ford: The Stability of Sub-miniature Mica Capacitors at the N. P. L., *J. Sci. Instr.*, vol. 28, p. 168, June, 1951.

Schmidt, P. S.: Mica Paper and Ceramic Capacitors, *Elec. Mfg.*, vol. 47, p. 244, 1951.

Rayner, G. H., and L. H. Ford: The Stability of Mica Standards of Capacitance, *J. Sci. Instr.*, vol. 28, no. 6, p. 168, June, 1951.

Javitz, A. E.: Research Progress in Dielectrics, 1951, *Elec. Mfg.*, vol. 49, p. 92 (Table I, specifically), January, 1952.

Bray, P. R.: Power Factor and Capacitance of Mica Capacitors at Low Frequencies, *J. Sci. Instr.*, vol. 30, pp. 49–51, February, 1953.

Lynch, A. C.: Variation of Capacitance with Temperature in Metallized Mica Capacitors, *Proc. Inst. Elec. Engrs. (London)*, vol. 100, pt. IIA, no. 3, p. 38, 1953.

Rayner, G. H., and L. H. Ford: The Performance of Dried and Sealed Mica Capacitors, *J. Sci. Instr.*, vol. 31, no. 1, p. 3, January, 1954.

Dokuchitz, P., and T. Tognola: Elimination of Strategic Mica Films as Dielectric Materials for High Temperature Capacitors, *Proc. Electronic Components Conference*, 1958.

Ceramic Capacitors, Dielectric Properties of Ceramics, Etc.

Schmidt, W.: Permittivity of Titania, *Ann. Physik*, vol. 4, p. 9, 1902.

Beldi, F.: Dielectric Losses and Breakdown Strength of Porcelain, *Brown Boveri Rev.*, vol. 18, p. 172, May, 1931.

Steger, W.: Advances in Ceramic Materials, *Z. Ver. Deut. Ing.*, vol. 77, p. 81, January, 1933.

Weicker, W.: Porcelain and Ceramic Insulating Materials, *Elektrotech. Z.*, vol. 54, p. 543, June, 1933.

Schonberg, E.: Insulating Materials of the Steatite Group, *Elektrotech. Z.*, vol. 54, p. 545, June, 1933.

Eucken, A., and A. Buchner: Permittivity of Titania, *Z. Physik. Chem.*, vol. 27, p. 326, 1934.

Soyck, W.: Dielectric Characteristics of Rutile Materials, *Verband Deutscher Elektrotechniken* (U.D.E. Fachbericht—Archive frur Elektrotechnik), p. 129, 1935.

Hartshorn, L., and W. H. Ward: Dielectric Properties of Frequentite, *Electrical Research Association (London)*, Report L/T 85, 1939.

Thurnauer, H.: Properties of Ceramic Materials, *Electronics*, vol. 12, p. 33, April, 1939.

Bellaschi, Z.: Dielectric Strength of Porcelain, *Trans. AIEE*, vol. 58, p. 651, December, 1939.

Richter, E. F.: On the A. C. Resistance of Ceramic Materials at Temperatures up to 600°C., *Phys. Z.*, vol. 40, p. 597, October, 1939.

————: Ceramic Materials, *Electrician (London)*, vol. 125, p. 137, September, 1940.

Berberich, L. J., and M. E. Bell: Dielectric Properties of the Rutile Form of TiO_2, *J. Appl. Phys.*, vol. 2, p. 681, 1940.

Robinson, W. G.: Ceramic Insulations for H. F. Work, *J. Inst. Elec. Engrs. (London)*, vol. 87, p. 527, November, 1940.

Richter, E. F., and W. Weicker: Ceramic Insulating Materials at High Temperature, *Elektrotech. Z.*, vol. 64, p. 103, February, 1943.

Rosenthal, E.: Dielectric or Puncture Strength of Porcelain and Other Ceramic Materials, *Electronic Eng. (London)*, vol. 15, p. 408, March, 1943.

Rigterlink, M. D.: Ceramics for H. F. Insulation, *Bell Labs Record*, vol. 21, p. 290, May, 1943.

Maida, F. X.: Rating of Ceramic Condensers, *Electronic Ind.*, vol. 2, pp. 80–82, July, 1943.

Wainer, E.: High Titania Dielectrics, *Trans. Electrochem. Soc.*, vol. 83, p. 189, 1943.

Vul, B. M., and G. V. Skanavi: High Frequency Ceramic Capacitors, *Bull. Acad. Sci. (U.S.S.R.)*, Serial Physics 1, vol. 8, no. 4, pp. 194–199, 1944 (in Russian).

Russell, R.: Low Loss Ceramics, *Electronics*, vol. 17, p. 136, May, 1944.

Rigterlink, M. D.: Improved Ceramic Dielectric Materials, *Rev. Sci. Instr.*, vol. 12, p. 527, November, 1944.

Vul, B. M., and I. M. Goldman: Dielectric Constant of Barium Titanate as a Function of Strength of an Alternating Field, *Bull. Acad. Sci. (U.S.S.R.)*, vol. 49, pp. 177–180, October, 1945 (in English).

Vrolet, F., and R. Lecuir: Evolution of Ceramic Technique in the Laboratories of the Compagnie General de Telegraphie sans Fil (C.S.F.) for the Preparation of High Precision Ceramics, *Annales de Radioeléctricité*, vol. 1, pp. 152–159, October, 1945, and January, 1946.

Coursey, P. R., and K. G. Brand: Dielectric Constants of Some Titanates, *Nature*, vol. 157, pp. 297–298, March, 1946.

Frohlich, H.: Dielectric Properties of Dipolar Solids, *Proc. Roy. Soc. (London)*, vol. 185, p. 399, April, 1946.

Von Hippel, A., R. G. Breckenridge, F. G. Chasley, and Laszlo Tisza: High Dielectric Constant Ceramics, *Ind. Eng. Chem.*, vol. 38, p. 1097, November, 1946.

De Brettersville, A.: Oscillograph Study of Dielectric Properties of Barium Titanate, *J. Am. Ceram. Soc.*, vol. 29, p. 303, 1946.

————: High Dielectric Ceramic for Limited Space Capacitors: Research at the National Bureau of Standards, *Product Eng.*, vol. 18, pp. 147–148, June, 1947.

Howatt, G. N., R. G. Breckenridge, and J. M. Brownlow: Fabrication of Thin Ceramic Sheets for Capacitors, *J. Am. Ceram. Soc.*, vol. 30, p. 237, August, 1947.

Thomas, A. M.: Experimental Low Temperature Coefficient Ceramics: Variation of Capacitance and Power Factor with Temperature, *Beama J. (London)*, vol. 54, p. 321, September, 1947.

Novosiltsev, H. S., and A. L. Khodakov: Dielectric Properties of Barium Titanate at High Frequencies, *J. Tech. Phys. (U.S.S.R.)*, vol. 6, pp. 651–656, 1947 (in Russian).

Bonning, M.: Deposition of Thin Films of Titania, *J. Am. Optical Soc.*, vol. 37, p. 188, 1947.

———: High Dielectric Ceramics Produced with Tam Titanium Dioxide and Titanates, *J. Am. Ceram. Soc.*, vol. 30, no. 8, p. 237, 1947.

Rosenthal, I. E.: Dielectric or Puncture Strength of Porcelain and Other Ceramic Materials, *Electronic Eng. (London)*, vol. 15, pp. 408–411, March, 1948.

Matthias, B., and A. Von Hippel: Domain Structure and Dielectric Response of Barium Titanate Single Crystals, *Phys. Rev.*, vol. 73, p. 1378, June, 1948.

Reddish, W.: Cyclic Variation of Capacitance, *Wireless Eng.*, vol. 25, p. 331, October, 1948.

Shelton, G. R., A. S. Creamer, and E. N. Bunting: Properties of Barium Magnesium Titanate Dielectrics, *J. Research Nat. Bur. Standards*, vol. 41, p. 17, 1948.

Blumenthal, W. B.: Preparation of Chemically Pure Anatase and Rutile, *Ceramic Age*, p. 320, June 1948.

Powles, J. G.: Dielectric Properties of Titanates at Ultra High Frequencies, *Nature*, vol. 162, p. 614, 1948.

Marks, B. H.: Ceramic Dielectric Materials, *Electronics*, vol. 21, no. 8, p. 116, August, 1948.

Devonshire, A. F.: Structure and Dielectric Properties of Barium Titanate and Similar Compounds, *Electrical Research Association (London)*, Report L/T 185, 1948.

Powles, J. G.: Dielectric Properties of Mixed Barium and Strontium, Titanates at 10^{10} C/sec, *Nature*, vol. 162, p. 655, 1948.

Hartington, J. R., G. V. Planer, and I. I. Boswell: Voltage Effects in Titanate Polycrystals, *Nature*, vol. 162, p. 151, July, 1948.

Roberts, W. G.: Ceramic Capacitors, *J. Brit. IRE*, vol. 9, no. 5, p. 184, May, 1949.

Powles, J. G., and W. Jackson: The Measurement of the Dielectric Properties of High Permittivity Materials at Centimeter Wavelengths, *Proc. Inst. Elec. Engrs. (London)*, vol. 96, pt. III, no. 43, p. 383, September, 1949.

Bauer, A. J.: Ceramic Transmitting Capacitors, *Electronics*, vol. 22, no. 3, p. 97, 1949.

Devonshire, A. F.: Theory of Barium Titanate—Part I, *Phil. Mag.*, vol. 40, p. 1040, October, 1949.

Verwey, E. J. W., and R. D. Bugel: Ceramic Materials with High Dielectric Constant, *Philips Tech. Rev.*, vol. 10, p. 231, February, 1949.

Kay, H. F., and P. Vousden: Symmetry Changes in Barium Titanate at Low Temperatures and Their Relation to Its Ferroelectric Properties, *Phil. Mag.*, vol. 40, p. 1019, October, 1949.

Blunt, R. F., and W. F. Love: Dielectric Properties of Barium Titanate at Low Temperatures, *Phys. Rev.*, vol. 76, pp. 1202–1204, October, 1949.

Jackson, W.: The Structure, Electrical Properties and Potential Applications of the Barium-Titanate Class of Ceramic Materials (also contains 75 references to work on barium-titanate ceramics), *Proc. Inst. Elec. Engrs. (London)*, vol. 97, pt. III, no. 49, p. 285, September, 1950.

Kiyoshi, A., and T. Tetsuro: Study on High Dielectric Constant Ceramics, *Bull. Inst. Chem. Research, Kyoto Univ.*, vol. 22, p. 79, 1950.

Devonshire, A. F.: Theory of Barium Titanate, *Phil. Mag.*, vol. 42, p. 1065, October, 1951.

Brownlow, J. M., and G. N. Howatt: Ceramic Capacitors in Circuit Miniaturization, *Tele-Tech*, vol. 10, pp. 56–57, October, 1951; vol. 11, pp. 56–57, November, 1951.

Graff, R. G.: Effect of Impurities on the Dielectric Properties of Barium Titanate, *Ceramic Age*, p. 16, December, 1951.

Shirane, G.: Dielectric Properties of Lead Zirconate, *Phys. Rev.*, vol. 84, p. 471, 1951.

Dranetz, A. Z.: Ceramics for Capacitors, *Tele-Vision (England)*, vol. 34, pp. 12–13, April, 1952.

Droughard, M. E., H. L. Funk, and D. Young: Dielectric Constant and Loss Measurement in BaTiO₃ Single Crystals while Traversing the Hysteresis Loops, *J. Appl. Phys.*, vol. 23, no. 9, p. 1166, September, 1952.

Popper, P.: Ceramic Dielectrics and Their Application to Capacitors for Use in Electronic Equipment, *Inst. Elec. Engrs. (London)*, Paper 1490, 1953.

Kramers, W. J.: Scientific Approach to New Ceramics (pts. I and II), *Research (London)*, p. 101, March, 1954, and p. 142, April, 1954.

Droughard, M. E., and D. Young: Domain Clamping Effect in Barium Titanate Single Crystals, *Phys. Rev.*, vol. 94, no. 6, p. 1561, June, 1954.

Slate, M. W.: Resonance Effects in Tubular Feed-Thru Capacitors, *Tele-Tech and Electronic Industries*, vol. 13, pp. 98–101, June, 1954.

Von Hippel, A., and Associates: "Tables of Dielectric Materials" (four volumes to date), Laboratory for Insulation Research, Massachusetts Institute of Technology, Boston.

Mertz, W. J.: Domain Formation and Domain Wall Motions in Ferroelectric BaTiO₃ Single Crystals, *Phys. Rev.*, vol. 95, no. 3, p. 690, August, 1954.

Glass and Vitreous-enamel Capacitors, Dielectric Properties of Glass, Etc.

Decker, W. C.: Power Losses in Commercial Glasses, *Elec. World*, vol. 89, p. 601, March, 1927.

Strutt, M. J. O.: Dielectric Properties of Various Glasses, *Arch. Elektrotech*, vol. 25, p. 715, October, 1931.

Bogorodickiy, N.: Dielectric Losses in Glass, *J. Tech. Phys. (U.S.S.R.)*, vol. 2, no. 4, p. 324, 1935.

Morey, G. W.: Glass as a Dielectric, *J. Franklin Inst.*, vol. 219, p. 315, March, 1935.

Hackel, W. H. F.: Permittivity and Power Factor of Glasses, *Ann. Physik*, vol. 29, no. 1, p. 63, March, 1937.

Bogorodickiy, N., and I. Friedberg: Dielectric Losses in Inorganic Glasses at R. F., *J. Tech. Phys. (U.S.S.R.)*, vol. 4, no. 9, p. 707, 1937.

Hartshorn, L., and W. H. Ward: Dielectric Properties of Glass, *Electrical Research Association (London)*, Report L/T 93, 1939.

Humphrys, J. M., and W. R. Morgan: Effect of Composition and Thermal History on Dielectric Constants of Soda Borosilicate Glass, *J. Am. Ceram. Soc.*, vol. 24, p. 123, 1941.

Skavani, G.: Dielectric Losses at H. F. in Glass Fabric, *J. Phys. (Moscow)*, vol. 4, p. 85, 1941.

Von Hippel, A., and R. J. Maurer: Pre-breakdown Currents in Glass, *Phys. Rev.*, vol. 59, p. 820, 1941.

Guyer, E. M.: Electrical Glass, *Proc. IRE*, vol. 32, p. 743, December, 1944.

————: Glass Useful as an Insulating Medium in Electrical Condensers for Radio Circuits, *Glass Ind.*, vol. 27, p. 134, March, 1946.

Bradford, C. I., B. L. Weller, and S. A. McNeight: Printed Vitreous Enamel Components: Produced by Sprayed-Enamel Process, *Electronics*, vol. 20, p. 106, December, 1947.

Forrest, J. S.: Electrical Properties of Semiconducting Ceramic Glazes, *J. Sci. Instr.*, vol. 21, p. 211, 1947.

Danzin, A., and P. Meunier: Dielectric Properties of a Glass, *Compt. Rend.*, vol. 228, no. 5, p. 391, 1949.

Stevels, J. M.: The Power Factor of Glasses, *Verres et Refractaires*, vol. 4, p. 83, 1950; *ibid.*, p. 4, 1951.

————: The Dielectric Losses in Glasses, *J. Soc. Glass Technol.*, vol. 34, p. 80, 1950.

Callinan, T. D., R. T. Lucas, and R. C. Bowers: The Properties of Glass Fibre Paper, *Elec. Mfg.*, vol. 48, pp. 94–97, 1951.

Keller, K. J.: Dielectric Losses and Breakdown in Ceramic Materials—I: Electrical Conduction and Breakdown of Solid Insulators, in Particular Glass, *Koninklijk Instituut van Ingenieurs*, nos. 29–31, p. 485, May, 1951.

Stevels, J. M.: The Loss Angle of Glasses, *Koninklijk Instituut van Ingenieurs*, no. 31, p. 485, May, 1951.

Naudin, F.: The Effect of Thermal Treatment on the Dielectric Constant and Loss Angle of Glass, *Compt. Rend.*, vol. 232, p. 831, 1951.

Plastic Capacitor, Dielectric Properties of Plastics, Etc.

Whitehead, J. B.: Dielectric Loss and Relaxation Time in Resins, *Physics*, vol. 2, p. 3, February, 1932.

Yager, W. A.: Dielectric Constant and Loss of Plastics Related to Their Composition, *Trans. Electrochem. Soc.*, vol. 74, p. 113, 1938.

Hartshorn, L.: Plastics and Electrical Insulation, *J. Inst. Elec. Engrs. (London)*, vol. 83, p. 474, October, 1938.

Hartshorn, L., and W. H. Ward: Dielectric Properties of Synthetic Resins, *Electrical Research Association (London)*, Report L/T 85, 1939.

Garton, C. G.: The Dielectric Properties of a Chemically Pure Resin, *J. Inst. Elec. Engrs. (London)*, vol. 85, p. 625, 1939.

Pelmore, D. R.: Dielectric Loss in Simple Alkyd Resins, *Proc. Roy. Soc. (London)*, vol. 175, p. 468, July, 1940.

Hartshorn, L., E. Rushton, and N. J. L. Megson: The Dielectric Properties of Thermoplastic Synthetic Resins, *Proc. Phys. Soc. (London)*, vol. 52, p. 796, November, 1940.

Hartshorn, L.: Dielectric Properties of Some Thermoplastics, *Proc. Phys. Soc. (London)*, vol. 52, p. 796, November, 1940.

————: Molecular Relaxation and Properties of Plastics, *Proc. Phys. Soc. (London)*, vol. 52, p. 817, November, 1940.

Thomas, A. M., and M. V. Griffith: Intrinsic Electric Strength and Conductivity of Varnish Films and Their Variation with Temperature, *J. Inst. Elec. Engrs. (London)*, vol. 89, pt. I, p. 487, 1942.

Yersley, F.: Electrical Properties of Neoprene, *Ind. Eng. Chem.*, vol. 35, p. 330, March, 1943.

Garton, C. G., and Savic: Dipolar Properties of Resins, *Electrical Research Association (London)*, Report L/T 135, 1943.

Simonds, H. R., C. Ellis, and M. H. Bigelow: "Handbook of Plastics," Chapman & Hall, Ltd., London, 1943.

Morrell, R. S., "Synthetic Resins and Allied Plastics," Oxford University Press, London, 1943.

Cares, A.: Perspex, Endeavour, vol. 3, p. 156, October, 1944.

Jackson, W., and J. S. A. Forsyth: The Development of Polythene as a High Frequency Dielectric, J. Inst. Elec. Engrs. (London), vol. 92, pt. III, p. 23, March, 1945.

Swallow. J. C.: Polythene, Endeavour, vol. 3, p. 26, January, 1946.

Weeks, J. R.: Polystyrene Capacitors: Construction and Performance, Bell Labs Record, vol. 24, p. 111, March, 1946.

——: Development of Polystyrene, Capacitors, Elec. Mfg., vol. 37, p. 146, 1946.

Nauth, R.: "The Chemistry and Technology of Plastics," Reinhold Publishing Corporation, New York, 1947.

Bown, C. E. H.: "Chemistry of High Polymers," Butterworth & Co. (Publishers) Ltd., London, 1948.

Cozens, J. H.: Plastic Film Capacitors, Wireless World, vol. 55, p. 11, June, 1949.

Reddish, W.: The Dielectric Properties of Polyethylene Terephthalate, Trans. Faraday Soc., vol. 46, no. 330, p. 459, June, 1950.

——: "The Plastics Encyclopaedia," Plastics Catalogue Corporation, New York (annually).

Sissman and Bopp: The Physical Properties of Irradiated Plastics, U.S. Atomic Energy Commission Report, ORNL–928, Oak Ridge Nat. Lab. (225 pages), June 29, 1951.

Matheson, L. A., and V. J. Caldecourt: Electrical Charge Storage in Polystyrene Capacitors, J. Appl. Phys., vol. 22, p. 11, September, 1951.

Ball, I. D. L.: The Intrinsic Electric Strength of Polyvinyl Alcohol and Its Temperature Variation, Proc. Inst. Elec. Engrs. (London), vol. 98, pt. I, p. 84, March, 1951.

Wooley, M. C., G. T. Kohman, and W. McMahon: Polyethylene Terephthalate as a Capacitor Dielectric, Electronic Eng. (London), vol. 71, p. 715, August, 1952.

——: Cross Linking of Polythene in the Atomic Pile, British Plastics, vol. 26, no. 286, p. 79, March, 1953.

Sun, K. H.: Effects of Atomic Radiation on High Polymers, Modern Plastics, vol. 32, p. 141, September, 1954 (contains extensive bibliography).

McLean, D. A., and H. G. Wehe: Miniature Lacquer Film Capacitors, Proc. IRE, vol. 42, pp. 1797–1805, December, 1954.

Ruby, J. A.: "Mylar" Film as Capacitor Dielectric, Tele-Tech and Electronic Industries, vol. 14, p. 72, April, 1955.

Mistic, G.: Capacitor Miniaturization with Plastic Films, Aero Dig., vol. 70, p. 54, May, 1955.

——: Temperature Compensating Capacitors (Composite Plastic Films), Elec. Mfg., vol. 57, pp. 83–86, February, 1956.

——: New Decade Capacitor with Polystyrene Dielectrics, General Radio Experimenter, July, 1956.

Electrolytic Capacitors

Smith, T. A., and J. Millen: Electrolytic Condensers, Radio, vol. 7, p. 808, December, 1925.

Siegmund, H. D.: The Aluminum Electrolytic Condenser, *Trans. Electrochem. Soc.*, vol. 53, p. 203, 1928.

Coursey, P. R.: Capacity of Dry Electrolytic Condensers, *Experimental Wireless and Wireless Engineering*, vol. 6, p. 128, March, 1929.

Edelman, P. E.: Dry Electrochemical Condensers, *Proc. IRE*, vol. 18, p. 1366, August, 1930.

Godsey, F. W.: Electrolytic Condensers for Radio Use, *Electronics*, vol. 2, p. 596, April, 1931.

————: A. C. Capacity of Electrolytic Condensers, *Trans. Electrochem. Soc.*, vol. 61, p. 515, April, 1932.

————: Film Characteristics of Electrolytic Condensers, *Trans. AIEE*, vol. 51, p. 432, June, 1932.

————: Power Losses in Electrolytic Condensers, *Trans. AIEE*, vol. 51, p. 439, June, 1932.

————: Electrolytic Condensers Produced in Aluminum by Impact Extrusion, *Iron Age*, vol. 130, p. 220, August, 1932.

————: Developments in the Design of Small Size Electrolytic Condensers, *Aerovox Research Worker*, November, 1933.

Covert, R. J.: The Dry Electrolytic Condenser, *Radio Eng.*, vol. 14, no. 6, p. 18, June, 1934.

Verwey, E. I. W.: The Structure of the Electrolytical Oxide Layer on Aluminium, *Z. anorg. Chem.*, vol. 91, p. 317, 1935.

————: Regulating Properties of Wet Electrolytic Condensers, *Aerovox Research Worker*, August, 1936.

Deeley, P. M.: "Electrolytic Capacitors," Cornell-Dubilier Corporation, South Plainfield, N.J., 1938.

Coursey, P. R., and S. N. Ray: Electrolytic Condensers, *J. Inst. Elec. Engrs. (London)*, vol. 85, p. 107, July, 1939.

Coursey, P. R.: "Electrolytic Condensers," Chapman & Hall, Ltd., London, 1939.

Edwards, J. D., and F. Keller: Formation of Anodic Coatings on Aluminium, *Trans. Electrochem. Soc.*, vol. 79, p. 135, 1941.

Deeley, P. M.: Condensers at R. F., *Electronics*, vol. 16, p. 209, April, 1943.

Georgiev, A. M.: "The Electrolytic Capacitor," Murray Hill Books, Inc., New York, 1945.

————: Electrolytic Capacitors Dry Out (Elektrolytblokke torrer ud), *Radio Ekko*, vol. 1, p. 92, May, 1948.

Miguelis, H. E.: Climatisation of the Electrolytic Condenser, *Radio Technical Digest*, vol. 3, p. 77, April, 1949 (in French).

Whitehead, M.: New Electrolytic Capacitors—Use of Tantalum for Electrodes, *F. M. and Television*, vol. 11, p. 26, February, 1951.

Dummer, G. W. A.: Electrolytic Capacitors, *Wireless World*, vol. 57, p. 510, December, 1951.

Foster, L. W.: Tantalytic Capacitors, *Gen. Elec. Rev.*, vol. 54, p. 30, October, 1951 (revised February, 1953).

Easter, C. D.: Electrolytic Capacitors at Low Temperatures, *Tele-Tech*, vol. 11, pp. 44–45, January, 1952.

Maxwell, J. W.: New Low-Temperature Capacitors Electrolytic Types for Operation to −55°C., *Tele-Tech*, vol. 11, p. 53, June, 1952.

Muriset, G.: Influence of Impurities in Foil, Electrolyte and Paper in Electrolytic Capacitor, *Electrochem. Soc.*, vol. 99, pp. 285–288, July, 1952.

Foster, L. W.: Tantalum Foil Capacitors Save Space, *Electronics*, vol. 26, p. 242, May, 1953.

Nquyen, T. C., and J. Vergnolle: Condensateurs Electrolytiques au Tantale, *Annales de Radioélectricité*, vol. 935, pp. 83–97, January, 1954.

Young, L.: Anodic Oxide Films on Tantalum Electrodes, *Trans. Faraday Soc.*, vol. 50, February, 1954.

Altenpohl, D.: Improvements in the Field of Electrolytic Capacitors, *Convention Record IRE*, pt. 3, p. 35, 1954.

Hovey, R. J., and S. S. Fry: Tantalum Capacitors, *Elec. Mfg.*, vol. 57, pp. 80–81, March, 1956.

Peck, D. B., S. W. Bubriski, and W. W. Schroeder: High Temperature Foil Type Tantalum Capacitors, *Elec. Mfg.*, vol. 57, pp. 134–135, May, 1956.

McLean, D. A., and F. S. Power: Tantalum Solid Electrolytic Capacitors, *Proc. IRE*, vol. 44, pp. 872–878, July, 1956.

McLean, D. A.: Tantalum Capacitors Use Solid Electrolyte, *Electronics*, vol. 29, pp. 176–177, October, 1956.

Lunchick, A., and E. Gikow: Characteristics of Tantalum Electrolytic Capacitors, *Elec. Mfg.*, pp. 79–84, December, 1956.

Burnham, J.: Dielectric Films in Aluminum and Tantalum Electrolyte and Solid Tantalum Capacitors, *IRE Trans. on Component Parts*, vol. CP–4, pp. 73–82, September, 1957.

Fraioli, A. V.: Recent Advances in the Solid-State Electrolytic Capacitor, *IRE Trans. on Component Parts*, pp. 72–75, June, 1958.

Kass, S.: On Tantalum Capacitors, *Semiconductor Products*, p. 39, May–June, 1958.

Vacuum, Air, and Gas-filled Capacitors

Rayner, E. H.: The Design and Use of an Air Condenser for High Voltages, *J. Sci. Instr.*, vol. 3, p. 33, November, 1925; p. 70, December, 1925; p. 104, January, 1926.

Astin, A. V.: Nature of Energy Losses in Air Capacitors at Low Frequencies, *J. Research Nat. Bur. Standards*, vol. 22, p. 673, 1939.

Michaelson, H. B.: Gas-Filled and Vacuum Capacitors, *Electronics*, vol. 17, no. 9, p. 124, September, 1944.

Floyd, G. H.: Vacuum Capacitors, *Proc. IRE*, vol. 32, p. 463, 1944.

Griffiths, H. A. H.: Vacuum Condensers, *Wireless World*, vol. 53, p. 23, January, 1947.

Moon, C., and C. M. Sparks: Standards for Low Values of Direct Capacitance, *J. Research Nat. Bur. Standards*, vol. 41, p. 497, November, 1948.

Ford, L. H.: Effect of Humidity on the Calibration of Precision Air Capacitors, *J. Inst. Elec. Engrs. (London)*, vol. 95, pt. II, pp. 709–712, December, 1948.

Borgars, S. J.: Development of Vacuum Capacitors, *Proc. Inst. Elec. Engrs. (London)*, vol. 99, pt. III, no. 61, p. 307, September, 1952.

Clothier, W. K.: A Fixed Gas-Dielectric Capacitor of High Stability, *Proc. Inst. Elec. Engrs. (London)*, vol. 101, pt. II, p. 453, August, 1954.

General Reviews on Variable Capacitors

Cheireix, H.: Variable Condensers with Plates of Special Form, *Lumière élect.*, vol. 31, p. 73, 1915.

Winters, S. R.: Straight Line Condensers, *Experimental Wireless and Wireless Engineering*, vol. 12, p. 24, April, 1925.

Forbes, H. C.: A Straight-Line Frequency Variable Condenser, *Proc. IRE*, vol. 13, p. 507, August, 1925.

Harris, S.: Straight-Line Frequency Condensers, *Radio*, vol. N7, p. 188, August–September, 1925.

Roos, O. C.: Simplified S. L. F. and S. L. W. Design, *Proc. IRE*, vol. 14, p. 773, December, 1926; Discussion by O. C. Roos, R. R. Batcher, and P. M. Mueller in vol. 15, p. 319, April, 1927.

Griffiths, W. H. F.: Accuracy and Calibration Permanence of Variable Air Condensers for Precision Wave-meters, *Experimental Wireless and Wireless Engineering*, vol. 5, p. 17, January, 1928.

Edgeworth, K. E.: What is the Correct Characteristic for a Variable Condenser? *Experimental Wireless and Wireless Engineering*, vol. 5, p. 148, March, 1928.

Crawford, J. D.: Straight-Line Wavelength and Frequency Variable Condensers, *General Radio Experimenter*, vol. 4, no. 10, p. 1, March, 1930.

Griffiths, W. H. F.: Losses in Variable Air Condensers, *Experimental Wireless and Wireless Engineering*, vol. 8, p. 124, March, 1931.

Koepping, E. D.: Gang Condensers of Variable Capacity, *Radio Eng.*, vol. 12, no. 9, p. 7, September, 1932.

McNamiee, B. F.: Padding Condensers, *Electronics*, vol. 4, p. 160, May, 1932.

Schwartzmann, H., and L. G. Burnell: Superhet Tuning Condenser Design, *Electronics*, vol. 7, p. 180, June, 1934.

Jackson, W.: Analysis of Air Condensers Loss Resistance, *Proc. IRE*, vol. 22, p. 957, August, 1934.

Field, R. F., and D. B. Sinclair: Method for Determining the Residual Inductance and Resistance of a Variable Air Condenser at Radio Frequencies, *Proc. IRE*, vol. 21, p. 255, February, 1936.

Ward, W. H.: Self-Inductance of Variable Air Capacitors, *J. Sci. Instr.*, vol. 13, p. 251, August, 1936.

Proctor, R. F.: Variable Air Condensers, *Wireless Eng.*, vol. 17, p. 257, June, 1940.

———: Straight-Line Rotating Plate Condensers with Large Angle of Rotation, *Electronic Eng. (London)*, vol. 15, pp. 434–435, March, 1943.

Wald, S.: Liquid Dielectrics for Variable Condensers, *Electronic Eng. (London)*, vol. 10, p. 7, April, 1948.

Kline, H. W.: Increasing the Self-Resonant Frequency of Variable Capacitors, *Radio News*, vol. 40, p. 13, July, 1948.

Wald, S.: Oil-Filled Miniature Tuning Capacitor, *Tele-Tech*, vol. 7, pp. 43–45, October, 1948.

Bowdler, G. W.: Wide-Range Variable Capacitor, *J. Sci. Instr.*, vol. 26, p. 117, April, 1949.

———: Easy Calculation of Variable Condensers (Fácil Cálculo de los Condensadores Variables), *Boletín Técnico de Fidelco*, pp. 16–17, April, 1949.

Pender, H., and K. McIlwain: "Electrical Engineers Handbook (Communications and Electronics Volume)," John Wiley & Sons, Inc., New York, 1949.

Henney, K.: "Radio Engineering Handbook," McGraw-Hill Book Company, Inc., New York, 1950.

Schweikert, G. G.: Construction and Calculation of Variable Capacitors, *Elektrotechnik (Berlin)*, vol. 5, p. 226, May, 1951.

Briganti, E.: Study and Evaluation of the Microphony due to Vibrations of the Plates of a Variable Condenser, *Telecommunicazioni*, vol. 21, p. 363, August, 1953.

Rockett, F.: Component Design Trends—New Variable Capacitors Extend Tuning Range, *Electronics*, vol. 27, p. 130, August, 1954.

Wilson, H. M.: Air Capacitor, Type 1420 Variable, *General Radio Experimenter*, July, 1956.

Precision Variable Capacitors

Griffiths, W. H. F.: Calibration Permanence and Overall Accuracy of the Series-Gap Precision Variable Air Condenser, *Experimental Wireless and Wireless Engineering*, vol. 6, p. 23, January–February, 1929.

Kouenhoren, W. B., and C. L. Lemmon: Phase-Defect Angle of an Air Capacitor, *J. Am. Inst. Elec. Engrs. (JAIEE)*, vol. 49, p. 945, November, 1930.

Griffiths, W. H. F.: The Losses in Variable Air Condensers, *Wireless Eng.*, vol. 8, p. 124, 1931.

Thomas, H. A.: The Electrical Stability of Condensers, *J. Inst. Elec. Engrs. (London)*, vol. 81, p. 227, 1936.

Griffiths, W. H. F.: The Temperature Compensation of Condensers, *Wireless Eng.*, vol. 19, p. 148, April, 1942.

Garton, G. C.: A Variable Air Capacitor of Zero Loss Angle, *Technique (Muirhead)*, vol. 2, no. 4, 1948.

Ford, L. H.: The Effect of Humidity on the Calibration of Precision Air Capacitors, *J. Inst. Elec. Engrs. (London)*, vol. 96, pt. III, p. 13, January, 1949.

Laws Relating Capacitance with Shaft Rotation

Duddell, W.: On a Variable Condenser with a Square Law, *J. Inst. Elec. Engrs. (London)*, vol. 52, p. 275, 1914.

Forbes, H. C.: The Straight-Line Frequency Variable Condenser, *Proc. IRE*, vol. 13, p. 507, 1925.

Griffiths, W. H. F.: Notes on the Laws of Variable Air Condensers, *Wireless Eng.*, vol. 3, p. 3, January, 1926.

———: Further Notes on the Laws of Variable Condensers, *Wireless Eng.*, vol. 3, p. 743, December, 1926.

———: Wide-Range Variable Condenser for Special Laws, *Wireless Eng.*, vol. 11, p. 415, August, 1934.

———: Law Linearity of Semi-Circular Plate Variable Air Condensers, *Wireless Eng.*, vol. 22, p. 107, March, 1945.

McDonald, L. J.: Contours of Capacitor Rotor Plates, *Electronics*, vol. 18, p. 126, March, 1945.

Conner, J. A.: R. F. Standard Capacitors for Minute Increments (Co-Axial Types), *Electronics*, vol. 24, p. 250, October, 1951.

Schmid, O.: Calculating the Profile of Variable Capacitors, *Frequenz*, vol. 6, p. 105, April, 1952.

Transmitter Variable Capacitors and Associated Useful Information

Reuhema, L. E.: The Relation between Frequency and Sparkover Voltage in a Sphere-Gap Voltmeter, *Trans. AIEE*, vol. 47, p. 38, January, 1928.

Miseré, F.: Breakdown of Air over a Frequency Range 200 to 1,000 Kc/s, *Arch. Elecktrotech*, vol. 26, p. 123, 1932.

Seward, E. W.: The Breakdown Strength of Air, *Electrician (London)*, vol. 117, p. 783, 1936.

Seward, E. W.: The Electric Strength of Air at High Frequencies, *J. Inst. Elec. Engrs. (London)*, vol. 84, p. 288, February, 1939.

Ekstrand, P. A.: Radio-Frequency Sparkover in Air, *Proc. IRE*, vol. 28, p. 262, June, 1940.

Varela, A. A.: Effect of D.C. Potential on Initiation of R.F. Discharge, *Phys. Rev.*, vol. 71, p. 124, 1947.

Pim, J. A.: Electrical Breakdown Strength of Air at Ultra-High Frequencies, *Nature*, vol. 161, p. 683, May, 1948.

————: The Electrical Breakdown Strength of Air at Ultra-High Frequencies (curves for 100 to 300 Mc/s), *Proc. Inst. Elec. Engrs. (London)*, vol. 97, pt. III, p. 117, March, 1949.

Wheeler, H. A.: Air Breakdown Chart for Radar Pulses, *Electronics*, vol. 25, p. 148, August, 1952.

Miscellaneous—Variable

Gordon, J. F.: Electrically Variable Gas Dielectric Capacitor, *Electronics*, vol. 29, p. 158, January, 1956.

INDEX

Variable capacitors, summary of impor-
     tant characteristics, 53
  symbols for, 203
  transmitter (*see* Transmitter capaci-
     tors)
  trimmer, 51, 235–246
Vermiculite, 101, 110
Vitreous-enamel-dielectric capacitor,
     138–140
  bibliography, 274
  characteristics of, 39
  insulation resistance, 39, 140
  moisture and, 139
  temperature coefficient, 39, 48, 139

Voltage, discharge inception, 23
  spark, 97
  working, electrolytic capacitors, 158–
     159
Volume resistivity, 18–19

Wagner earth, 59
Waveguide method of dielectric meas-
     urement, 65
Wet electrolyte capacitors, 162, 171
Winding technique for plastic films,
     143–145
Working voltage, electrolytic capaci-
     tors, 158–159